Electric and Magnetic Fields

Harcourt, Brace & World, Inc. *New York / Chicago / Burlingame*

D. H. TOMBOULIAN
Cornell University

Electric and Magnetic Fields

to R L T

Contents

Chapter 13.   Mechanical Waves   327

Chapter 14.   Electromagnetic Waves   361

Electric and Magnetic Fields

"I was never able to make a fact my own without seeing it."
Michael Faraday (1791–1867)

Chapter 1.
Sources of the Electrostatic Field

1.1   Electrification

Investigations in atomic and nuclear physics lead to the conclusion that all matter is composed of protons, neutrons, and electrons. Protons and electrons possess a property that manifests itself in repulsive or attractive interactions. The force between a pair of protons or a pair of electrons is repulsive; the force between a proton and an electron is attractive. The presence of such forces is attributed to the *charged* or *electrified* nature of these particles.

There are two kinds of electric charge. The charge associated with the proton is labeled arbitrarily as positive; the charge associated with the electron is labeled as negative. The atoms which make up the different chemical elements are composed of positive and negative charges. Positive charges are associated with the protons in the nucleus. Negative charges are associated with the electrons surrounding the nucleus.

An undisturbed atom—that is, an atom not subject to external influences, such as fields or collisions with other particles—is electrically neutral, for the number of positive charges on the nucleus is equal to the integral number of negative extranuclear electrons. When an electron is removed from a neutral atom or molecule, the result is a positively charged particle, which is referred to as a positive ion. An assemblage of molecules and atoms subjected to external influences may contain a number of positive ions and electrons as well as neutral particles. In an extreme case, where matter is dissociated into atoms and the atoms in turn are entirely stripped of their extranuclear electrons, the resulting assemblage consists exclusively of positive ions and an equivalent number of negative electrons. A gaseous aggregate composed of equal numbers of electrons and positive ions is referred to as a *plasma.* A plasma may or may not contain neutral particles. Problems in plasma physics are actively studied in connection with conduction of electricity through gases and also in investigations of thermonuclear reactions.

Matter in the solid state consists of an arrangement in space of atomic nuclei surrounded by electrons. In certain types of solids, one or more electrons associated with an atom in the isolated state are no longer bound rigidly to that atom when the latter is incorporated in the lattice structure of the crystal. Such electrons cannot, however, escape from the boundaries of the solid without the expenditure of energy by some external agent—through, for example, the influence of thermal excitation, exposure to radiation, or bombardment by particles.

When we say that a body is *charged,* we mean that by some process we have been able to separate one kind of charge from the other. If the body has lost electrons and therefore has an excess of protons, then we say that it is positively charged. If the body has acquired additional electrons, we say that it is negatively charged. Hence from a macroscopic (large-scale) viewpoint, the term charge refers to the net or excess charge. As already stated, electrical charge is a property of elementary particles. Although within a closed system various means may be employed to redistribute or separate the negative and positive components, the total charge within the isolated system is conserved. This principle of charge conservation may be written as

$$\sum_{m=1}^{n} q_m = \text{Constant}$$

for a closed system containing n discrete charges, the mth charge having the magnitude q_m.

1.2   The Law of Force between Charges at Rest

The formulation of the law of force between charged bodies was based on mechanical experiments in which high precision was impossible. In 1785 Coulomb discovered that when a small charged body was attached to the end of a torsion rod, it was acted upon by a second small charged body placed near it. The force between the charges gave rise to a torque about the suspension of the torsion rod.

Observations of this sort led to the conclusions that (1) the force between like charges was repulsive, while the force between unlike charges was attractive, (2) the force exerted by one charge on another was a central force—that is, it acted along the line joining the charges, and (3) the magnitude of the force was directly proportional to the product of the two charges and inversely proportional to the square of the distance between them.

The statements presuppose that the dimensions of the bodies on which the charges reside are negligibly small relative to their separation. Charge distributions satisfying this condition are known as "point charges." The net force between charged bodies is found to depend on the nature of the surrounding medium and on the presence of boundaries. (The effects arising from the presence of material media will be discussed in Chapter 4, on electrical properties of matter.)

We can express the fundamental relation describing the interaction between point charges at rest relative to the observer as follows:

$$F = C\frac{q_1 q_2}{r^2} \tag{1.1}$$

where, as is summarized in Fig. 1.1, F is the magnitude of the force exerted by the point charge q_1 on the point charge q_2, r is the separation between the charges, and C is a constant.

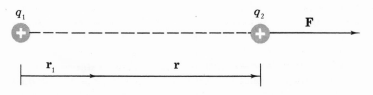

Figure 1.1   Coulomb's law.

Since force and displacement are vector quantities, we can designate both the magnitude and the direction of the force by writing Coulomb's law in vector form:

$$\mathbf{F} = C\frac{q_1 q_2}{r^2}\mathbf{r}_1 = C\frac{q_1 q_2}{r^3}\mathbf{r} \tag{1.2}$$

THE ELECTROSTATIC FORCE

The ancients knew that bits of straw or feathers were attracted by amber. As time went on, men discovered that many other substances could be made to attract light objects. Eventually, the phenomenon of attraction came to be known as *vis electrica* (electrical force) after *ēlektron*, the Greek word for amber.

In 1785, Coulomb (1736–1806) carried out pioneering quantitative measurements to establish the law of force between charges. For this purpose Coulomb used a torsion balance resembling the one that Cavendish used to measure gravitational forces. A schematic diagram of the balance is shown in the accompanying diagram.

A is a metal sphere mounted on one end of an insulating rod AB, which is suspended by a wire W attached to a torsion head H.

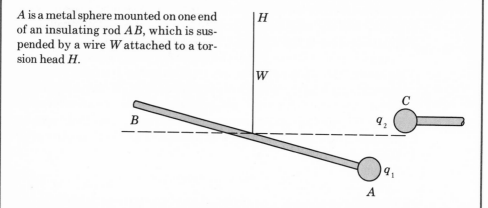

Coulomb carried out the experiment by attaching a second small sphere C to an insulating rod and by giving a charge to the sphere. He allowed the uncharged sphere A to come into contact with the charged sphere C. As a result, the spheres acquired charges of like sign but of varying magnitudes q_1 and q_2. The repulsive force between the charges caused the spheres to separate. When equilibrium was reached, the torque arising from the repulsive force was balanced by the restoring torque of the suspension. The repulsive force was computed from the known torque constant of the suspension and the measurement of the angle through which the rod was turned. The distance between the spheres was read on a scale placed opposite the end B. For a second setting, the torsion head H was twisted until the distance between the spheres was reduced by a known factor m (say 2); the repulsive force was measured again and its magnitude was found to be m^2 (or 4) times as great. This observation proved that the force between q_1 and q_2 varied inversely with the square of the distance.

Moreover, Coulomb established that the force was proportional to the product of the two charges. Once again, after charging the spheres C and A as before, he removed the sphere C and allowed it to touch an identical uncharged sphere. In this operation C lost half of its initial charge. When C was returned to its original position, the repulsive force between the spheres was only half as great.

Do you have any reason to think that the verification of Coulomb's law by the torsion balance is unsatisfactory? Is the charge distributed uniformly over the spheres? What about the effect of charges induced on various parts of the apparatus? Does the magnitude of the charge on each sphere remain constant during the manipulations? Is the measurement of the distance between spheres and of the repulsive force sufficiently refined?

Here the boldface letters indicate vector quantities. As pictured in Fig. 1.1, $\mathbf{r}_1$ is a vector of unit length directed from q_1 to q_2, and $\mathbf{F}$ is the force exerted by q_1 on q_2. Another form of the law also appears in (1.2) where $\mathbf{r}$ is the vector displacement from q_1 to q_2, since $\mathbf{r} = \mathbf{r}_1 r$. (A preliminary discussion of vector algebra appears in Appendix A.)

The mks rationalized system of units will be used exclusively in this text. (For other systems of units, see Appendix B.) In the mks system the unit of force is the newton, the unit of length is the meter, and the unit of charge is the coulomb. The coulomb is defined in terms of the ampere, the unit of current established from magnetic experiments. Since the units of $\mathbf{F}$, $\mathbf{r}$, and q are defined independently of the relation in (1.1), the proportionality constant appearing in (1.1) must be evaluated by the application of this relation. Conceptually, the procedure involves an experiment in which $\mathbf{F}$ is measured in newtons, q in coulombs, and r in meters. In practice, the value of C is arrived at indirectly. The magnitude of the constant is

$$C = 8.987 \times 10^9 \text{ new-m}^2/\text{coul}^2 \qquad (1.3)$$

For the purpose of simplifying relations that are used more frequently in the study of electromagnetism, C is arbitrarily replaced by the substitution

$$C = \frac{1}{4\pi\varepsilon_0} \text{ new-m}^2/\text{coul}^2 \qquad (1.4)$$

The constant ε_0 is called the *permittivity of free space*. Its numerical value is given by

$$\varepsilon_0 = \frac{1}{4\pi C} = 8.854 \times 10^{-12} \text{ coul}^2/\text{new-m}^2 \qquad (1.5)$$

It has already been stated that if a pair of charges is not situated in a vacuum but is immersed in a material medium, or if there is any matter in the vicinity of the pair of charges, additional forces will generally be exerted on q_2. In particular, if q_1 and q_2 are located in an extensive, homogeneous and isotropic, nonconducting medium, the net force on q_2 will arise not only from q_1 but also from charges induced in the surrounding medium. In this highly special case, the numerical value of the constant C will depend on the nature of the particular medium.

The relation in (1.1) is universally applicable. Coulomb's law, with the constant C defined appropriately for free space as in (1.3), applies to the interaction force between a pair of charges.

Indirect effects produced by the presence of matter do not limit the law's validity. So long as we use the mks units we agreed on, we can rewrite the interaction force between a pair of charges as follows:

$$\mathbf{F} = \frac{1}{4\pi\varepsilon_0} \frac{q_1 q_2}{r^2} \, \mathbf{r}_1 \qquad (1.6)$$

Coulomb's law leads to correct results both when it is applied to the interaction between fundamental particles such as protons and electrons, and also when it is applied to the repulsive forces between nuclei at distances in excess of 10^{-15} m. On the atomic scale, support for its validity has been obtained from experiments dealing with the scattering of alpha particles (doubly charged He nuclei) traversing thin metal foils. Such particles interact with atomic electrons and suffer numerous small angular deviations. The occasional large-angle scattering of an alpha particle is attributed to collisions with massive positively charged nuclei.

Experimental evidence for the validity of the inverse square law has also been derived from tests conducted on the macroscopic scale. The verification is based on the prediction that within a cavity completely surrounded by a conductor, the force on a test charge should vanish if the law of force depends inversely on the square of the distance. High-precision measurements indicate that the exponent of r does not deviate from 2 to within one part in a billion.

1.3   Electric Field

If a test charge q placed at any point within a region experiences a force $\mathbf{F}$, the region is said to be an electric field of force. This concept enables us to determine the force on a charge at rest placed at a particular point even though we have no detailed knowledge of the sources (that is, other charges fixed in magnitude and location) to which the force may be attributed. The electric intensity or the strength of the field is denoted by the vector $\mathbf{E}$, which is defined by the ratio

$$\mathbf{E} = \frac{\mathbf{F}}{q} \qquad (1.7)$$

The test charge q will induce charges on the boundary of the field and thus cause a rearrangement of the original charge in the neighborhood of q. If such a disturbance is significant, the ratio defined by (1.7) will not have a unique value; instead, $\mathbf{E}$ will be a function of the magnitude of the test charge. In such a case, (1.7) defines the actual field at the location of q.

We can refine the definition of $\mathbf{E}$ in the following manner: Let $q_1, q_2, q_3, \ldots$ represent sequentially diminishing values of the test charge, and let $\mathbf{F}_1, \mathbf{F}_2, \mathbf{F}_3, \ldots$ denote the corresponding forces experienced by the test charges. In each case, form the ratio $\mathbf{F}/q$. With each reduction in the magnitude of q, the disturbance in the source charges will also be reduced, and the ratio $\mathbf{F}/q$ may approach a constant. Hence as q is reduced indefinitely, the field intensity may be defined as

$$\mathbf{E} = \lim_{q \to 0} \frac{\mathbf{F}}{q} \qquad (1.8)$$

If the location and distribution of charges are given, the electric intensity may be calculated. For instance, the field intensity due to an isolated point charge q is

$$\mathbf{E} = \frac{1}{4\pi\varepsilon_0} \frac{q}{r^2} \mathbf{r}_1 \qquad (1.9)$$

where r now stands for the distance from the fixed charge q to the field point. In free space the vector $\mathbf{E}$ is directed along the line joining q and the field point. This directional property is described by the unit vector $\mathbf{r}_1$. By convention, $\mathbf{E}$ is directed away from q if q is positive, and toward q if q is negative.

If the electric field arises from a number of point charges, we must first determine the contribution of each of the individual charges to the resultant intensity at the field point. Then we obtain the resultant intensity by adding the individual contributions vectorially. In symbols, for n point charges in free space, we write

$$\mathbf{E} = \left[\mathbf{E}_1 + \mathbf{E}_2 + \cdots + \mathbf{E}_n \right] = \frac{1}{4\pi\varepsilon_0} \sum_{m=1}^{n} \frac{q_m \mathbf{r}_m}{r_m^3} \qquad (1.10)$$

where $\mathbf{r}_m$ is the vector displacement from the point charge q_m to the field point and r_m is its magnitude. The summation in (1.10) invokes the superposition principle for electric fields, which states that the resultant field at the field point is the vector sum of the individual field intensities produced by the various charges.

Point charge distributions are idealizations. And yet in a given physical situation we must be able to calculate the electric field due to the excess charge that resides within the volume and on the surface of an isolated body of finite dimensions. From the atomic point of view, electric charge occurs in multiples of a discrete unit, and on this scale we must regard charge as discontinuous. In dealing with ordinary large-scale electrification, however, we regard the charge distributions as continuous. This is a valid approach, since the calculation of the field quantities will be formulated in terms of differential elements of charge. These elements contain a very large number of electronic charges and have physical dimensions that are small relative to the distances between them. The approach is similar to that adopted in fluid mechanics, where the fluid, in spite of its molecular structure, is treated as a continuous distribution of matter.

On the microscopic scale, charged particles in matter are in motion. This would seem to imply that Coulomb's law, which applies to point charges at rest relative to the observer, cannot be considered valid when we are dealing with the interaction between physically small elements of charge. The nature of the force action between charges in motion will be discussed in Chapter 6, where it will be pointed out that in addition to the Coulomb interaction, there is a force which is dependent on the velocities of the moving charges. At a given instant, the force on a moving test charge arising from the movements of a large number of charges will average out to zero if the velocities of the charges in the assemblage are randomly oriented and if the moving charges reside in a volume element all points of which are essentially equidistant from the test charge.

For these reasons, Coulomb's law may be used to develop expressions for the field intensities produced by charges located in a volume of space or by charges spread over a surface. In the solution of such problems, it is convenient to introduce the concept of density of charge.

For a continuous distribution of charge in space, we introduce the quantity ρ, which defines the volume density of charge according to the relation

$$\rho = \lim_{V \to 0} \frac{Q}{V} \tag{1.11}$$

where Q is the excess charge in the volume V. The limit of this ratio as V shrinks about the point $P(x, y, z)$ gives the value of ρ at P. In general, ρ is a scalar function of position. If the charge distribution is uniform, then every volume element contains the same charge and ρ is a constant. In the mks system, ρ is expressed in coulombs per cubic meter.

In like manner, if the charge is distributed over an area, the surface density σ is defined by

$$\sigma = \lim_{A \to 0} \frac{Q}{A} \qquad (1.12)$$

and is expressed in coulombs per square meter.

Finally, if the charge resides on a thin filament, the quantity λ is used to denote the linear density, again represented by

$$\lambda = \lim_{L \to 0} \frac{Q}{L} \qquad (1.13)$$

and measured in coulombs per meter.

These three types of density are useful in expressing differential elements of charge dq. For example, in the cartesian coordinate system

$$dq = \rho \, dx \, dy \, dz$$

or

$$= \sigma \, dx \, dy \qquad (1.14)$$

or again

$$= \lambda \, dx$$

for the volume, surface, and linear distributions respectively. The dimensions of the differential element must be small relative to the distance from the element to the field point in question. In such a circumstance, the element of charge dq may be treated as a point charge.

1.4 **The Calculation of Electric Field Intensity Due to Sources in Free Space**

The field produced by a number of point charges at rest—or, more generally, the field produced by a static continuous charge distribution—can be evaluated directly by the application of (1.9). The method is outlined below:

(1) Write an expression for the contribution to the field at a given point in space. For discrete charges this is given directly by (1.9) for each charge. For a distribution, write the magnitude of the elementary vector $d\mathbf{E}$ at the selected field point. In this case the magnitude of $d\mathbf{E}$ is given by

$$dE = \frac{dq}{4\pi\varepsilon_0 r^2} \qquad (1.15)$$

where dq is the suitably chosen element of charge located at a distance r from the field point.

(2) In both cases referred to above, the contribution is a vector. Resolve this vector into components according to the system of coordinates chosen for the solution. For instance, in rectangular coordinates, resolve the vector $d\mathbf{E}$ into x, y, and z components.

(3) Along a given direction, the magnitudes of the components may be added as scalar quantities. The sum represents the corresponding component of the resultant. For distributions, resolve $d\mathbf{E}$ in a similar way and integrate over the given charge distribution to obtain a particular component of the resultant field.

(4) Find the magnitude of the resultant from each of its components and specify the direction of the resultant.

Several illustrations of this procedure follow:

(a) *Field arising from a number of discrete charges in empty space.* Consider point charges q_1, q_2, and q_3 located in the x,y plane as indicated in Fig. 1.2. Let $q_1 = -16 \times 10^{-9}$ coul, $q_2 = -3 \times 10^{-9}$ coul, and $q_3 = +50 \times 10^{-9}$ coul. It is desired to compute the electric intensity at the point O, the origin of coordinates. Due to q_1,

$$E_1 = 9 \times 10^9 \frac{16 \times 10^{-9}}{(4)^2} = 9 \text{ new/coul}$$

Figure 1.2   The field due to three point charges in a vacuum.

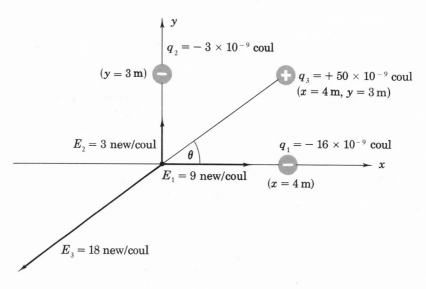

where $\mathbf{E}_1$ is directed toward q_1 along the $+x$-axis, since q_1 is negative. For convenience, the value of the constant C is taken as equal to 9×10^9 rather than the more precise value of 8.987×10^9.

Similarly,

$$E_2 = 9 \times 10^9 \frac{3 \times 10^{-9}}{(3)^2} = 3 \text{ new/coul}$$

and is directed toward q_2 along the $+y$-axis. And

$$E_3 = 9 \times 10^9 \frac{50 \times 10^{-9}}{(5)^2} = 18 \text{ new/coul}$$

and is directed along the line joining q_3 to O. The line makes an angle θ with the x-axis, where $\tan \theta = \frac{3}{4}$; hence $\sin \theta = \frac{3}{5}$ and $\cos \theta = \frac{4}{5}$. The sense of $\mathbf{E}_3$ is away from q_3.

Resolving $\mathbf{E}_1$, $\mathbf{E}_2$, and $\mathbf{E}_3$ into x and y components, we have

Source	x components, new/coul	y components, new/coul
q_1	+9.0	0.0
q_2	0.0	3.0
q_3	−14.4	−10.8

Hence the x and y components of the resultant are -5.4 and -7.8 new/coul respectively, and the magnitude of resultant $= \sqrt{(5.40)^2 + (7.80)^2} = 9.49$ new/coul. The resultant is directed along a line which makes an angle ϕ with the x-axis, where $\phi = \arctan (7.8/5.4) = 55.2°$.

(b) *Field due to a positive charge spread uniformly along a straight line.* Let the constant linear density be λ coul/m and let the filament of charge be located along the $+x$-axis, with the near end at $x = b$ and the far end at $x = c$ (see Fig. 1.3). At the point P, located at $y = -a$, the contribution $d\mathbf{E}$ due to an element of charge $dq = \lambda \, dx$ is

$$d\mathbf{E} = C \frac{\lambda \, dx}{r^2} \mathbf{r}_1$$

where $d\mathbf{E}$ is directed away from dq. Resolving into x and y components, we have

$$dE_x = dE \sin \theta = \frac{C\lambda x \, dx}{r^3} = \frac{C\lambda x \, dx}{(a^2 + x^2)^{3/2}} = \frac{C\lambda}{a} \sin \theta \, d\theta$$

$$dE_y = dE \cos \theta = \frac{C\lambda a \, dx}{r^3} = \frac{C\lambda a \, dx}{(a^2 + x^2)^{3/2}} = \frac{C\lambda}{a} \cos \theta \, d\theta$$

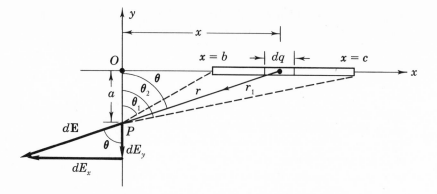

Figure 1.3   Electric intensity arising from a uniform charge residing along a line.

where the expressions at the extreme right were obtained by a change in variable in accordance with

$$x = a \tan \theta, \qquad dx = a \sec^2 \theta \, d\theta, \qquad r = a \sec \theta$$

E_x and E_y due to the entire distribution are found by integration with respect to x or with respect to θ. If x is chosen as the variable, the limits are $x = b$ to $x = c$. If θ is chosen as the variable, the limits become the constant angles θ_1 and θ_2. Thus

$$E_x = \frac{C\lambda}{a} \int_{\theta_1}^{\theta_2} \sin \theta \, d\theta \qquad \text{and} \qquad E_y = \frac{C\lambda}{a} \int_{\theta_1}^{\theta_2} \cos \theta \, d\theta$$

In the special case of a very long wire, extending equally along the x-axis in either direction, the evaluation may readily be achieved by allowing θ to vary from $-\pi/2$ to $+\pi/2$. Thus

$$E_x = \frac{C\lambda}{a} \int_{-\pi/2}^{+\pi/2} \sin \theta \, d\theta = 0$$

and

$$E_y = \frac{C\lambda}{a} \int_{-\pi/2}^{+\pi/2} \cos \theta \, d\theta = \frac{2C\lambda}{a}$$

In this case the vanishing of E_x can also be deduced from symmetry considerations, since for every element dq on the positive half of the x-axis there is a symmetrically placed element located on the negative x-axis. Considering these differential charge elements in pairs, we see that the corresponding differential contributions to the x component of the field cancel out. In the y

direction, dE_y is always in the same sense no matter where dq is located. This results in a nonvanishing result for E_y. The resultant is found from

$$E = \sqrt{E_x^2 + E_y^2} = \frac{\lambda}{2\pi\varepsilon_0 a} \qquad (1.16)$$

upon substituting the value for C. The resultant at P is directed along the y-axis away from the line distribution if λ is positive. The result in (1.16) shows that for an "infinitely" long uniformly charged straight line, the field strength is inversely proportional to a, the *first* power of the distance of the field point from the wire.

Physically, a uniformly charged thin long wire satisfies the conditions of the problem approximately. Indeed, a well-known detector of radiation (the GM counter) is provided with such a wire. The electric field outside the wire is correctly predicted by (1.16).

(c) *Electric intensity at an axial point of a uniformly charged cylindrical shell.* Consulting the diagram in Fig. 1.4 for the contribution from a surface element of charge to the field at an axial point P, we may write

$$d^2E = C\,\frac{dq}{r^2} = C\,\frac{\sigma a\,d\phi\,dx}{r^2}$$

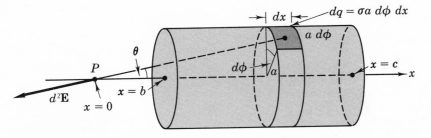

Figure 1.4　Field at axial points due to a uniformly charged cylindrical shell.

The field point is chosen at $x = 0$, and the surface element is located on the short cylindrical surface of radius a and thickness dx. The charge on the element is $\sigma a\,d\phi\,dx$, where σ is the surface charge per unit area.

We integrate the axial component of d^2E, taking into account only the charge on the narrow belt of width dx. The axial component is $d^2E \cos\theta$, and if we integrate over ϕ we obtain the field intensity at P due only to the charged shell of width dx. Thus

$$dE_{\text{axial}} = \frac{C\sigma ax\,dx}{r^3} \int_0^{2\pi} d\phi = \frac{\sigma ax\,dx}{2\varepsilon_0 r^3}$$

Because of axial symmetry, the integral of the radial component $d^2E \sin\theta$ vanishes.

Next we integrate dE_{axial} over the length of the cylinder to obtain the field at P due to the charge on the entire cylindrical surface. This yields

$$E_{\text{axial}} = \frac{\sigma a}{2\varepsilon_0} \int_{x=b}^{x=c} \frac{x\,dx}{(a^2 + x^2)^{\frac{3}{2}}} = \frac{\sigma a}{2\varepsilon_0} \left[-\frac{1}{(a^2 + x^2)^{\frac{1}{2}}} \right]_b^c \qquad (1.17)$$

$$E_{\text{axial}} = \frac{\sigma a}{2\varepsilon_0} \left[\frac{1}{(a^2 + b^2)^{\frac{1}{2}}} - \frac{1}{(a^2 + c^2)^{\frac{1}{2}}} \right]$$

If the field point is on the axis at one end, then $b = 0$, so that

$$E_{\substack{\text{axial} \\ \text{at end}}} = \frac{\sigma a}{2\varepsilon_0} \left[\frac{1}{a} - \frac{1}{(a^2 + c^2)^{\frac{1}{2}}} \right] \qquad (1.18)$$

Sources of the Electrostatic Field: **Problems**

Let $C = \frac{1}{4\pi\varepsilon_0} = 9 \times 10^9$ new-m²/coul².

1.1 A point charge is placed at the point O in an extended region in which a uniform electric field E_0 (magnitude 10^4 new/coul) has previously been established parallel to the line OP and directed from O to P. At the point P, 0.03 m from O, the resultant electric field is found to vanish. Determine the magnitude and the sign of the charge placed at O.

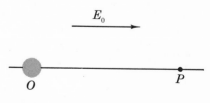

1.2 Three small objects, each having an electric charge of 2×10^{-6} coul, are placed at the corners of an equilateral triangle 3 cm on a side. Determine (a) the electric force acting on one of the objects, (b) the electric field at the center of the triangle.

1.3   In a certain region of space the electric field is directed downward
      and has a magnitude of 100 new/coul. A small charged particle of
      mass equal to 5.10×10^{-6} kg remains at rest when placed in the field.
      What are the magnitude and the sign of the charge on the particle?

1.4   A straight, slender rod, L m long, is
      charged positively and uniformly.
      The charge per unit length is λ
      coul/m. The rod is located on the
      positive x-axis. Find an expression
      for the magnitude of the electric in-
      tensity at the field point P located
      at the origin $(x = 0)$. The point P is
      at a distance of d m from the near
      end of the rod. Specify the direction
      of the field and state the units of
      the result.

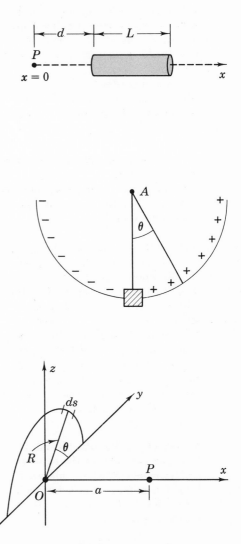

1.5   Two wires, each 4.5 m long, are
      joined to a small insulating block
      and are bent to form a semicircle.
      The wires to the right and left of
      the insulator are uniformly charged
      to a linear density of $+10^{-9}$ coul/m
      and -10^{-9} coul/m, respectively.
      What are the magnitude and the
      direction of the resultant field at
      point A, the center of the semi-
      circle?

1.6   A slender wire is bent into a semi-
      circle of radius R. The semicircle is
      located in the y,z plane with its cen-
      ter at the origin O. The wire is elec-
      trified uniformly with a positive
      linear charge density λ equal to
      $\frac{1}{3} \times 10^{-9}$ coul/m.

      (a) Treat the charge residing on the element of arc ds as a point
      charge and write an expression for the magnitude of the vector $d\mathbf{E}$,
      the contribution to the electric field at the point P due only to the

charge on ds. P is located on the x-axis a m from the origin. Reproduce the diagram and on it show the vector $d\mathbf{E}$.

(b) Set up an expression for the x component of the resultant electric field at P due to the entire charge on the semicircle.

(c) Evaluate the integral and give the units of the result.

1.7 A thin nonconducting wire in air is bent into a semicircle of radius R m. The wire is electrified in such a way that the linear density of charge is given by

$$\lambda = A \cos \theta \text{ coul/m}$$

where A is a constant and the angle θ is shown in the diagram.

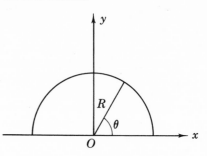

(a) Draw a graph showing how the linear density of charge varies with the angle θ.

(b) Calculate the magnitude of the electric intensity at the point O, the center of the semicircle. Specify the direction and the units of the electric intensity.

1.8 AB and DC are thin wires lying on the opposite sides of the square $ABCD$, whose side is 2 m in length. The wires are electrified uniformly with a positive linear charge density of $\frac{1}{3} \times 10^{-9}$ coul/m. Calculate the magnitude of the electric intensity at the point P, which is located at the midpoint of the side AD. Specify the direction and the units of the result. Assume the charged wires are located in free space.

1.9 Two slender lucite rods AB and BC form the two sides of the equilateral triangle ABC whose side is 5 m long. The rods are charged in such a way that λ, the linear density of charge, is given by

$$\lambda = \frac{r^3}{k} \text{ coul/m}$$

where $k = 9 \times 10^9$ mks units, and r is the distance in meters from a

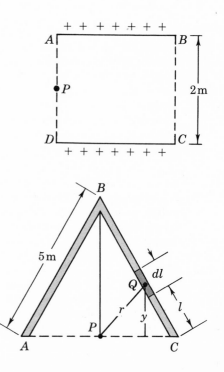

point Q on the rod to the point P, which is the midpoint of the third side AC.

(a) What is the magnitude of the contribution to the field at P due to the charge on an element of length dl?

(b) Calculate the magnitude of the electric intensity at P due to the charge distribution on AB and BC. Specify the direction and unit of the answer. Hint: Use y as the variable of integration.

1.10   One face of a thin circular disk of radius R is charged uniformly with a positive surface charge density σ.

(a) Derive an expression for the magnitude of the electric intensity at a point on the axis of the disk at a distance x from the center of the disk, considering the distribution to be a plane sheet of charge.

(b) By allowing $R \rightarrow \infty$, obtain the magnitude of the field at the point x due to a uniformly charged plane of large area.

1.11   An electron (mass 9.11×10^{-31} kg, charge -1.60×10^{-19} coul) is projected into a uniform electric field whose strength is 25×10^3 new/coul. The field is directed along the positive y-axis. Determine the x and y coordinates of the position of the electron after an elapsed time t sec when the electron is projected with a speed of 2×10^4 m/sec (a) along the positive y-axis, (b) along the positive x-axis.

1.12   A point charge $+q$ is placed at a distance $2l$ from a charge $-q$. The charges are positioned on the x-axis, so that the origin O is at the midpoint of the line joining the charges. Determine the magnitude and direction of the electric field at the following points:

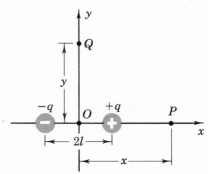

(a) The origin. (b) The point P on the x-axis at a distance x from O. (c) The point Q on the y-axis at a distance y from O. (d) Simplify the results when the distance to field points P and Q is made much larger than $2l$.

1.13   By integrating Coulomb's law, calculate the magnitude of the electric intensity at a point outside a uniformly charged spherical surface. Hint: Start with the expression for the field on the axis of a uniformly charged ring. For the charge element, use a ring-shaped charge distribution on the surface of the sphere.

Chapter 2.
Potential

2.1 Electrostatic Potential

In the electrostatic field $\mathbf{E}$, a given charge q is subject to a force $\mathbf{F} = \mathbf{E}q$. If the charge is given a vector displacement $d\mathbf{l}$ by the application of an equal but oppositely directed force $-\mathbf{F}$ provided by an external agent, the element of work done is given by

$$dW = -\mathbf{F} \cdot d\mathbf{l} \tag{2.1}$$

Since the applied force has the same magnitude as the force due to the field, the charge is not accelerated. However, the work dW done on the charge increases its potential energy. [The quantity $\mathbf{F} \cdot d\mathbf{l}$ is the dot product of the two vectors $\mathbf{F}$ and $d\mathbf{l}$. The dot product is a scalar whose magnitude is $F\,dl\cos\theta$, where θ is the angle between $\mathbf{F}$ and $d\mathbf{l}$. See Appendix A. This quantity may be regarded as the product of dl, the magnitude of the displacement and $(F\cos\theta)$, the component of the force along the displacement. This product, by definition, is the measure of the work done.] If both sides of (2.1) are divided by q, the result is

$$\frac{dW}{q} = -\mathbf{E} \cdot d\mathbf{l} \tag{2.2}$$

The quantity dW/q, which represents the work per unit charge, is defined as the increase in the potential of the charge q. Denoting this increase by dV, we have

$$dV = -\mathbf{E} \cdot d\mathbf{l} \tag{2.3}$$

In the present discussion, we must regard the charge q as a test charge which is sufficiently small so that dW/q and hence dV, the increase in potential, do not depend on q.

18

The applied force **F** can be resolved into rectangular components F_x, F_y, and F_z. Similarly the vector displacement $d\mathbf{l}$ has components dx, dy, and dz. The work dW done by the force **F** can be equated to the total work done by each of its components. Thus $-F_x \, dx$ is the element of work done by the x component of the applied force. Similarly $-F_y \, dy$ and $-F_z \, dz$ represent the work done by the other components. Hence

$$dW = -(F_x \, dx + F_y \, dy + F_z \, dz)$$

and
$$\frac{dW}{q} = dV = -(E_x \, dx + E_y \, dy + E_z \, dz) \tag{2.4}$$

where E_x, E_y, and E_z are the magnitudes of the rectangular components of the field vector **E**.

The potential difference between two points can be calculated by evaluating the integral

$$V_1 - V_2 = -\int_2^1 E \cos \theta \, dl \tag{2.5}$$

provided E can be expressed as a function of the coordinates. Equation (2.5) defines the potential difference between the points 1 and 2 as the negative of the line integral of the electric field intensity from point 2 to point 1. Physically $(V_1 - V_2)$ is equal to the work per unit charge done against electrostatic force when a test charge is carried from point 2 to point 1.

Point 1 is said to be at a potential higher than that of point 2 if work is done by an external agent against the electrostatic force when a positive charge is transported from point 2 to point 1.

Potential difference is expressed in volts. The potential difference between two points is said to be one volt if one joule of work per coulomb is done in moving charge from one point to the other.

Let us calculate the potential difference between two points P_1 and P_2 in the field of a point charge q at the origin. As a special circumstance, let P_1 and P_2 be located on the x-axis at $x = a$ and $x = b$, as shown in Fig. 2.1. In this case, $E_x = Cq/r^2$ and

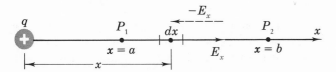

Figure 2.1 Potential difference between points P_1 and P_2 in the field of a point charge at the origin. The points P_1 and P_2 lie on the same straight line.

$E_y = E_z = 0$, so that $dV = -E_x\,dx$. By definition the potential difference between P_1 and P_2 is the work done per unit charge against electrostatic force in transporting a test charge from P_2 to P_1. The potential difference is denoted as $V_{1,2}$ or as $(V_1 - V_2)$. By applying (2.5), we obtain

$$V_1 - V_2 = \int_{P_2}^{P_1} dV = -\int_{x=b}^{x=a} E_x\,dx = Cq\left[\frac{1}{a} - \frac{1}{b}\right] \quad (2.6)$$

If the integration is carried out for the case where the test charge is moved from a point at infinity to a point a units away from the charge q, the result is Cq/a and is called the potential at P_1. This calculation also implies that Cq/b is the potential at P_2. As $b \to \infty$, $Cq/b \to 0$, so that in this case the zero of potential may be taken at infinity.

It is instructive to calculate the work done per unit charge with the use of vectorial representation. In Fig. 2.2 let $d\mathbf{l}$ represent a small vector displacement at a distance $\mathbf{r}$ from q. The work done by the field is the scalar product $\mathbf{E} \cdot d\mathbf{l}$. The differential increase in potential dV is defined as the work done against the field, so that

$$dV = -\mathbf{E} \cdot d\mathbf{l} = -E\cos\theta\,dl \quad (2.7)$$

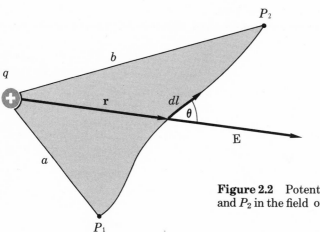

Figure 2.2   Potential difference between P_1 and P_2 in the field of a point charge q.

which may be interpreted as the product of the component of $\mathbf{E}$ along the displacement $d\mathbf{l}$; as before, it represents work done per unit charge. In vector notation, $\mathbf{E} = Cq\mathbf{r}_1/r^2$. Substitution of $\mathbf{E}$ in (2.7) gives

$$dV = -\frac{Cq}{r^2}\,\mathbf{r}_1 \cdot d\mathbf{l} \quad (2.8)$$

where $\mathbf{r}_1$ is a unit vector along $\mathbf{r}$. Since the magnitude of $\mathbf{r}_1$ is unity, the dot product in (2.8) is equal to ($dl \cos \theta$), or simply dr. Equation (2.8) can thus be written as $dV = -Cq\ dr/r^2$, and the difference in potential between P_1 and P_2 is

$$V_1 - V_2 = -Cq \int_{r=b}^{r=a} \frac{dr}{r^2} = Cq\left(\frac{1}{a} - \frac{1}{b}\right) \tag{2.9}$$

as before.

It may be instructive to make the same calculation using rectangular components. Inspection of Fig. 2.3 shows that $E_x = Cqx/r^3$, $E_y = Cqy/r^3$, and $E_z = 0$. Returning to (2.5),

$$dV = -Cq\left[\frac{x\ dx}{(x^2 + y^2)^{3/2}} + \frac{y\ dy}{(x^2 + y^2)^{3/2}}\right] \tag{2.10}$$

whence

$$V_1 - V_2 = -Cq\left[\int_{x_2}^{x_1} \frac{x\ dx}{(x^2 + y_1^2)^{3/2}} + \int_{y_2}^{y_1} \frac{y\ dy}{(x_2^2 + y^2)^{3/2}}\right]$$

$$= Cq\left(\frac{1}{a} - \frac{1}{b}\right) \tag{2.11}$$

In integrating over x, we proceed from R to P_1. Hence $y = y_1 =$ Constant in the expression for the distance from the origin to any

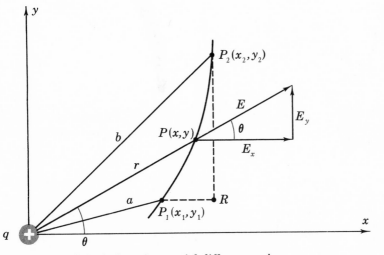

Figure 2.3   Calculation of potential difference using rectangular components.

point along P_1R. Similarly, in integrating over y, we proceed from P_2 to R, and hence $x = x_2 = $ Constant. The total work done in traversing from P_2 to R to P_1 along paths parallel to the y- and x-axes is thus found to be equal to the work done in passing from P_2 to P_1 along the arbitrary path P_2PP_1.

The approach followed in deducing the results given in (2.9) or (2.11) makes it clear that the difference in potential between two points is independent of the path traversed and depends only on the coordinates of the end points. A field in which the potential difference is independent of the path is called a conservative field.

Consider the two fixed points 1 and 2 in Fig. 2.4. If a test charge is taken from 2 to 1 via path A, the work done per unit charge, or the potential difference, is $(V_1 - V_2)$ and constitutes a rise in potential. However, if the test charge is moved from 2 to 1 via path B, the amount of work done is also $(V_1 - V_2)$. If the path B is traversed from 1 to 2, there is a drop in potential numerically equal to the rise encountered in going from 2 to 1 via path A; that is, $(V_1 - V_2) + (V_2 - V_1) = 0$. As a consequence, no net work is done on the test charge if it is taken from point 2 to 1 via path A and is returned to the starting point 2 via path B. Applying the definition given in (2.3), we write for the work done per unit charge in going around a closed path

$$\int_{\substack{2 \\ \text{path } A}}^{1} -\mathbf{E} \cdot d\mathbf{l} + \int_{\substack{1 \\ \text{path } B}}^{2} -\mathbf{E} \cdot d\mathbf{l} = (V_1 - V_2) + (V_2 - V_1) \equiv 0 \qquad (2.12)$$

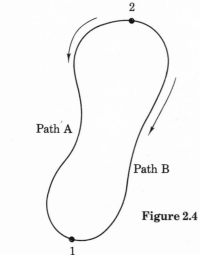

Figure 2.4   The circuital law for the electrostatic field.

The line integrals over path A and path B may be combined and represented as

$$\oint \mathbf{E} \cdot d\mathbf{l} = 0 \tag{2.13}$$

where the symbol $\bigcirc$ (loop around the integral sign) means that the integration is carried out over a closed path. (Consult Appendix A.) The vanishing of the line integral around a closed path is a characteristic property of the electrostatic field in general.

Since potential differences are additive, the same type of reasoning would hold if, instead of a single point charge, the source of the static field consisted of any static distribution of charge. The relation in (2.13) is known as the circuital law of the electrostatic field.

2.2   **The Potential Function**

Suppose that in the calculation leading to the result in (2.6), P_2 is taken as a fixed reference point whose coordinate is x_0, while P_1 is considered to be any point on the x-axis at a distance x from the charge q. Then (2.6) may be written as

$$V_1 - V_2 = Cq\left(\frac{1}{x} - \frac{1}{x_0}\right) \tag{2.14}$$

which shows that the potential difference is a function of x, the coordinate of P_1. Since P_2 is fixed, V_2 is a constant and (2.14) can be put in the form

$$V_1 - V_2 = V(x) - V(x_0) \tag{2.15}$$

The right-hand member of (2.15) represents a one-dimensional potential function. If the reference point is a point at infinity, then $V(x_0) = -Cq/x_0$ can be set equal to zero and the potential function for this case of motion along the x-axis reduces to

$$V(x) = \frac{q}{4\pi\varepsilon_0} \cdot \frac{1}{x} \tag{2.16}$$

In the more general case, P_1 and P_2 are specified by three coordinates (x, y, z) and (x_0, y_0, z_0). For an assemblage of point charges or finite charge distributions, similar to those found in nature, the reference point may be taken at infinity and the constant term $V(x_0, y_0, z_0)$ may be made equal to zero. (For certain charge distributions encountered in exercises, the reference potential may not always be set equal to zero.) The potential function in general will depend on three variables and in the rectangular system is denoted by $V(x, y, z)$.

In (2.4) the increase in potential was expressed in terms of the rectangular components of the field and in terms of the x, y, and z component displacements along the axes. In cartesian coordinates a differential change in potential resulting from a displacement dl with components dx, dy, and dz can be expressed in terms of the total differential—that is,

$$dV = \frac{\partial V}{\partial x} dx + \frac{\partial V}{\partial y} dy + \frac{\partial V}{\partial z} dz \qquad (2.17)$$

The partial derivatives in (2.17) imply that in differentiating the potential function $V(x, y, z)$ only one variable at a time is allowed to vary. The partial derivative $\partial V/\partial x$ denotes that in differentiating $V(x, y, z)$, y and z are to be regarded as constants and that only x is allowed to vary. Similar statements apply to the remaining partial derivatives. A comparison of (2.4) and (2.17) brings out the connection between $V(x, y, z)$ and the components of the field, namely

$$\frac{\partial V}{\partial x} = -E_x, \qquad \frac{\partial V}{\partial y} = -E_y, \qquad \frac{\partial V}{\partial z} = -E_z \qquad (2.18)$$

Thus, if $V(x, y, z)$ is given, the components of $\mathbf{E}$ may be obtained by partial differentiation.

A theorem dealing with the properties of line integrals such as

$$\oint \mathbf{E} \cdot d\mathbf{l} = \oint (E_x \, dx + E_y \, dy + E_z \, dz)$$

states that the necessary and sufficient condition for the vanishing of the integral over a closed curve is

$$\frac{\partial E_x}{\partial y} = \frac{\partial E_y}{\partial x}, \qquad \frac{\partial E_y}{\partial z} = \frac{\partial E_z}{\partial y}, \qquad \frac{\partial E_z}{\partial x} = \frac{\partial E_x}{\partial z} \qquad (2.19)$$

Another way of describing the property physically is to say that the work done in transporting charge between a pair of fixed points is not dependent on the path if equalities of the partial derivatives in (2.19) are satisfied. The equalities in (2.19) make it possible to test whether or not a given set of components E_x, E_y, and E_z are associated with an electrostatic or a conservative field. If the given components fulfill the relations in (2.19), then these components are derivable from a potential function in accordance with (2.18).

To illustrate the principles involved, let the components of an electric field in the x,y plane be described by

$$E_x = -\frac{y}{(x^2 + y^2)^{1/2}}, \qquad E_y = \frac{x}{(x^2 + y^2)^{1/2}}$$

Does the field represent an electrostatic field? Applying the test, we find

$$\frac{\partial E_x}{\partial y} = -\frac{x^2}{(x^2 + y^2)^{3/2}}, \qquad \frac{\partial E_y}{\partial x} = \frac{y^2}{(x^2 + y^2)^{3/2}}$$

Hence the field is not conservative, and the work done in transporting a test charge from one fixed point to another depends on the path chosen.

On the other hand, if

$$E_x = \frac{-2x}{x^2 + y^2} \qquad \text{and} \qquad E_y = \frac{-2y}{x^2 + y^2}$$

then

$$\frac{\partial E_x}{\partial y} = \frac{\partial E_y}{\partial x} = \frac{4xy}{(x^2 + y^2)^2}$$

Hence the given components represent an electrostatic field. Also from

$$dV = \frac{2x}{(x^2 + y^2)} \, dx + \frac{2y}{(x^2 + y^2)} \, dy$$

we find $V(x, y) - V(x_0, y_0) = \ln(x^2 + y^2) - \ln(x_0^2 + y_0^2)$

2.3   Calculation of Potential Difference

If the electric field is known, then the defining relation given in (2.5) may be used directly. However, if its charge distribution is given, we may consider this distribution to be made up of elements of charge, each of which can be treated as a point charge. According to (2.16), the contribution to the potential at a fixed point in the field is given by

$$dV = \frac{dq}{4\pi\varepsilon_0 r} \tag{2.20}$$

where dq is an element of charge belonging to the distribution, and r is the distance of dq from the field point. The potential V

due to the entire charge distribution at the fixed point is deduced from

$$V = \frac{1}{4\pi\varepsilon_0} \int \frac{dq}{r} \qquad (2.21)$$

where the integration is carried out over the charge distribution—that is, the limits of the integral are determined by the range of values assumed by the coordinates of dq. Since no vector addition is involved, the method is simpler than the procedure where we compute the components of $\mathbf{E}$ from the charge distribution and then integrate $\mathbf{E}$ between two field points to arrive at the potential difference.

As an illustration, let us calculate the potential on the axis of a ring of charge. Let λ represent the charge per unit arc length. Then $dq = \lambda\, ds$, where ds is an element of arc length. With the aid of Fig. 2.5, we see that the contribution to the potential at P is

$$dV = \frac{1}{4\pi\varepsilon_0} \frac{dq}{r} = \frac{\lambda a\, d\phi}{4\pi\varepsilon_0 r}$$

where a is the radius of the ring and ϕ is the central angle in the plane of the ring. The potential at P due to the entire ring distribution is then given by integrating from $\phi = 0$ to $\phi = 2\pi$. Hence

$$V = \frac{\lambda a}{4\pi\varepsilon_0 r} \int_0^{2\pi} d\phi = \frac{2\pi a\lambda}{4\pi\varepsilon_0 r} = \frac{a\lambda}{2\varepsilon_0 r}$$

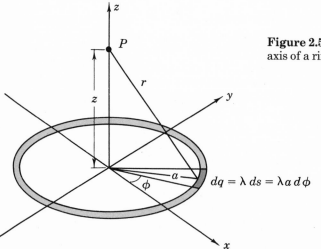

Figure 2.5 The potential on the axis of a ring of charge.

$dq = \lambda\, ds = \lambda a\, d\phi$

In terms of the axial distance of the field point,

$$V = \frac{a\lambda}{2\varepsilon_0 \sqrt{z^2 + a^2}}$$

For axial points only, the z component of the field is obtained from

$$E_z = -\frac{\partial V}{\partial z} = \frac{a\lambda z}{2\varepsilon_0(z^2 + a^2)^{3/2}} = \frac{Qz}{4\pi\varepsilon_0(z^2 + a^2)^{3/2}}$$

where Q is the total charge on the ring.

2.4   Equipotential Surfaces and Lines of Force

The electrostatic field may be represented graphically by a set of lines and a set of surfaces. If the potential function is constant at all points of a surface, then $dV = 0$. Consequently, for a displacement $d\mathbf{l}$ along the surface, $-\mathbf{E} \cdot d\mathbf{l} = 0$, which means that $\mathbf{E}$ is either zero or perpendicular to $d\mathbf{l}$. (Recall that the magnitude of the dot product is $E \cos \theta \, dl$, so that for a nonzero value of E, $\cos \theta$ must equal zero, or the angle between $\mathbf{E}$ and $d\mathbf{l}$ is $\pi/2$.) Physically, no work is done on a charge as the latter is moved along an equipotential surface. The line, whose tangent at any point has the direction of the electric field, is called a line of force. Hence, lines of force intersect an equipotential surface at right angles.

For a point charge q at the origin, equipotential surfaces are concentric spherical surfaces with the center at the origin. Lines of force are straight lines in the radial direction. Such surfaces can be labeled by indicating the constant value of the potential relative to a reference value of the potential. Figure 2.6(a) illustrates the map of the electrostatic field associated with a point charge. Taking $q = 4\pi\varepsilon_0 = (\frac{1}{9}) \times 10^{-9}$ coul, a spherical surface with a radius of 0.01 m will be a constant potential surface at all points of which the potential will be 100 v, relative to a point at infinity which is taken as the zero of potential. Similarly, the constant value of the potential on the spherical surface with a radius of 0.1 m is 10 v. Figure 2.6(b) shows the equipotentials and lines of force for two equal and opposite point charges.

If we know the components of the electric intensity at all points of the field, we can derive the equation of the family of

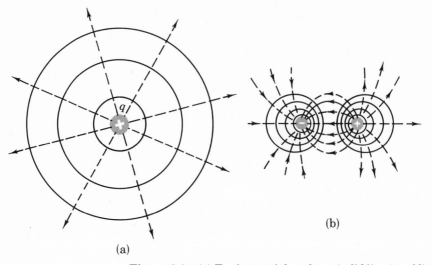

(a)

(b)

Figure 2.6   (a) Equipotential surfaces (solid lines) and lines of force (dashed lines) for a point charge at the origin. (b) Two equal point charges, one positive and one negative. The maps represent intersections of three-dimensional surfaces with the plane of the diagram.

Figure 2.7   The components of the electric field intensity and the tangent of the line of force.

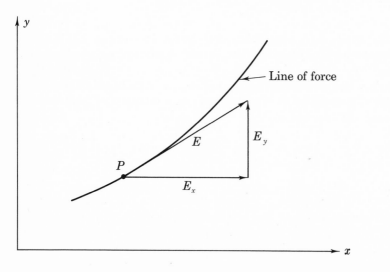

curves representing the lines of force as follows: In Fig. 2.7, the vector **E**, tangent to the line of force at P, has a slope E_y/E_x. But this is exactly the slope of dy/dx of the line of force at the point P, so that

$$\frac{dy}{dx} = \frac{E_y}{E_x} \tag{2.22}$$

As an illustration, let the components of the field in a certain region be given by

$$E_x = \frac{-kx}{(x^2 + y^2)}, \qquad E_y = \frac{-ky}{(x^2 + y^2)}, \qquad E_z = 0$$

where k is a positive constant. Substitution in (2.22) results in the equation

$$\frac{dy}{dx} = \frac{y}{x} \qquad \text{or} \qquad \frac{dy}{y} = \frac{dx}{x}$$

whence $$\ln y = \ln x + \ln C$$

or $$y = Cx$$

where C is a constant of integration. The lines of force are a family of straight lines in the x,y plane passing through the origin. The equipotential traces in the x,y plane are circles.

2.5 Illustrative Examples

Example 1. A point charge q_1 equal to $+80 \times 10^{-9}$ coul is situated on the x-axis at the origin. A second point charge q_2 equal to -60×10^{-9} coul is placed at $x = +0.20$ m. The field point A is located on the x-axis at $x = 0.10$ m. A second field point B is situated in the x,y plane at a distance of 0.16 m from q_1 and 0.12 m from q_2.

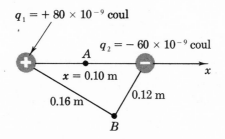

$q_1 = +80 \times 10^{-9}$ **coul**

$q_2 = -60 \times 10^{-9}$ **coul**

A

$x = 0.10$ m

0.16 m

0.12 m

x

B

(a) Calculate the potential at the point A.

$$V_A = 9 \times 10^9 \left(\frac{80 \times 10^{-9}}{0.10} - \frac{60 \times 10^{-9}}{0.10} \right) = 1800 \text{ v}$$

(b) Calculate the potential at the point B.

$$V_B = 9 \times 10^9 \left(\frac{80 \times 10^{-9}}{0.16} - \frac{60 \times 10^{-9}}{0.12} \right) = 0.0 \text{ v}$$

(c) Calculate the work done in transferring a charge of $+20 \times 10^{-6}$ coul from B to A.

$$W_{AB} = (V_A - V_B)q = (1800 - 0) \times 20 \times 10^{-6} = 0.036 \text{ joule}$$

The point A is at the higher potential. Hence work must be done by an external force.

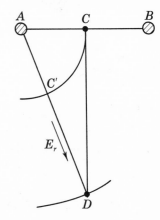

Example 2. Two long, thin electrified wires intersect the plane of the paper normally at A and B. The magnitude of the electric field due to each wire is $(1/r)$ new/coul, its direction being radially away from the wire. Calculate the potential difference between the points C and D. Consider CD the perpendicular bisector of AB. Let $AC = CB = 4.00$ m, $CD = 10.12$ m, and $AD = 10.88$ m.

First consider the wire passing through A. In the field of this charged wire draw the circular equipotential traces passing through C and D. Then for wire A

$$V_{CD} = V_{C'D} = - \int_{10.88}^{4.00} E_r \, dr = \int_{4.00}^{10.88} \frac{dr}{r}$$

$$= \ln \frac{10.88}{4.00} = \ln 2.72 = 1.00 \text{ v}$$

In the field of *both* wires the potential difference is 2.00 v.

Example 3. An uncharged conducting sphere of radius a is immersed in an extensive uniform field E_0, directed on the z-axis.

The location of a field point P at a distance r $(r > a)$ from the center of the sphere may be specified by spherical coordinates r, θ, and ϕ. Because of symmetry, the electric field is independent of ϕ. By more advanced methods, it is found that the potential outside the sphere is

$$V = -\left(1 - \frac{a^3}{r^3}\right) E_0 r \cos\theta$$

Find the components of the electric field outside the sphere.

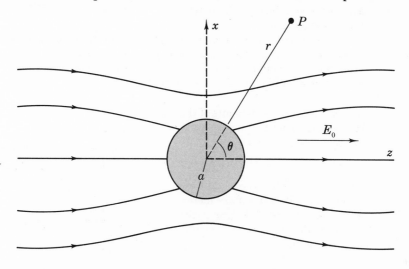

The component along the radius vector $\mathbf{r}$ is obtained by partial differentiation of V with respect to r. Hence

$$E_r = -\frac{\partial V}{\partial r} = \left(1 + \frac{2a^3}{r^3}\right) E_0 \cos\theta$$

In the direction of increasing θ, that is, at right angles to the radius vector, we have

$$E_\theta = -\frac{1}{r}\left(\frac{\partial V}{\partial \theta}\right) = -\left(1 - \frac{a^3}{r^3}\right) E_0 \sin\theta$$

This example illustrates the use of the spherical coordinate system. If the potential also depends on the azimuthal angle ϕ, E_ϕ is derivable from

$$-\frac{1}{r\sin\theta}\frac{\partial V}{\partial \phi}$$

Potential: **Problems**

2.1   A straight, thin rod, L m long is charged positively with uniform linear density of λ coul/m. As shown in the diagram, the rod is located on the positive x-axis.

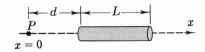

Starting with the expression for the potential in the field of a point charge, calculate the potential at the point P located at the origin $(x = 0)$. The point P is at a distance of d m from the near end of the rod. Specify the units of the result.

2.2   The rectangular components of the electrostatic field $\mathbf{E}$ at any point in the x,y plane are given by

$$E_x = Cx, \qquad E_y = Cy, \qquad E_z = 0$$

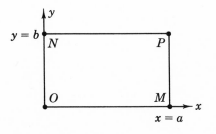

where C is a positive constant expressed in volts per square meter, and where x and y represent the distance of the field point in meters from the origin O.

(a) What are the direction and magnitude of the electric intensity at any point in the x,y plane? From this, sketch the lines of force in the x,y plane.

(b) Consider the rectangular path $OMPN$. Calculate the potential difference between the point P and O, by integrating the electric field first along PN, then along NO.

(c) Evaluate the line integral of $\mathbf{E}$ around the rectangular path. What property of the electrostatic field is illustrated by this example?

2.3   Under undisturbed conditions, there is a downward-directed electric field above the surface of the earth. If y represents the height in meters measured from the surface, E_y, the magnitude of the field over a limited range in y, can be represented as

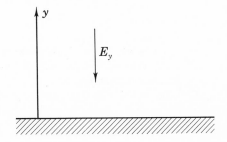

$$E_y = -(300 - 0.010y) \text{ v/m}$$

Over the range of validity of E_y, obtain an expression for the potential above the surface, taking the surface to be at zero potential.

2.4 A thin semicircular wire of radius R m is located in the y,z plane with its center at the origin O. Let the wire be electrified in such a way that the linear charge density λ is given by

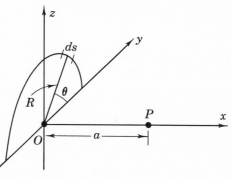

$$\lambda = 10^{-9} \cos^2 \theta \text{ coul/m}$$

where θ is the angle shown in the diagram.

(a) Consider the charge residing on the element of arc length ds as a point charge and write an expression for the potential at the point P due only to the charge on ds. The point P is on the x-axis, a m from the origin.

(b) Set up an integral for the potential at P arising from the charge on the entire semicircle.

(c) Evaluate the integral and give the units of the answer. Take $1/(4\pi\varepsilon_0) = 9 \times 10^9$ mks units. Hint: $\cos 2\theta = 2 \cos^2 \theta - 1$.

2.5 A thin circular ring is electrified uniformly with positive charge. The magnitude of the electric field $\mathbf{E}$ at any point on the axis of the ring at a distance of x m from the center is given by

$$E = \frac{x}{(x^2 + 1)^{3/2}} \quad \text{new/coul}$$

Compute the work done in transferring a charge of 9×10^{-9} coul from a point on the axis located at $x = 2\sqrt{2}$ m to the center of the ring.

2.6 The components of a field are given by $E_x = -ay$, $E_y = ax$, and $E_z = 0$, where a is a positive constant.

(a) Is the field a conservative one?

(b) What is the magnitude of the line integral of $\mathbf{E}$ around a square whose side is L?

(c) What is the "potential difference" between the center and one corner of the square? Is this a meaningful question?

(d) Determine the equation which represents a line of force.

2.7 Two charged plane conducting surfaces, OA and OB, are set at an
angle $\alpha = \pi/4$ radians but do not
quite touch along the line of inter-
section. Traces of the electric lines
of force are circles whose common
center is at O (see diagram). The
electric intensity at any point P in
the space between the plates is
$400/\pi r$ new/coul, where r is the
radial distance in meters from O to
P. Neglecting edge effects, calculate
the potential difference between
OA and OB.

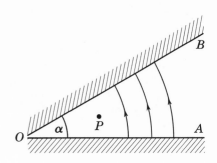

2.8 In the region between the plane electrodes of a vacuum diode the potential is given by

$$V = Cx^{4/3}$$

where C is a positive constant and x is the distance measured normally from one of the electrodes.

Let the potential of the cathode (the electrode at $x = 0$) be zero.
Let an electron leave the cathode normally with negligible velocity.

(a) What is the total energy (K.E. + P.E.) of the electron at any
point x units away from the cathode? Neglect relativistic effects—i.e.,
regard the mass of the electron as independent of velocity.

(b) If the second electrode (anode) is located at $x = a$, how long
does it take for the electron to go from one plate to the other?

(c) The electronic charge is -1.60×10^{-19} coul and its mass is
9.11×10^{-31} kg. If the potential of the anode is 100 v and $a = 1$
cm, evaluate the velocity of the electron on arrival at the anode and
the time of flight.

2.9 One face of a thin circular disk of radius R is charged uniformly with
a positive surface-charge density.

(a) Derive an expression for the potential at a point on the axis of
the disk at a distance x from the center of the disk. Consider the distribution to be a plane sheet of charge.

(b) From your answer to (a), derive an expression for the electric
intensity at this point. What is its direction?

(c) From your answer to (b), obtain the field at the point x due to a
uniformly charged plane of large area, by allowing $R \to \infty$. (See
Problem 1.10.)

2.10   In a certain region of space the rectangular components of the electric field intensity are given by

$$E_x = \frac{Cx}{(x^2 + y^2)^{3/2}}, \qquad E_y = \frac{Cy}{(x^2 + y^2)^{3/2}}, \qquad E_z = 0$$

where the constant C has the numerical value of 10 v-m when distances are expressed in meters.

Find the difference in potential between two points A and B located on the positive x-axis at $x = 2.00$ m and $x = 5.00$ m respectively.

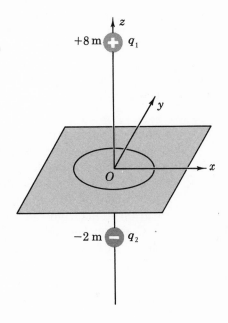

2.11   A point charge

$$q_1 = +36 \times 10^{-12} \text{ coul}$$

and a second point charge

$$q_2 = -18 \times 10^{-12} \text{ coul}$$

are located on the z-axis at $z = +8$ m and $z = -2$ m respectively. In the x,y plane, the circle of radius 4 m and center at the origin O represents an equipotential trace.

What is the potential difference between the origin and any point on the circle? Which point is at the higher potential? Take

$$\varepsilon_0 = 9 \times 10^{-12} \text{ farad/m}$$

2.12   In a certain region in space the "potential" is taken as

$$V = \frac{K}{(x^2 + y^2 + z^2)}$$

Calculate the components of the field and decide whether the components represent an electrostatic field.

Chapter 3.
Fundamental Theorem of Electrostatics

3.1   Gauss's Law

So far in our discussion of electrostatic phenomena we have dealt with the concepts of charge, fields of force, and potential difference. We now introduce a generalization which may serve as the starting point for determining the relationships between the distribution of source charges and the field quantities. The generalization stems from Coulomb's law.

Consider the field due to a single positive point charge q, as shown in Fig. 3.1. Let an imaginary spherical surface of radius r

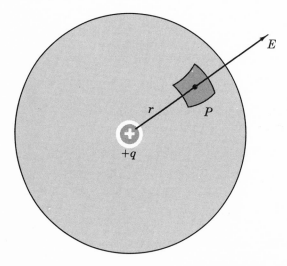

Figure 3.1   Point charge $+q$ surrounded by an imaginary spherical surface.

36

be drawn through the field point P, with the center of the surface located at the point charge. The magnitude of the vector $\mathbf{E}$ has the constant value of $q/4\pi\varepsilon_0 r^2$ at all points of this surface, and the vector is directed radially outward from the center. Suppose the magnitude of $\mathbf{E}$ is multiplied by the surface area of the sphere $4\pi r^2$. Then q/ε_0 is the result, which is independent of the radius of the imaginary spherical surface that surrounds the charge q. We have already seen that a line of force may be used to designate the *direction* of the field. The above observation suggests a way of designating the *magnitude* of the field.

Picture lines of force spaced in such a way that the number of lines per unit area crossing a surface drawn normally to the field is equal to the strength of the field. The total number of lines crossing a given surface is called the *flux* of $\mathbf{E}$ and will be denoted by Φ. In the example of the spherical surface enclosing a charge q, the flux of $\mathbf{E}$ is q/ε_0.

In general, a surface drawn in an electric field will not be at right angles to the field. Moreover, the magnitude of $\mathbf{E}$ will vary from point to point. In this instance the flux of $\mathbf{E}$ can be expressed as follows: In Fig. 3.2, let dA represent an element of area whose normal $\mathbf{n}_1$ makes an angle θ with the field. The projection of dA perpendicular to $\mathbf{E}$ is $dA \cos \theta$. Thus the element of flux $d\Phi$ through dA is

$$d\Phi = E \cos \theta \, dA \qquad (3.1)$$

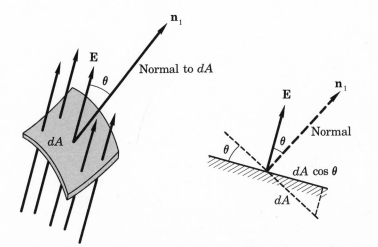

Figure 3.2 Electric field directed obliquely to an element of surface.

If $\mathbf{n}_1$ is a unit vector along the normal, then the vector $d\mathbf{A} = \mathbf{n}_1 \, dA$ has the magnitude of the element of area and the direction of its normal. Hence in vector notation, (3.1) can be written as the dot product

$$d\Phi = \mathbf{E} \cdot d\mathbf{A} \tag{3.2}$$

Since $E \cos \theta = E_n$, the component of $\mathbf{E}$ normal to dA, we can write alternately

$$d\Phi = E_n \, dA \tag{3.3}$$

Let us digress for a moment to comment on the measurement of solid angles. In Fig. 3.3, consider lines drawn from all points of the periphery of the area A_1 to O, the center of the spherical surface on which A_1 is located. The conical aperture described in this manner specifies the solid angle ω.

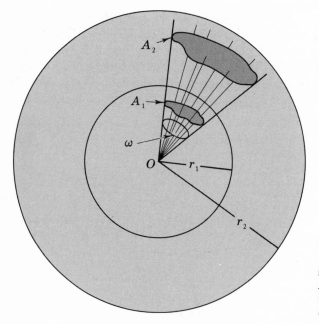

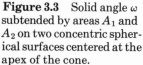

Figure 3.3 Solid angle ω subtended by areas A_1 and A_2 on two concentric spherical surfaces centered at the apex of the cone.

A plane angle whose apex is at the center of a circle of radius r is measured by the ratio s/r, where s is the arc length subtended by the central angle. The angle so defined is expressed in radians and is independent of the radius of the circle, since the circumference is directly proportional to the radius.

In defining a solid angle, a similar procedure is followed. The surface area of a sphere is proportional to the square of its radius.

Therefore the magnitude of the solid angle is measured by the
ratio A/r^2, where A is the area intercepted by the conical aperture on a spherical surface of radius r. Figure 3.3 shows two areas,
A_1 and A_2, cut out on spheres of radius r_1 and r_2. The solid angle
ω is defined either by A_1/r_1^2 or by A_2/r_2^2 independently of the radius. Solid angles are measured in steradian, and one steradian
(sr) is defined as the conical aperture subtended by an area of
1 m² on the surface of a sphere whose radius is 1 m. The plane
angle subtended by the circumference is 2π radians, and the
total solid angle subtended by a spherical surface is $4\pi r^2/r^2$ or
4π sr.

In Fig. 3.3, used to define steradian, all points of the area cut
out by the cone were equidistant from the apex. We shall need
to express solid angles in terms of areas cut out on irregular surfaces. In Fig. 3.4, let dA represent such an element of area. The
solid angle $d\omega$ subtended by dA at the point charge $+q$ is

$$d\omega = \frac{dA \cos \theta}{r^2} \qquad (3.4)$$

assuming that dA is small so that $dA \cos \theta$ is approximately equal
to an element of area on a spherical surface.

Consider a closed surface of arbitrary shape completely surrounding the charge $+q$. Figure 3.5 shows an element dA of
such a surface. From (3.1) and (3.4) we can write the flux of **E**
crossing dA as

$$d\Phi = E \cos \theta \, dA = \frac{q \, dA \cos \theta}{4\pi\varepsilon_0 r^2} = \frac{q \, d\omega}{4\pi\varepsilon_0} \qquad (3.5)$$

The sign associated with $d\Phi$ is determined according to the following convention: In the case of a closed surface, the outward
normal is taken as positive, so that if the angle θ between **E** and

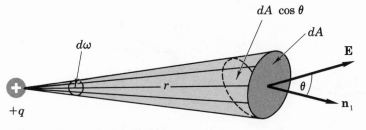

Figure 3.4   An element of a solid angle.

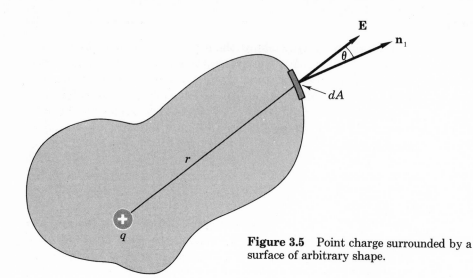

Figure 3.5 Point charge surrounded by a surface of arbitrary shape.

$\mathbf{n}_1$ is acute, $d\Phi$ is positive; if θ is obtuse, $d\Phi$ is negative. If the expression in (3.5) is integrated over the entire closed surface, the total outward flux is

$$\Phi = \int_{\substack{\text{closed} \\ \text{surface}}} E \cos \theta \, dA = \frac{q}{4\pi\varepsilon_0} \int_{\substack{\text{closed} \\ \text{surface}}} d\omega = \frac{q}{\varepsilon_0} \tag{3.6}$$

since the solid angle subtended at the point charge by the closed surface is 4π.

Next consider the case where q is outside the closed surface. As shown in Fig. 3.6, the cone of angular opening $d\omega$ intercepts an area dA_1 centered at point 1 and area dA_2 at point 2. The outward flux through dA_1 and dA_2 taken together is $d\Phi = E_1 \cos \theta_1 \, dA_1 + E_2 \cos \theta_2 \, dA_2 = -E_1 \cos \alpha_1 \, dA_1 + E_2 \cos \theta_2 \, dA_2$, since the angle θ_1 between the positive directions of $\mathbf{n}_1$ and $\mathbf{E}_1$ is obtuse, so that $\cos \theta_1 = \cos (\pi - \alpha_1) = -\cos \alpha_1$.

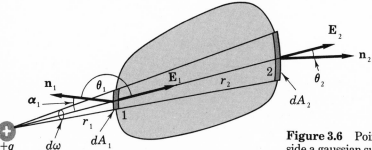

Figure 3.6 Point charge outside a gaussian surface.

The negative sign appearing in the term $-E_1 \cos \alpha_1 \, dA_1$ means that the flux through dA_1 is directed inward. But from the geometry of the figure

$$d\omega = \frac{dA_1 \cos \alpha_1}{r_1^2} = \frac{dA_2 \cos \theta_2}{r_2^2}$$

consequently,

$$d\Phi = \frac{q}{4\pi\varepsilon_0}\left(-\frac{\cos \alpha_1 \, dA_1}{r_1^2} + \frac{\cos \theta_2 \, dA_2}{r_2^2}\right) = 0$$

Hence it follows that the net outward flux vanishes when one considers a pair of surface elements which subtend the same solid angle $d\omega$ at the point charge. By extending the reasoning to other pairs of elements of areas the entire surface can be covered. As shown above, in each case the inward flux through one element of area is equal to the outward flux through the other; consequently, the net outward flux through the entire closed surface vanishes when the charge is located outside.

If the closed surface contains a number of discrete charges, $q_1, q_2, q_3, \ldots,$ or if charge is distributed continuously with volume density ρ, an extension of the preceding reasoning indicates the net outward flux of **E** is always equal to Q/ε_0, where

$$Q = q_1 + q_2 + q_3 + \cdots \quad \text{or} \quad Q = \int_{\text{volume}} \rho \, dv$$

where Q represents the sum of the discrete charges within the closed surface or the total charge contained in the closed surface found by integrating the charge density over the volume bounded by the surface.

Therefore, in general,

$$\int_{\substack{\text{closed}\\\text{surface}}} E \cos \theta \, dA = \int_{\substack{\text{closed}\\\text{surface}}} \mathbf{E} \cdot d\mathbf{A} = \frac{Q}{\varepsilon_0} \qquad (3.7)$$

which is known as Gauss's law and may be stated as follows: The surface integral of the normal component of the electric intensity over any closed surface is equal to the total charge enclosed by the surface divided by ε_0, the permittivity of free space. This law represents one of the fundamental relations of electromagnetic theory.

In the accompanying diagram, consider a point P within the empty interior of a uniformly charged spherical shell. Taking P as the apex, draw the symmetric cones which cut out areas A_1 and A_2 on the surface of the sphere. If r_1 and r_2 denote the distances from P to these areas, then $A_1/A_2 = r_1^2/r_2^2$ (see Section 3.1). Also Q_1 and Q_2, the charges on A_1 and A_2, obey the equality $Q_1/Q_2 = A_1/A_2 = r_1^2/r_2^2$. Now F_1, the magnitude of the force exerted by Q_1 on a test charge q at P, is equal to CQ_1q/r_1^n, where it is assumed that the force varies as the nth power of the distance. Similarly, Q_2 exerts a force F_2 given by CQ_2q/r_2^n, and the forces produced at P by the two surface elements of charge are in the ratio

$$\frac{F_1}{F_2} = \frac{Q_1/r_1^n}{Q_2/r_2^n}$$

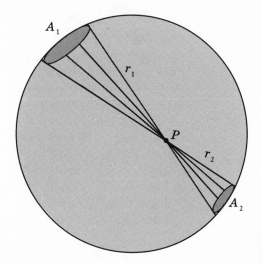

If n, the power of r, is exactly 2, then the above ratio is unity and F_1 cancels F_2, since these forces have opposite senses. The entire surface of the shell can be divided into similar pairs of surfaces, and the force produced by each pair of surface elements will again vanish. Consequently, the force on a charge at an interior point P vanishes if the exponent of r in the force law is exactly 2. Therefore, to test the inverse square law, we need only to ascertain whether the force within a uniformly charged shell is zero.

On the atomic scale, the inverse square law has received strong support from experiments on the scattering of alpha particles. When alpha particles (positively charged helium nuclei) bombard thin metallic foils, a certain number of the incident particles are deflected through large angles approaching 180°. This result is consistent with the view that the alpha particles interact strongly with a highly localized positive charge associated with an atom in the foil. Consequently, it is postulated that a repulsive force obeying the inverse square law is present between the atomic core and the incident alpha particles. The assumption of an inverse square type of force led to calculated results which were in harmony with the observed large-angle scattering, provided that the positive charge associated with the core of an atom was concentrated in a region whose radial dimension was of the order of 10^{-14} m. Such a model of the nuclear atom has received ample substantiation from many other considerations.

3.2   Calculation of E by Gauss's Law

If the charge distribution is sufficiently symmetric, we can use
Gauss's law to determine the magnitude of the electric intensity.
The success of the method depends on choosing a suitable gaussian surface which passes through the field point. [The term
gaussian surface refers to the imaginary closed surface implied
in (3.7).] The surface is chosen so that the electric field is constant and normal to certain portions of the surface but parallel
to the remaining portions. Only when **E** has the same magnitude at all points of the surface and is normal to the surface can
the surface integral be written as $E \int dA$. If **E** is parallel to
some surfaces, then $\int \mathbf{E} \cdot d\mathbf{A} = 0$. This circumstance makes it
possible to evaluate the left-hand member of (3.7) readily and to
solve for the magnitude of the intensity. To evaluate the right-
hand member of (3.7) we must determine the net charge contained within the chosen gaussian surface. Since the mathematical details of the calculation depend on the particular
charge distribution involved, we shall offer several illustrations.
The results obtained by this method may be used to verify the
results obtained by other types of calculation.

   1. *Field of infinite line charge.* Let positive charge be distributed along the z-axis with constant linear density λ. As is shown
in Fig. 3.7, the field at the point P is directed radially away from

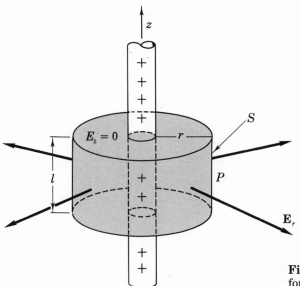

Figure 3.7   Gaussian surface S
for an infinitely long line charge.

the line charge (z-axis) and has the same magnitude E at all points at the constant distance r from the z-axis. These considerations, derived from the symmetry of the charge distribution, suggest that the appropriate gaussian surface S is a right circular cylindrical surface of length l and radius r coaxial with the z-axis. The ends of the cylindrical surface are closed by plane circular areas normal to the axis. The gaussian surface so constructed passes through the field point P and is located very far away from the ends of the physical distribution. This implies that E_z, the component of $\mathbf{E}$ parallel to the z-axis, may be taken as zero. Thus the outward flux over the ends of the gaussian surface is zero. However, the surface integral of E_r, the component of $\mathbf{E}$ normal to the curved surface, is $2\pi r l E_r$. Hence, the total outward flux over the entire closed surface is also $2\pi r l E_r$. By Gauss's law, this quantity must be equated to the total charge λl enclosed by the surface divided by ε_0. Analytically,

$$2\pi r l E_r = \lambda l/\varepsilon_0$$

whence
$$E_r = \frac{\lambda}{2\pi\varepsilon_0} \cdot \frac{1}{r} \tag{3.8}$$

It is seen that E_r is independent of the length of the cylinder. Direct integration of Coulomb's law also yields the same result.

2. *Field around a long cylinder charged uniformly.* A situation that can be approximated in practice consists in a charge distributed on the surface of a long cylinder of radius a. (The preceding calculation, which is applicable to a filamentary charge distribution, is the limiting case where $a \to 0$.) We construct the gaussian surface as in the preceding case, except that the charge enclosed in its interior is $2\pi a l \sigma$, where σ is the uniform surface density of charge. Following the same reasoning,

$$2\pi r l E_r = 2\pi a l \sigma/\varepsilon_0$$

whence
$$E_r = \frac{a\sigma}{\varepsilon_0} \cdot \frac{1}{r} \tag{3.9}$$

The charge per unit length of cylinder is $2\pi a \sigma$. If we denote this by λ, we can write (3.9) as

$$E_r = \frac{\lambda}{2\pi\varepsilon_0} \cdot \frac{1}{r} \tag{3.10}$$

which has the same form as (3.8) for the field in the vicinity of a long "line" charge. Thus, for points at a distance r from the axis outside the charged cylinder of radius a, we can describe the field due to the actual surface distribution on the cylinder by assuming that the charge is concentrated on the axis of the cylinder with linear density λ.

3. *Field due to an infinite plane sheet of charge.* Here we want to find the field at a point P, on one side of a plane sheet of charge distributed with uniform surface density σ. The distance of P from the plane is to be small compared to the linear dimension of the sheet. The symmetry implies that E_n, the field at P, is normal to the charged plane. A cylindrical gaussian surface, with its elements normal to the plane, is therefore appropriate. Figure 3.8 shows the gaussian surface S in the form of a right cylinder, with plane end surfaces of area A parallel to the sheet of charge.

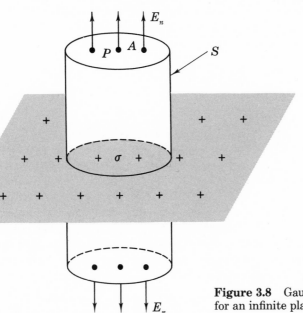

Figure 3.8   Gaussian construction for an infinite plane sheet of charge.

The cross section of the cylinder may be circular as shown, or it may assume any other form. The outward flux from the top of the cylinder is AE_n. A similar amount emerges from the bottom. Since the flux is zero over the curved surface, the total outward flux of **E** is $2AE_n$. The enclosed charge is σA. The application of Gauss's law yields

$$2AE_n = \sigma A/\varepsilon_0$$

or
$$E_n = \frac{\sigma}{2\varepsilon_0} \tag{3.11}$$

a result which is independent of the distance of P from the charged plane.

4. *Field due to a uniformly charged spherical shell.* In Fig. 3.9, the spherical shell of radius a is charged uniformly with surface density σ. Consider first an external point P_1, at a distance r from the center, where $r > a$. To find the magnitude of the field at P_1 we select the spherical gaussian surface S_1 concentric with the charged shell. Due to the symmetry of the charge configuration, E_r, the field at P_1, will be radial and constant in magnitude over the gaussian surface of radius r. Thus,

$$4\pi r^2 E_r = 4\pi a^2 \sigma / \varepsilon_0$$

Consequently

$$E_r = \frac{a^2 \sigma}{\varepsilon_0} \cdot \frac{1}{r^2} \tag{3.12}$$

which may also be written as

$$E_r = \frac{Q}{4\pi\varepsilon_0} \cdot \frac{1}{r^2} \tag{3.13}$$

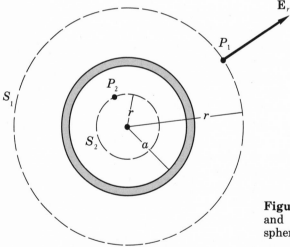

Figure 3.9 Gaussian surfaces S_1 and S_2 for a uniformly charged spherical shell.

where Q is the total charge on the spherical shell. The expression for E_r given by (3.13) is independent of the radius a of the spherical charge distribution. For field points external to the charged shell ($r > a$), the intensity is indistinguishable from that produced by a point charge of magnitude Q located at the center. In other words, the external field due to the charged shell is the same as the field that would be produced if the entire charge on the shell were concentrated at its center.

Next consider the point P_2, which lies within the charged shell. Since the space within the shell is free of charge, the application of (3.7) results in the statement

$$\int_{S_2} E \cos \theta \, dA = 4\pi r^2 E_r = 0 \qquad (3.14)$$

where S_2 is a concentric gaussian sphere which passes through P_2, and where E_r again denotes the radial component or the component of **E** normal to S_2. The result in (3.14) states that the net outward flux over S_2 is zero; in this instance of radial symmetry the net outward flux over S_2 is zero only if $E_r = 0$ at all points of S_2.

However, in drawing conclusions regarding **E** from the vanishing of the surface integral, we must proceed with caution. Consider for instance a cylindrical gaussian surface located in a uniform field, with the lines of force parallel to the elements of the cylinder. Assume that no charge is present within the surface. Once again the net outward flux vanishes, but in this case, even though the net outward flux over the cylinder is zero, we cannot conclude that **E** is zero at all points of the plane areas which close the ends of the gaussian surface.

In the case of the spherical shell, no uniform fields are superimposed on the field of the spherical charge configuration, and zero net flux means that the field vanishes at all interior points. This property may also be verified by considering the contributions to the field at any interior point coming from charges located on elements of surface area subtended by equal conical angles whose common vertex is at the interior field point.

5. *Field due to charge distributed continuously within a spherical volume.* Finally, let us consider a spherical volume of radius R_0 within which charge is distributed with a volume density $\rho = kr^2$, where r is the distance from the center and k is a constant. To calculate the electric field at an external point P_1 at a distance a where $a > R_0$, pass through P_1 a hypothetical spherical surface S_1 concentric with the sphere S containing the charge. Since ρ is a function only of the radius r, the field E_1 is normal to S_1 and has the same value at all points of S_1. (See Fig. 3.10.) The flux directed outward from S_1 is equal to $4\pi a^2 E_1$, and we calculate the charge enclosed within S_1 by considering the element of charge contained in a spherical shell of radius r and

thickness dr. The volume of this shell is $4\pi r^2\,dr$, and the charge contained therein is $4\pi r^2 \rho\,dr$, or $4\pi k r^4\,dr$. For the charge Q in the sphere of radius R_0, we write

$$Q = 4\pi k \int_0^{R_0} r^4\,dr = 4\pi k R_0^5/5$$

Hence, by Gauss's law,

$$4\pi a^2 E_1 = 4\pi k R_0^5/5\varepsilon_0$$

which leads to $$E_1 = \frac{kR_0^5}{5\varepsilon_0}\cdot\frac{1}{a^2}\qquad (a > R_0)\qquad(3.15)$$

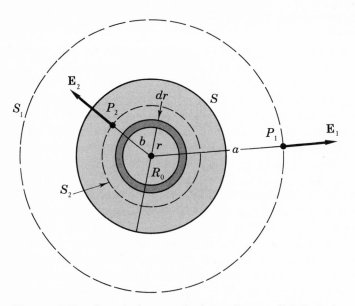

Figure 3.10 Gauss's law applied to charges distributed throughout the volume of a sphere S.

Thus the field at external points due to the volume distribution is the same as the field that would be produced by a charge $(4\pi k R_0^5/5)$ concentrated at the center.

To find E_2, we again make use of the radial symmetry and adopt the gaussian surface S_2. As before,

$$4\pi b^2 E_2 = 4\pi k b^5/5\varepsilon_0$$

whence $$E_2 = \frac{kb^3}{5\varepsilon_0}\qquad (b < R_0)\qquad(3.16)$$

At the surface where $a = b = R_0$, E_1 as given by (3.15) agrees
with the value of E_2 as given by (3.16).

3.3   Conductors in Static Equilibrium

On the basis of electrical properties, we can divide matter into
two broad categories. In one category we find charge carriers
that are essentially free—that is, they are not strongly bound to
atomic centers. Such carriers (electrons, in most instances) may
be made to move through matter under the action of applied
electric fields. The resulting flow of charge constitutes an electric current. Materials that behave in this fashion are called
conductors.

In the second category, which consists of materials called in-
sulators or dielectrics, the component charges are bound together more or less strongly. The application of an electric field
of moderate strength does not result in the steady drift motion
of charge through the substance. Instead, dielectrics become polarized—that is, negatively charged particles are displaced relative to positive charges. These statements are idealizations, of
course. In practice, dielectric materials may act as weak conductors.

Between the two extremes are materials classified as semi-
conductors, whose electrical properties are intermediate between
those of conductors and dielectrics.

In the discussion that follows we shall be concerned with the
behavior of conductors in electrostatic equilibrium. We shall
discuss the properties of dielectrics in connection with polarization effects.

Let us begin with a few examples. The diagram in Fig. 3.11
shows a positively charged, hollow conductor. The conductor
became charged when electrons were removed from the surface,
with the attendant migration of electrons from the interior.
When the equilibrium state is reached, the free charges in the
interior of the body are so distributed that the electric field
within the interior of the conductor is zero everywhere. In a
metal such as copper, the free electron density is of the order of
10^{29} electrons/m^3. This number is high enough so that a zero
field in the interior can always be achieved on a macroscopic
scale. (On a microscopic scale, there are strong fields in the neighborhood of atomic nuclei and extranuclear electrons.) What we

are referring to here is the average field over a volume, which from the macroscopic viewpoint may be regarded as very small, yet from the atomic viewpoint is large enough to contain a great many atoms. A cube of copper 100 atoms on a side has a volume of

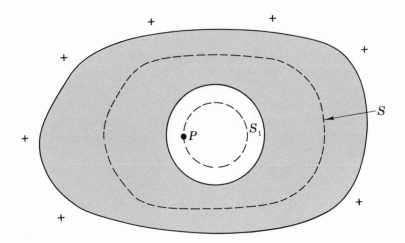

Figure 3.11   A charged thick-walled conductor with a cavity.

nearly 10^{-22} m^3 and still contains 10^6 atoms or 10^6 free electrons. (Such a volume is referred to as "physically small.") Indeed, the vanishing of the field inside the body of the conductor may be taken as a definition of a conductor in electrostatic equilibrium; a nonvanishing of the field would imply the motion of charge, which is contrary to the assumption that charges are at rest.

Interesting consequences may be deduced from the field-free state of a conductor in static equilibrium. One consequence is that all the charge must reside on the outer boundary of the conductor. The proof of this statement follows from Gauss's law. In Fig. 3.11, let S represent a gaussian surface which lies wholly within the body of the conductor. Since **E** is everywhere zero over S, the net charge within S is zero. This statement is valid for all surfaces S, no matter how close to the outer surface of the conductor they are drawn. Hence all the charge must be located on the outer boundary of the conductor.

A second consequence of the absence of a field inside the conductor is that the conductor is an equipotential. This means that points within the conductor, on the surface of the cavity, and on the outer surface of the conductor are at the same potential. The equipotential character of the surfaces and of the region within the conductor follows directly from the defining relation $dV = -\mathbf{E} \cdot d\mathbf{l}$, which identically vanishes for all displacements, since $\mathbf{E} = 0$.

A third consequence is that if the cavity (refer again to Fig. 3.11) does not contain a charge it is also a field-free region, and points within it are at the same potential as the conductor. Let us suppose that V, the potential of an interior point P, is higher than the constant potential V_0 of the inner surface of the conductor. Let S_1 be an equipotential surface which lies within the cavity and passes through P. The assumption $V > V_0$ signifies that there is a component of the field which is directed outward from the closed surface S_1 and that there is a net outward flux. By Gauss's law, this implies the presence of a positive charge within S_1. But the presence of such a charge is contrary to our hypothesis. Similar reasoning shows that the inequality $V < V_0$ cannot hold either. Therefore $V = V_0$, and a similar statement can be made for other points within the cavity.

The property just discussed is put to practical use in electrostatic shielding. A cavity completely surrounded by a metal remains a field-free region no matter what the charge distribution on the outer boundary of the conductor is. The vanishing of the field within an enclosure surrounded by a conducting medium follows from Coulomb's law of force between charges. If the Coulomb force did not vary inversely with the square of the distance, there would be a field within the enclosure. Recent experiments designed to detect the presence of fields within such a cavity indicate that if the exponent of the distance in the denominator of Coulomb's law is different from 2, it must differ from 2 by 1 part in 10^9. This constitutes an indirect but highly sensitive proof of Coulomb's law.

We proceed to calculate the field "just outside" (this phrase is explained at the end of this paragraph) a conductor in terms of σ, the surface density of charge. The electric field just outside the surface must be normal to the surface. There can be no component parallel to the surface, since the surface is an equipotential. Otherwise the charges would be in motion. A short cylinder, with small cross-sectional area ΔA, is chosen as the gaussian surface. As shown in Fig. 3.12, the cylinder is located partly in free space above the charged conductor and partly within the body of the conductor. The elements of the cylinder are parallel to the field, and the outward flux over the end with-

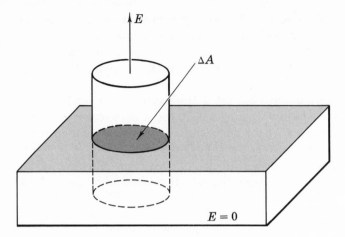

Figure 3.12 Field normal to the surface
of a charged conductor.

in the conductor is zero, since this is a field-free region. The flux
through the end in free space is $E \, \Delta A,$ and the net charge enclosed by the gaussian surface is $\sigma \, \Delta A$. Consequently, Gauss's
law gives

$$E \, \Delta A \,=\, \sigma \, \Delta A / \varepsilon_0$$

or $$E \,=\, \frac{\sigma}{\varepsilon_0} \tag{3.17}$$

Strictly speaking, the charge is not located on a geometrical surface; rather, it lies in a thin transition layer which extends into
the conductor. This layer could be divided by a number of surfaces parallel to the outer boundary of the conductor. If σ' is the
charge density on a surface intermediate between the inner boundary of the transition layer and the outer boundary of the conductor, the electric intensity at the intermediate surface is

$$E' \,=\, \frac{\sigma'}{\varepsilon_0} \tag{3.18}$$

where σ' is less than σ which appears in (3.17). This explains the
meaning of the phrase "just outside" used at the beginning of
this paragraph.

Referring to (3.9) and (3.12), we see that at the surfaces of the
cylindrical and spherical charge distributions the electric inten-
sity reduces to σ/ε_0 when the value a is substituted for r. This is

equivalent to taking a field point located on the charged surface and agrees with the result in (3.17) for a charged conductor of arbitrary shape.

3.4   Charged Body Placed Inside a Hollow Conductor

If a charge $+Q$ is placed inside the cavity of an otherwise uncharged conductor (see Fig. 3.13), the charge induced on the inner surface of the cavity may be found by the use of the gaussian surface S. This surface, located inside the body of the conductor, is arbitrarily close to the cavity wall. Since the field is zero in the interior of the conductor, the net outward flux over S is zero. Hence

$$\int_S \mathbf{E} \cdot d\mathbf{A} = 0 = \frac{Q + Q_i}{\varepsilon_0} \tag{3.19}$$

where Q_i is the total induced charge. It follows from (3.19) that $Q_i = -Q$, that is, the induced charge has the same magnitude as the inducing charge but is of opposite sign. The induced charge

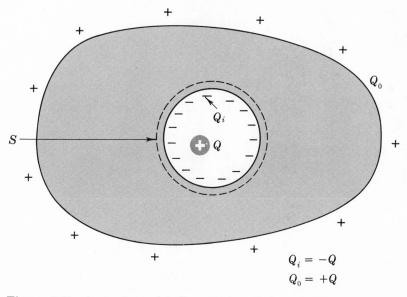

$$Q_i = -Q$$
$$Q_0 = +Q$$

Figure 3.13 An uncharged hollow thick-walled conductor with charge $+Q$ inserted in cavity.

A Van de Graaf electrostatic generator. The spherical aluminum conductors store charge-developing potentials of up to 2 million volts. The generator shown in this photograph was originally used to bombard atomic nuclei with electrons, protons, deuterons, and alpha particles; it now stands in the Boston Museum of Science. (Courtesy of Massachusetts Institute of Technology.)

must lie on the inner surface of the cavity, because, as we have seen, no matter how close the surface S is drawn to the cavity boundary, the net charge within S must still remain zero.

Originally, the conductor was uncharged. After the rearrangement of charges subsequent to the insertion of Q into the cavity, the net charge on the entire conductor must still be zero, as demanded by the conservation law discussed in Section 1.1. Accordingly, a charge Q_0 equal to Q must appear on the outer surface of the conductor. If Q is moved about in the cavity, the distribution of negative charge on the inner wall will be altered. The distribution on the outer surface will not be altered, however, since Q and Q_i form an isolated neutral system. Also, there is a field within the cavity and a field outside the conductor, but there is *no* field within the conductor. The field in the cavity starts at the charged body Q and terminates on the inner surface; it may be destroyed by allowing the charged body to touch the cavity wall. In any case, the surfaces of the conductor under static equilibrium are equipotential surfaces.

3.5   Differential Form of Gauss's Law

We can transform the integral form of Gauss's law that appears in (3.7) into a differential form by applying the relation to a volume element in space. This modification is useful in representing fundamental relations of electromagnetism and in solving a variety of problems that are not limited to charge distributions of high symmetry. The purpose of the transformation is to associate either the electric intensity or the potential at a point $P(x, y, z)$ in space with $\rho(x, y, z)$, the volume density of charge at the same point.

Consider the rectangular volume element whose edges Δx, Δy, and Δz are parallel to the cartesian coordinate axes. (See Fig. 3.14.) Let E_{x_1} represent the x component of the field at some point R within face 1, which is perpendicular to the x-axis. At the point T inside face 2, E_{x_2}, the x component of the intensity, may be represented by

$$E_{x_2} = E_{x_1} + \Delta E_x = \left(E_{x_1} + \frac{\partial E_x}{\partial x}\bigg|_{x_0} \Delta x \right) \qquad (3.20)$$

The substitution for ΔE_x may be understood by examining the

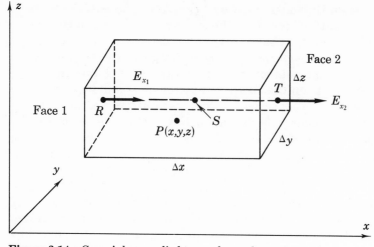

Figure 3.14   Gauss's law applied to a volume element in rectangular coordinates.

diagram in Fig. 3.15, where $\partial E_x/\partial x|_{x_0}$ is the slope of the E_x vs x curve evaluated at $x = x_0$, a value of x which is intermediate between x_1 and x_2. The point x_0 is the x coordinate of the point S, which lies on the line RT (in Fig. 3.14) drawn parallel to the x-axis. In Fig. 3.15, the x coordinates of R and T are designated by x_1 and x_2.

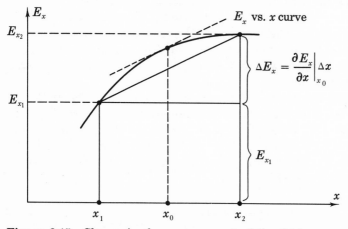

Figure 3.15   Change in the x component of the field as a function of the coordinate x, for fixed values of y and z.

Consider only faces 1 and 2. The net flux of E_x outward from the rectangle is given by

$$\int_{\Delta y \Delta z} E_{x_2} \, dy \, dz - \int_{\Delta y \Delta z} E_{x_1} \, dy \, dz \qquad (3.21)$$

where the negative sign indicates that the flux over face 1 is directed inward. Combining (3.20) with (3.21), we get

$$\int_{\Delta y \Delta z} \left. \frac{\partial E_x}{\partial x} \right|_{x_0} \Delta x \, dy \, dz \qquad (3.22)$$

This expression involves an integration over the end surface $\Delta y \, \Delta z$. Before evaluating it we must recall that the integrand is a function of y and z. Had we considered the dependence of E_x on x along another line parallel to RT, still within the rectangular volume, the partial derivative would have been evaluated at some interior point whose x coordinate was different from x_0. The integration may be carried out by using the theorem of the mean for integrals, namely,

$$\int \left. \frac{\partial E_x}{\partial x} \right|_{x_0} \Delta x \, dy \, dz = \left(\frac{\partial E_x}{\partial x} \right) \Delta x \, \Delta y \, \Delta z \qquad (3.23)$$

where the value of $(\partial E_x / \partial x)$ is intermediate between the lowest value and the highest value of the derivative encountered within the volume. [The reader is familiar with the mean-value theorem for definite integrals in a single variable—that is,

$$\int_a^b f(x) \, dx = (b - a) f(\xi)$$

where $a \leq \xi \leq b$. Similarly it may be shown that for double integrals

$$\int_A f(y, z) \, dA = A f(\eta, \zeta)$$

where (η, ζ) is a point of the closed area A.]

Treating the remaining two pairs of faces in a similar fashion gives rise to the terms $(\partial E_y / \partial y) \, \Delta x \, \Delta y \, \Delta z$ and $(\partial E_z / \partial z) \, \Delta x \, \Delta y \, \Delta z$, where as before the derivatives are evaluated at appropriate points within a rectangular volume. Over the closed surface of the rectangular box, the net outward flux is given by the sum

$$\left(\frac{\partial E_x}{\partial x} + \frac{\partial E_y}{\partial y} + \frac{\partial E_z}{\partial z} \right) \Delta x \, \Delta y \, \Delta z \qquad (3.24)$$

The relation appearing in (3.29) is one of the most celebrated equations of mathematical physics. It bears the name of the French mathematician and astronomer Pierre Simon Laplace (1749–1827), who used it extensively in his studies of planetary mechanics and gravitation. Laplace was a master of mathematical analysis. He deduced the manner in which lunar acceleration depended on changes in the eccentricity of the earth's orbit. He succeeded in solving completely the problem of the gravitational force exerted on an external particle by a spheroidal distribution of matter.

We state here, without offering proof, the contribution of Laplace's equation to electrostatics. At the boundaries of the electrostatic field, charge will distribute itself in some manner, and the potential at all points of the boundary will assume a definite value. (If the boundary surface is that of a conductor, the charge will distribute itself so that the potential at all points of the surface has the *same* value.) Moreover, if there is no charge in the space between the boundaries, then Laplace's equation,

$$\nabla^2 V = 0$$

holds. Now, if we can find a solution of this equation that satisfies the boundary conditions—that is, a solution that represents appropriately the potential at every point of the boundary—then the potential is *uniquely* determined at all points in the space between the boundaries.

Laplace's equation is encountered not only in potential theory but in problems dealing with the flow of fluids and the conduction of heat. A related equation is found in the treatment of wave motion.

Now within the volume of the rectangle the charge density ρ varies from point to point. If $\bar{\rho}$ is the average value of this quantity within the volume $\Delta x \, \Delta y \, \Delta z$, the net charge enclosed by the gaussian surface in the form of a rectangular box is

$$\bar{\rho} \, \Delta x \, \Delta y \, \Delta z \tag{3.25}$$

Then, by Gauss's law

$$\left(\frac{\partial E_x}{\partial x} + \frac{\partial E_y}{\partial y} + \frac{\partial E_z}{\partial z} \right) \Delta x \, \Delta y \, \Delta z = \frac{\bar{\rho} \, \Delta x \, \Delta y \, \Delta z}{\varepsilon_0} \tag{3.26}$$

Let us imagine that the rectangular volume $\Delta x \, \Delta y \, \Delta z$ shrinks and approaches a physically small volume centered about the fixed point $P(x, y, z)$. In the limit, all the derivatives may be regarded as evaluated at P. Also, ρ takes on the value of the charge density at the same point. We may now write (3.26) as

$$\frac{\partial E_x}{\partial x} + \frac{\partial E_y}{\partial y} + \frac{\partial E_z}{\partial z} = \frac{\rho}{\varepsilon_0} \tag{3.27}$$

And it is possible to express (3.27) in terms of the potential function. Since

$$E_x = -\frac{\partial V}{\partial x}, \qquad E_y = -\frac{\partial V}{\partial y}, \qquad E_z = -\frac{\partial V}{\partial z}$$

substitution in (3.27) results in

$$\frac{\partial^2 V}{\partial x^2} + \frac{\partial^2 V}{\partial y^2} + \frac{\partial^2 V}{\partial z^2} = -\frac{\rho}{\varepsilon_0} \tag{3.28}$$

The potential must be a solution of (3.28), which is called Poisson's equation. In a region free from charges, $\rho = 0$ and (3.28) reduces to the well-known relation

$$\frac{\partial^2 V}{\partial x^2} + \frac{\partial^2 V}{\partial y^2} + \frac{\partial^2 V}{\partial z^2} = 0 \tag{3.29}$$

which is known as Laplace's equation.

3.6 Derivatives of Fields

The developments in the preceding section indicate the necessity for describing the variations of the field components with position. In dealing with space differentiation the concept of differential operators is convenient. (See Appendix A.) In our study of the potential function V, we expressed the increase in potential [see (2.17)] as

$$dV = \frac{\partial V}{\partial x} \, dx + \frac{\partial V}{\partial y} \, dy + \frac{\partial V}{\partial z} \, dz \qquad (3.30)$$

where the partial derivatives imply that in differentiating the scalar function $V(x, y, z)$ only a single variable is allowed to vary. We can use the differential operator represented symbolically by

$$\boldsymbol{\nabla} \equiv \mathbf{i} \frac{\partial}{\partial x} + \mathbf{j} \frac{\partial}{\partial y} + \mathbf{k} \frac{\partial}{\partial z} \qquad (3.31)$$

to obtain several useful scalar and vector quantities associated with fields. For instance, if $\boldsymbol{\nabla}$ operates on the scalar function of position V, we obtain

$$\boldsymbol{\nabla} V = \mathbf{i} \frac{\partial V}{\partial x} + \mathbf{j} \frac{\partial V}{\partial y} + \mathbf{k} \frac{\partial V}{\partial z} \qquad (3.32)$$

which we find, with the aid of (2.18), to be just the negative of the electric field vector. Thus

$$\boldsymbol{\nabla} V = -(\mathbf{i} E_x + \mathbf{j} E_y + \mathbf{k} E_z) = -\mathbf{E} \qquad (3.33)$$

The quantity $\boldsymbol{\nabla} V$ is often referred to as the gradient of V, or grad V. The symbol $\boldsymbol{\nabla}$ (pronounced "del") is not a vector but simply an indication that certain differentiations are to be performed.

From the point of view of energetics, $dV = -\mathbf{E} \cdot d\mathbf{l}$ [see (2.7)]. Recalling that $d\mathbf{l} = \mathbf{i} \, dx + \mathbf{j} \, dy + \mathbf{k} \, dz$, we may express dV as

$$dV = -\mathbf{E} \cdot d\mathbf{l} = \boldsymbol{\nabla} V \cdot d\mathbf{l} \qquad (3.34)$$

When we substitute (3.32) in (3.34) and carry out the algebraic operations, we immediately obtain the form appearing on the right side of (3.30). Physically, the gradient represents a vector whose magnitude and direction are those of the maximum space rate of change of the scalar function V.

The differential form of Gauss's law appearing in (3.27) may also be represented in terms of the differential operator $\boldsymbol{\nabla}$. By writing $\mathbf{E} = \mathbf{i} E_x + \mathbf{j} E_y + \mathbf{k} E_z$ and forming the dot products, we get

$$\boldsymbol{\nabla} \cdot \mathbf{E} = \frac{\partial E_x}{\partial x} + \frac{\partial E_y}{\partial y} + \frac{\partial E_z}{\partial z} \qquad (3.35)$$

The quantity $\boldsymbol{\nabla} \cdot \mathbf{E}$ is a scalar and is called the *divergence* of the vector **E**, sometimes written as div **E**. In the light of the discussion in Section 3.5, the $\nabla \cdot \mathbf{E}$ denotes the net outward flux of **E** per unit volume. Historically, the mathematical formulation was developed in hydrodynamics, where the term *flux* was connected with the net amount of fluid crossing a surface. The term is still used in connection with the electric field, though we need not imagine the flow of a material substance. The *flux* of **E** through an element of surface is defined as the normal component of **E** multiplied by the area of the surface element.

The second-order partial-differential equations (3.28) and (3.29) can also be expressed in terms of the operator ∇ in the following manner. Consider the dot product $\nabla \cdot \nabla V$, the divergence of the gradient of V. From (3.31) and (3.33) we find that

$$\nabla \cdot \nabla V = \frac{\partial^2 V}{\partial x^2} + \frac{\partial^2 V}{\partial y^2} + \frac{\partial^2 V}{\partial z^2} \tag{3.36}$$

The operator $\nabla \cdot \nabla$ is a scalar operator given symbolically by

$$\nabla \cdot \nabla = \frac{\partial^2}{\partial x^2} + \frac{\partial^2}{\partial y^2} + \frac{\partial^2}{\partial z^2} \tag{3.37}$$

It appears often in physical problems and is called the *Laplacian*.

Finally, we shall express the circuital law of electrostatics in differential form. This law is given by the line integral

$$\oint \mathbf{E} \cdot d\mathbf{l} = 0 \tag{3.38}$$

as derived in Section 2.1. Let us apply (3.38) to the closed rectangular path in the x,y plane. The field point $P(x, y)$ is located at one corner of the rectangle. As shown in Fig. 3.16, the field **E** is resolved into the components E_x and E_y. If Δx and Δy are sufficiently small, E_x and E_y will not change along sides 1 and 4 respectively. On sides 2 and 3, the corresponding components are given by

$$E_y + \frac{\partial E_y}{\partial x} \Delta x \qquad \text{and} \qquad E_x + \frac{\partial E_x}{\partial y} \Delta y$$

Tracing the rectangle in the counterclockwise sense, we find that the value of the line integral becomes

$$\oint \mathbf{E} \cdot d\mathbf{l} = E_x \Delta x + \left(E_y + \frac{\partial E_y}{\partial x} \Delta x \right) \Delta y -$$
$$\left(E_x + \frac{\partial E_x}{\partial y} \Delta y \right) \Delta x - E_y \Delta y \tag{3.39}$$

The minus signs are necessary because over sides 3 and 4 we traverse the path against the field. Upon simplification we obtain

$$\oint \mathbf{E} \cdot d\mathbf{l} = \left(\frac{\partial E_y}{\partial x} - \frac{\partial E_x}{\partial y} \right) \Delta x \, \Delta y \qquad (3.40)$$

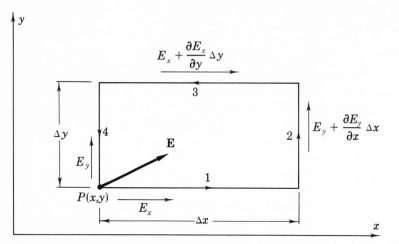

Figure 3.16   Evaluation of the line integral of $\mathbf{E}$ around a small rectangular path located in the x,y plane.

Now consider the cross product of the differential operator and $\mathbf{E}$. This is written as $\mathbf{\nabla} \times \mathbf{E}$ and is referred to as "del" cross $\mathbf{E}$, or curl $\mathbf{E}$. $\mathbf{\nabla} \times \mathbf{E}$ is a vector and, as indicated in Appendix A, its x, y, and z components are shown in the expansion, namely

$$\mathbf{\nabla} \times \mathbf{E} = \mathbf{i} \left(\frac{\partial E_z}{\partial y} - \frac{\partial E_y}{\partial z} \right) + \mathbf{j} \left(\frac{\partial E_x}{\partial z} - \frac{\partial E_z}{\partial x} \right)$$
$$+ \mathbf{k} \left(\frac{\partial E_y}{\partial x} - \frac{\partial E_x}{\partial y} \right) \qquad (3.41)$$

By comparing the right-hand sides of (3.40) and (3.41) we make the interesting observation that the line integral in (3.40) is equal to the z component of the curl $\mathbf{E}$ times the area ΔA given by $\Delta x \, \Delta y$. That is,

$$\oint_{\text{rectangle}} \mathbf{E} \cdot d\mathbf{l} = (\mathbf{\nabla} \times \mathbf{E})_z \, \Delta A \qquad (3.42)$$

But the z component really means the component of $\mathbf{\nabla} \times \mathbf{E}$ perpendicular to the element of area ΔA. This relation furnishes us with a definition stating that the component of the vector (curl **E**) or ($\nabla \times$ **E**) normal to a surface of area ΔA is equal to the line integral of the vector **E** around the periphery of the surface divided by the area ΔA. The definition is really valid for the limiting case where $\Delta A \to 0$.

This treatment of the special case may be extended to the case where the line integral is evaluated around any closed path. Formally, the result is

$$\oint_{\text{closed path}} \mathbf{E} \cdot d\mathbf{l} = \int_A (\nabla \times \mathbf{E})_n \, dA = \int_A (\nabla \times \mathbf{E}) \cdot d\mathbf{A} \quad (3.43)$$

where $(\nabla \times \mathbf{E})_n$ is the normal component of the curl at any point within the area A whose periphery coincides with the path of integration. In carrying out the line integration, the sense of circulation is related to the positive normal to the open surface by the right-hand screw rule.

From the relation given by (3.43) we see that the line integral of $\mathbf{E} \cdot d\mathbf{l}$ around a loop is zero if $\nabla \times \mathbf{E} = 0$ at all points of the area described by the loop. This condition can be satisfied if **E** itself is the gradient of a scalar function—i.e., if $\mathbf{E} = -\nabla V$. This is easily verified by writing

$$E_x = -\frac{\partial V}{\partial x}, \qquad E_y = -\frac{\partial V}{\partial y}, \qquad E_z = -\frac{\partial V}{\partial z}$$

From (3.41) the x component of $\nabla \times \mathbf{E}$ is given by

$$(\nabla \times \mathbf{E})_x = +\left(\frac{\partial E_z}{\partial y} - \frac{\partial E_y}{\partial z}\right) = -\left(\frac{\partial^2 V}{\partial y \, \partial z} - \frac{\partial^2 V}{\partial z \, \partial y}\right) = 0 \quad (3.44)$$

Similarly, the y and z components of $\nabla \times \mathbf{E}$ vanish identically.

We thus attain the important result that a vector field, such as the electrostatic field, is conservative if its curl vanishes identically. In symbols, if **E** is a conservative field

$$\nabla \times \mathbf{E} = 0 \quad (3.45)$$

3.7 The Properties of the Electrostatic Field

As an outcome of our discussion in the preceding section, we can describe the behavior of the electrostatic field by the following mathematical relations:

Integral form:
$$\int\limits_{\substack{\text{closed} \\ \text{surface}}} \mathbf{E} \cdot d\mathbf{A} = \frac{1}{\varepsilon_0} \int\limits_{\text{volume}} \rho \, dv = \frac{Q}{\varepsilon_0} \qquad (3.46)$$

$$\oint \mathbf{E} \cdot d\mathbf{l} = 0 \qquad (3.47)$$

Differential form:
$$\mathbf{\nabla} \cdot \mathbf{E} = \frac{\rho}{\varepsilon_0} \qquad (3.48)$$

$$\mathbf{\nabla} \times \mathbf{E} = 0 \qquad (3.49)$$

Furthermore, there exists for the electrostatic field a scalar function $V(x, y, z)$ which satisfies

$$\mathbf{\nabla} \cdot \mathbf{\nabla} V = -\frac{\rho}{\varepsilon_0} \qquad (3.50)$$

and the electric field can be derived from V by the use of

$$\mathbf{E} = -\mathbf{\nabla} V \qquad (3.51)$$

In principle, the solution of problems in the electrostatic field is a straightforward process if we know the charge distribution $\rho(x, y, z)$. When $\rho(x, y, z)$ is known, we can compute the potential function at a fixed field point by integration over the charge distribution. We can then derive the field from the potential by using (3.51).

Fundamental Theorem of Electrostatics: **Problems**

3.1   A spherical surface of radius R m is positively electrified with a constant surface density of σ coul/m². The charge resides on the outer surface; there is no charge in the interior of the sphere. Consider the layer of charge to be immersed in empty space.

(a) Apply Gauss's law and deduce an expression for the magnitude of the electric intensity at any point outside the spherical surface. Justify application of the law by reasoning based on the symmetry of the charge distribution. Make the necessary substitutions so that the charge density σ appears in your answer.

(b) Repeat for a point located in the interior of the sphere.

(c) Calculate the potential difference between any point inside the spherical surface and a point at infinity by integrating the field intensity obtained in parts (a) and (b). State which point is at the higher potential. Indicate the units of results in parts (a) and (b), assuming that all distances are expressed in meters.

3.2 An infinite line charge electrified
positively with uniform charge
density of λ coul/m coincides with
the *y*-axis. An identical line charge
parallel to the *y*-axis passes
through the point $(-1, 0)$. The region surrounding the charge distribution is empty space.

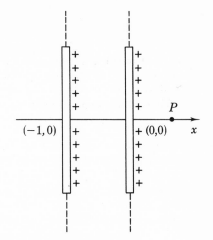

(a) Apply Gauss's law and obtain an expression for the electric
field at any point *P* on the positive
x-axis due only to the line charge
which crosses the *x*-axis at the origin. Justify the application of the
law by reasoning based on the symmetry of the charge distribution.

(b) Next consider the effect of the line charge passing through
the point $(-1, 0)$ and write a formula which represents the magnitudes of the electric intensity at *P* due to both line charges.

(c) Calculate the potential difference between the points $x = 1$
and $x = 2$ by integrating the field intensity. State which point is
at the higher potential. Give the units of results in parts (a) and
(c), assuming that all distances are expressed in meters.

3.3 In a certain region of space E_x, the *x* component of the electric field,
is given by

$$E_x = 20,000 \ (0.01 - x) \ \text{new/coul}$$

where *x* is measured in meters. The *y* and *z* components of the field
are zero at all points.

(a) Evaluate the potential difference between the origin and a
point on the *x*-axis at $x = 0.01$ m. Which point is higher in potential?

(b) Consider the space enclosed by a right circular cylinder of
radius 0.03 m whose axis coincides with the *x*-axis. The centers of
the circular areas at the ends of the cylinder are located at $x =$
0.01 m and at $x = 0.02$ m respectively. What is the net charge enclosed within the volume of the cylinder? (Note that the electric intensity at all points of a plane perpendicular to the axis has the
same magnitude.) Use Gauss's law. Consider the charge distribution
to be located in free space.

3.4 A charged, solid conducting sphere *A* is surrounded by a concentric
metallic shell *S* which is grounded (at zero potential). The radius of
the sphere is 1 cm and the inner radius of the shell is 10 cm. The potential of the sphere is 180 v.

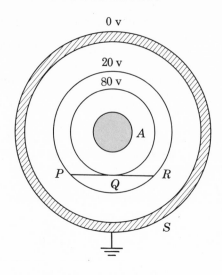

(a) Consult the diagram, which shows the traces of equipotential surfaces in an equatorial plane. What is the radius of the surface all points of which are at a potential of 80 v?

(b) PQR is a chord belonging to a second equipotential trace at 20 v. The chord is tangent to the first equipotential trace at Q. What is the difference in potential between the points P and Q? P and R?

3.5   The volume density of positive charges at any point P within a sphere of radius 3 m depends only on the radial distance r in accordance with the relation $\rho = (10^{-7})r$ coul/m³, where r is in meters.

(a) What is the total charge enclosed by the sphere?

(b) With the help of Gauss's law, find the electric field at a point 2 m from the center of the sphere.

(c) Calculate the potential difference between the center of the sphere and the outside edge. State which is at the higher potential.

3.6   In fair weather, the earth has a negative surface charge density which produces a downward-directed electric field at the earth's surface. A typical value is 300 v/m. Ions present in the atmosphere cause the magnitude of this field to vary with altitude. If the electric field at an altitude of 1400 m is also directed downward and has a magnitude of 20 v/m, what is the mean charge density in the atmosphere below 1400 m? Is this charge density negative or positive? Consider the earth to be a flat conductive plane of infinite extent.

3.7   In the accompanying figure AB and CD represent portions of two parallel-plane sheets of great extent charged uniformly with a surface density of σ coul/m². (AB and CD do not represent the boundaries of conducting plates.) By the application of Gauss's law determine the magnitude of the electric intensity at

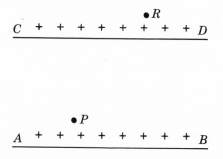

(a) a point P which lies between the planes CD and $AB;$

(b) a point R which lies above the plane CD. Defend your solution by a detailed explanation of the method used.

3.8 Positive charge is distributed throughout a sphere of radius R. The volume density ρ at any point P within the sphere is given by

$$\rho = r^2/4\pi \ \text{coul/m}^3$$

where r is the distance in meters of the point P from the center. If the charge within the sphere is 6.40 coul, what is the value of R?

3.9 The electrostatic potential of a point charge located at the origin in a cartesian system of coordinates is

$$V(x, y, z) = \frac{A}{\sqrt{x^2 + y^2 + z^2}}$$

where A is a constant. By differentiation, show that this function satisfies Laplace's equation for all values of the coordinates, except those at the location of the point charge.

3.10 A point charge q is located on the axis of a circular area at a height h above the plane of the circle whose radius is r. Calculate the flux of $\mathbf{E}$ through the circular area.

3.11 The potential function at any point in the x,y plane is given by $V = -Cxy$, where C is a positive constant.

(a) What is the potential at all points of the x-axis?

(b) The electric intensity $\mathbf{E}$ at any point in the plane may be expressed vectorially by $\mathbf{E} = \mathbf{i}E_x + \mathbf{j}E_y$, where $\mathbf{i}$ and $\mathbf{j}$ are unit vectors along the x and y directions respectively. Determine the values of E_x and E_y in terms of C and the coordinates.

(c) If dy/dx denotes the slope of the lines of force, complete the relation $dy/dx =$

3.12 The cartesian components in a certain field are described by

$$E_x = Cx^2, \qquad E_y = Cyz^2, \qquad E_z = Cy^2z$$

where C is a constant. Evaluate the curl $\mathbf{E}$ and decide whether the field is derivable from a scalar potential. If possible, determine the charge distribution ρ which would give rise to this field.

3.13 Consider two long, coaxial, hollow cylinders. The radius of the inner cylinder is a; that of the outer cylinder is b; $(a < b)$. Show that the potential at any point between the cylinders at a distance r from the axis can be put into the form

$$V(r) = V_a - (V_a - V_b)\frac{\ln\,(r/a)}{\ln\,(b/a)}$$

where $a < r < b$, and where V_a and V_b are the potentials of the inner and outer cylinders respectively.

3.14 Due to the existence of a cloud of electrons between two parallel plates, the potential at any point P in the space between the plates is

$$V = 120 \left(\frac{x}{0.01}\right)^{4/3} \text{ v}$$

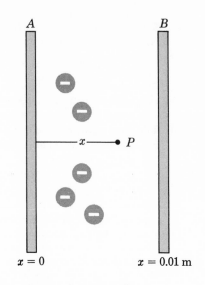

where x is the distance (in meters) of P from the plate A; the other plate is located at $x = 0.01$ m.

(a) What is the potential of plate B?

(b) Obtain an expression for the magnitude of the electric intensity at any point between the plates.

(c) What is the numerical value of the electric intensity at the inner surface of each plate?

(d) Consider the surface of the volume of space between the plates. Neglecting edge effects, apply Gauss's law to this surface and determine the number of electrons within this surface. The area of each plate is 2.0 m², and the electronic charge is -1.60×10^{-19} coul. Take $\varepsilon_0 = 9 \times 10^{-12}$ farad/m.

3.15 The volume density of positive charge at any point P within a sphere of radius R m depends only on the radial distance r according to the relation

$$\rho = Cr \text{ coul/m}^3$$

(a) If $R = 2$ m and $C = 1/\pi \times 10^{-6}$ coul/m⁴, what is the charge enclosed by the sphere?

(b) With the aid of Gauss's law find the electric field at a point ½ m from the center of the sphere. What symmetry property makes it possible to use Gauss's law?

3.16 The accompanying diagram shows a cross-sectional view of two long, coaxial, hollow metallic cylinders. The inner cylinder is charged positively and is insulated from the outer cylinder, which is grounded.

The magnitude of the electric intensity at any point P in the evacuated region between the cylinders is given by

$$2/r \text{ new/coul}$$

where r is the radial distance in meters from the common axis to the field point P, and a and b are the radii of the inner and outer cylinders.

(a) If $a = 0.100$ m and $b = 0.272$ m, calculate the potential of the inner cylinder.

(b) Would the potential of the inner cylinder be altered if the radius b of the grounded cylinder were made larger? Explain.

(c) Apply Gauss's law and calculate the charge per unit length present on the inner cylinder. Express your answer in terms of ε_0.

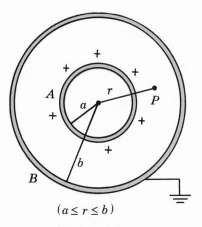

$(a \le r \le b)$

3.17 A large metallic plate lies in the horizontal plane. A similar plate is placed vertically and in contact with the first. (The diagram shows a sectional view of the plates in the x,y plane, the line of contact being the z-axis.) The conducting plates are charged. The electric intensity at any point P in the x,y plane on the 45° line OR is directed along OR away from the origin O. Its magnitude is

$$2r \text{ new/coul}$$

where r stands for the distance OP in meters.

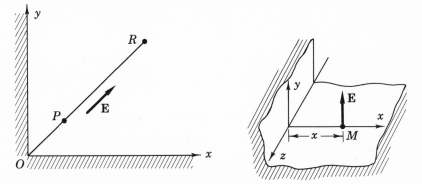

(a) What is the potential difference between the points O and R if the distance $OR = 3$ m? State which point is at the higher potential.

(b) At any point M on the surface of the horizontal plate at a distance of x m from the z-axis, the electric intensity is directed outward from the plate and its magnitude is equal to $2x$ new/coul. By the use of Gauss's law obtain an expression for the surface density of charge at M. What is the sign of the charge on the horizontal plate? Is the charge distributed uniformly over the plate? Give the reason for your answer.

3.18   A positive charge of 10^{-6} coul is distributed throughout a spherical region whose radius a is equal to 1 m. At any point within the sphere, the volume density ρ in coul/m³ is given by

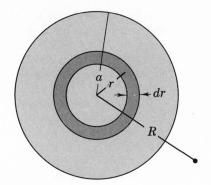

$$\rho = C(a - r) \qquad (a > r > 0)$$

where r is the distance of the point from the center and C is constant.

   (a) Determine the value of the constant C and specify its unit.

   (b) By applying Gauss's law calculate the magnitude of the electric intensity at any point *outside* the sphere ($R > a$) and specify its direction. Justify the application of the law by referring to the symmetry of the charge distribution.

Chapter 4.
Dielectrics

4.1   Polarization

So far we have dealt with the electric field produced by free charges, either on the surface of conductors or as distributions in space. We shall now consider the electrostatic field in a dielectric medium. In this preliminary study we shall make three assumptions: (1) that the medium is an ideal dielectric—that is, that it does not have free charges; (2) that its properties are isotropic—that is, that they are the same in all directions at a given point; and (3) that its properties are homogeneous—that is, that they are the same from point to point within the medium. In reality, certain dielectrics in the bulk, such as glass, plastics, mica, sulfur, and certain crystals, satisfy these assumptions to varying degrees. For example, a film of oxide formed on certain metals has unusual anistropic properties. Such a film has low resistance to flow of charge in one direction, but presents high resistance in the opposite direction. The majority of solids have a microcrystalline structure and are generally not homogeneous on an atomic scale.

From the molecular viewpoint, the most prominent characteristic of a dielectric lies in the strong binding of the charged entities (electrons and nuclei) of the molecule. The application of an external electric field causes a force to be exerted on each charged component. This results in a displacement of the charged particles, the positive particles being displaced in the direction of the field and the negative particles in the opposite direction. For ordinary fields, owing to the presence of restoring

71

The flashes of lightning demonstrate the increase in the capacitance of the air when the space between charge-carrying clouds (electrodes) is filled with water particles (a dielectric). (Courtesy Noel M. Klein, Weather Bureau, U. S. Department of Commerce.)

forces between the particles, displacements of this sort are confined to distances which are small relative to the molecular dimensions. The application of a field does not produce a drift of charge (as it does in conductors); instead, its overall effect is to displace the total positive charge relative to the total negative charge.

In the absence of an external field, the positive and negative charges in a physically small volume of an uncharged dielectric overlap. However, if such a dielectric is immersed in an external field, in the equilibrium state each volume element may be thought to have equal and opposite charges separated from each other. Such a configuration is called an electric dipole. A medium in which such a charge separation has taken place is said to be *polarized* (see Fig. 4.1). A polarized dielectric gives rise to a field at interior as well as exterior points and modifies the electric field which induced the dipoles.

A capacitor consists of a pair of similarly shaped conductors (parallel plates, or coaxial cylinders) which are insulated from each other. The capacitance C of such an arrangement is given by the ratio Q/V, where Q is the magnitude of the charge on either conductor, and V is the potential difference between them.

The phenomenon of polarization may be illustrated by the increase in the capacitance of a capacitor of a given geometry when the evacuated region between the electrodes is filled with a dielectric medium such as mineral oil. Measurements indicate that the ratio of the capacitance in the two cases is independent of the geometrical configuration but is characteristic of the dielectric used. Thus, if C_0 denotes the capacitance when the space between the electrodes is evacuated and C the capacitance when the space is filled with a dielectric without altering the geometry, then k, defined by the ratio C/C_0, is characteristic of the medium and is

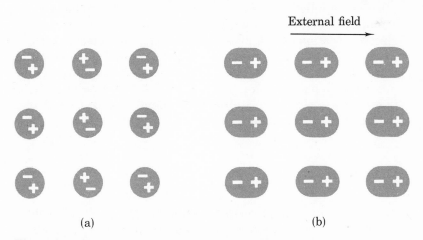

Figure 4.1 Representation of (a) unpolarized and (b) polarized dielectric from a macroscopic viewpoint.

known as the dielectric constant. (Other designations, such as dielectric coefficient and specific inductive capacity, are also used.)

An inference may be drawn regarding the change which takes place in the magnitude of the electric intensity as the dielectric material occupies the evacuated region. Let Q stand for the charge given to a capacitor in the absence of matter between the plates. Let the space between the electrodes be filled completely by a nonconducting medium of constant k in such a way that the charge on the capacitor remains unchanged during the operation. Consider the sequence of equalities $k = C/C_0 = (Q/V)/(Q_0/V_0) = V_0/V$, in which V_0 and V denote the initial and final values, respectively, of the potential difference. Since $Q = Q_0$ and $k > 1$, we may conclude that the introduction of the dielectric reduces V_0 by a factor k. But the potential difference across the capacitor is numerically equal to the line integral of the electric intensity from one plate to the other, whether or not a dielectric is present. The value of this integral is also reduced by a factor k. Hence the electric intensity itself has been reduced by the same factor. Although this result does not depend on the geometry of the particular capacitor, it can readily be verified in the case of a parallel-plate capacitor. Utilizing the relation $V = Ed$ and recalling that d is the distance between the plates, we find $(E_0 d)/(Ed) = (E_0/E) = k$. We shall see that the mechanism responsible for this reduction in E is the appearance of charge on the surfaces of the dielectric.

In some dielectrics the displacement of charge persists even after the applied field has been removed. If Carnuba wax, for example, is allowed to solidify in the presence of an electric field, electrets (permanent dipoles) are formed. An electret suspended in an external field experiences a torque that aligns the electret along the field direction. This resembles the behavior of a magnetic needle placed in a magnetic field. A few crystalline solids (e.g., barium titanate) exhibit permanent polarization at temperatures below a critical value.

4.2   The Electric Dipole

It follows from the preceding discussion that a dipole—that is, a pair of closely spaced equal charges of opposite sign—is an important configuration in describing the field produced by a polarized dielectric.

We shall now find expressions for the potential and the electric field in the neighborhood of the dipole shown in Fig. 4.2, where the point charges $-q$ and $+q$ are separated by the distance a. At the field point P, whose polar coordinates are r and θ, the combined potential due to the two point charges is

$$V = \frac{1}{4\pi\varepsilon_0}\left(\frac{q}{r_1} - \frac{q}{r_2}\right) = \frac{q}{4\pi\varepsilon_0}\left(\frac{r_2 - r_1}{r_1 r_2}\right) \tag{4.1}$$

If a is small relative to r, then approximately $r_1 r_2 = r^2$, and $(r_2 - r_1) = a\cos\theta$. Hence

$$V = \frac{qa\cos\theta}{4\pi\varepsilon_0 r^2} = \frac{\mathbf{p}\cdot\mathbf{r_1}}{4\pi\varepsilon_0 r^2} \tag{4.2}$$

In (4.2), $\mathbf{r_1}$ is a unit vector in the direction of $\mathbf{r}$, and $\mathbf{p}$ is referred to as the electric dipole moment of the pair of charges. The dipole moment $\mathbf{p}$ is a vector of magnitude qa. It is directed from

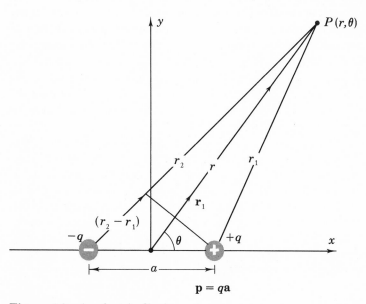

Figure 4.2 An electric dipole.

the negative to the positive charge. The radial component E_r of the electric intensity is obtained from

$$E_r = -\frac{\partial V}{\partial r} = \frac{2p\cos\theta}{4\pi\varepsilon_0 r^3} \tag{4.3}$$

And E_θ, the transverse component of the field, or the component of E in the direction of increasing θ, is given by

$$E_\theta = -\frac{1}{r}\frac{\partial V}{\partial \theta} = \frac{p \sin \theta}{4\pi\varepsilon_0 r^3} \tag{4.4}$$

In polar coordinates, the equipotential traces represented by $\cos \theta/r^2 = $ Constant are shown in Fig. 4.3 by the solid lines. To find the equation for the lines of force, recall that the slope of the tangent to the line of force at P is $r\,d\theta/dr$. Hence

$$\frac{r\,d\theta}{dr} = \frac{E_\theta}{E_r} = \frac{\sin \theta}{2 \cos \theta} = \frac{1}{2}\tan \theta$$

Integration results in

$$\frac{\sin^2 \theta}{r} = \text{Constant} \tag{4.5}$$

In Fig. 4.3 the lines of force are shown by the dashed lines.

The forces $\mathbf{E}q$ exerted by the field $\mathbf{E}$ on the two charges of the dipole give rise to a couple of magnitude $Eqa \sin \theta$ (see Fig. 4.4). The torque on the dipole about an axis through its midpoint per-

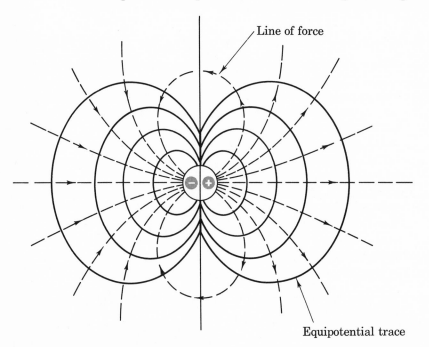

Figure 4.3   The dipole field.

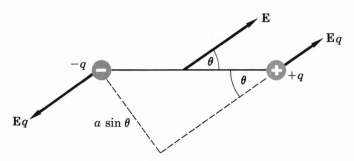

Figure 4.4   Torque on dipole.

pendicular to the plane of **p** and **E** has the value $pE \sin \theta$. In vectorial notation, the torque is given by

$$\mathbf{L} = \mathbf{p} \times \mathbf{E} \qquad (4.6)$$

where the right-hand member represents the torque as a vector product. The torque is in the counterclockwise direction.

4.3   The Molecular Viewpoint

From the molecular viewpoint the dipole moment of a volume element must be associated with the dipole moments of individual atoms or molecules contained in the volume element. Certain dielectrics consist of *nonpolar* molecules which do not possess a dipole moment in the absence of an applied field but which acquire such a moment when placed in the external field. In the case of these nonpolar molecules, the dipole moment of a given volume is the vector sum of the induced moments of the individual atomic or molecular constituents.

There are dielectrics whose component molecules possess a dipole moment even in the absence of a field. These are called *polar* molecules. An external field can also polarize a dielectric by orienting molecules which have permanent moments. When the external field is zero, the orientation of individual polar molecules is random. Hence the resultant dipole moment of an aggregate of polar molecules is zero. When the field is applied, each permanent dipole is subjected to a torque which aligns it with the field. Actually the thermal motions of the molecules tend to destroy the complete alignment of dipoles. However, the sum of partially lined-up moments within a volume element or cell gives rise to a nonvanishing resultant moment. In the case of nonpolar molecules, the induced moment is proportional to the strength of the applied field. In the case of polar molecules, the strength of the field at a given temperature again determines the resultant dipole moment of the cell, since a stronger field brings about a more complete alignment of dipoles within the cell. Since the alignment effect is temperature-sensitive, the two types of dielectrics may be sorted out by investigating the temperature dependence of a given sample. In the subsequent discussion we shall consider only the case of dipole moments induced in nonpolar dielectrics.

4.4   The Polarization Vector

The potential or the field produced at an external point by a polarized dielectric may be calculated by defining a vector quantity known as the polarization. The polarization vector $\mathbf{P}$ is defined as the dipole moment per unit volume induced in the medium. In symbols,

$$\mathbf{P} \equiv \frac{\Sigma \, \mathbf{p}}{v} \tag{4.7}$$

where $\Sigma \, \mathbf{p}$ denotes the vector sum of individual dipoles in the small volume v. The direction of the vector is the direction of the resultant dipole moment. It is possible to regard a block of dielectric material as made up of elements of volume v and to associate a vector $\mathbf{P}$ with each element. As in the case of other field quantities, $\mathbf{P}$ may be assumed to vary smoothly from point to point within the actual dielectric if v is sufficiently small.

The quantity $\mathbf{P}$ is then used to set up expressions for the potential due to the entire block, and the resulting field components may be deduced by differentiation. The general analysis is complicated. However, it indicates that at a point external to the block the potential function is that which is produced by surface and volume distributions of charge. The evaluation of the electric field inside the dielectric also indicates that the macroscopic field can be found from a consideration of the bound volume and surface charge densities. In considering the field at points inside, it must be realized that on an atomic scale the field varies rapidly in time and in position. The fluctuations from point to point arise from the nonuniform motions and thermal vibrations. The macroscopic field is taken to be the time and space average of the rapidly varying microscopic field.

We shall examine the polarization mechanism in a less formal way by making a direct evaluation of the polarization charge that crosses an element of area dA, and then applying the result to find the magnitude of the bound charge that leaves a closed surface S. Consider first a small element of surface area dA [see Fig. 4.5(a)] within the dielectric. When the external field $\mathbf{E}$ is applied, on the average a charge separation s is brought about. Positive charge crosses dA by being displaced in the direction of $\mathbf{E}$, and negative charge crosses dA in the opposite sense [see Fig. 4.5(b)]. For the

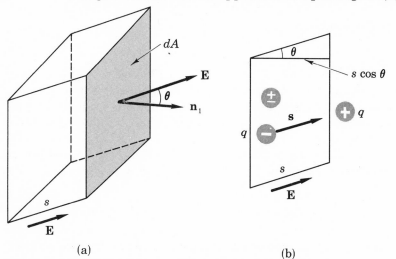

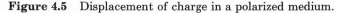

(a)   (b)

Figure 4.5   Displacement of charge in a polarized medium.

purposes of our present discussion, regard the charges as point charges, and assume that the negative charge is fixed and that the positive charge is the one that suffers a displacement s. The volume dv of the parallelopiped in Fig. 4.5(a) is

$$dv = \mathbf{s} \cdot \mathbf{n}_1 \, dA = s \cos \theta \, dA \qquad (4.8)$$

In (4.8) $\mathbf{n}_1$ is a unit vector normal to dA, and θ is the angle between $\mathbf{s}$ (or $\mathbf{E}$) and $\mathbf{n}_1$. Denoting by dQ_i the charge that crosses dA, we have

$$dQ_i = Nqs \cos \theta \, dA \qquad (4.9)$$

where N is the number of dipoles per unit volume and qs is the moment $\mathbf{p}$ of each dipole. With the help of the defining relation (4.7), $Nq\mathbf{s} = \mathbf{P}$. Hence

$$dQ_i = P \cos \theta \, dA \qquad (4.10)$$

This means that the polarization charge which crosses dA is just equal to the component of **P** normal to dA. If dA is a surface element on the outer boundary of a block of dielectric, dQ_i is the charge in a layer of thickness $s \cos \theta$. The layer thickness is of molecular dimensions, so dQ_i may be considered the charge which appears on the outer surface. We thus arrive at the significant result that P_n, the component of **P** normal to the dielectric surface, is equal to σ_i, the induced surface density of charge dQ_i/dA appearing in (4.10). In symbols,

$$\sigma_i = P_n \qquad (4.11)$$

or, in vectorial notation,

$$\sigma_i = \mathbf{P} \cdot \mathbf{n}_1 \qquad (4.12)$$

The surface density σ_i appearing in (4.12) is also called the bound, or polarization, charge density, to distinguish it from the free, or conduction, charge density σ alluded to in our discussion of conductors. From (4.11) we see that the unit of P is the coulomb per square meter.

Next we evaluate the net charge Q_i which passes out of the entire surface S enclosing a volume T (see Fig. 4.6). By integration of (4.10),

$$Q_i = \int_S P \cos \theta \, dA = \int_S \mathbf{P} \cdot d\mathbf{A} \qquad (4.13)$$

where $d\mathbf{A}$ is a vector whose direction is that of the outward normal and whose magnitude is dA (i.e., $d\mathbf{A} = \mathbf{n}_1 \, dA$). $\mathbf{P} \cdot d\mathbf{A}$ is positive when the charge passes outward through the element of surface and is negative when the charge enters. If as much charge

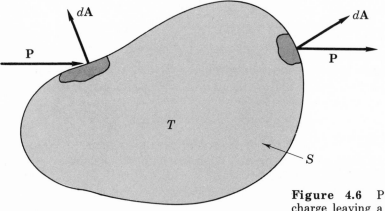

Figure 4.6 Polarization charge leaving a closed surface S which bounds volume T.

enters as leaves the surface S, then in (4.13) $Q_i = 0$. This is the case if $\mathbf{P}$ is uniform—that is, if $\mathbf{P}$ has the same magnitude and is parallel to a given direction at all points of S. However, there may be an accumulation of bound charges within S. Such a charge distribution may be described in terms of ρ_i, the volume density of induced charge at any point within T.

Prior to polarization, ρ_i at any point within S was zero—that is, the dielectric was neutral. Upon polarization, Q_i is the amount of induced charge which left the surface S. Hence, by the conservation law of charge, $-Q_i$ is the net charge left within the volume T. But the charge remaining *within* the volume is expressed as

$$-Q_i = \int_T \rho_i \, dv \tag{4.14}$$

where ρ_i is the charge density at points *inside* T. Combining (4.13) and (4.14), we have the important result

$$\int_T \rho_i \, dv = -\int_S \mathbf{P} \cdot d\mathbf{A} \tag{4.15}$$

which states that in a nonuniformly polarized dielectric the total charge remaining in a given volume is the negative of the surface integral of the polarization $\mathbf{P}$ over the surface which encloses the volume. Equation (4.15) resembles Gauss's law, and by a procedure followed previously it can be expressed in differential form that associates the volume density of induced charge ρ_i with P_x, P_y, and P_z, the rectangular components of the vector $\mathbf{P}$. The relation is

$$-\boldsymbol{\nabla} \cdot \mathbf{P} = -\left(\frac{\partial P_x}{\partial x} + \frac{\partial P_y}{\partial y} + \frac{\partial P_z}{\partial z}\right) = \rho_i \tag{4.16}$$

As in the case of σ_i, ρ_i represents the induced, or bound, or polarization charge density. Bound charge is produced by virtue of the small displacement of positive and negative charges during the process of polarization.

4.5   Parallel Plates Separated by a Dielectric

To clarify the concepts involved in the preceding discussion let us select the special but important example of two charged plane parallel metallic plates. When the intervening space is free of matter, equal and opposite free surface charge densities, $+\sigma$ and

$-\sigma$, are present on the plates. See Fig. 4.7(a). The electric intensity E_0 is uniform and has the value σ/ϵ_0. Keeping the charge on the conductors unchanged, let a dielectric slab be inserted so as to fill the region completely. In Fig. 4.7(b) a gap is shown, for clarity.

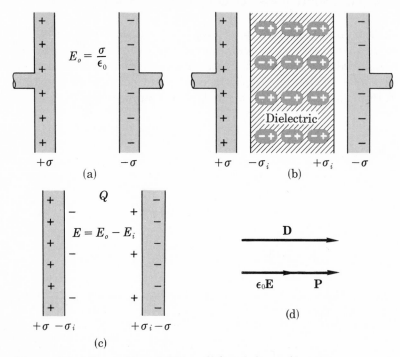

(a)   (b)

(c)

(d)

Figure 4.7   The resultant field in a dielectric located between charged plates.

Under the action of the field due to the charges on the plates, induced dipoles are formed. At the left-hand boundary of the dielectric, adjacent to the positively charged plate, there appears a layer of negative charge of surface density $-\sigma_i$. A corresponding layer of density, $+\sigma_i$, appears at the right-hand boundary adjacent to the negatively charged plate. These surface layers represent the induced charges. Unlike the free charges which were transferred to the metallic plates of the capacitor in the charging process, the induced charges belong to a system of dipoles and are bound. In the interior of the dielectric the net charge in a given volume remains equal to zero, since in this special example the polarization is uniform.

   To evaluate the magnitude of the macroscopic electric field in the dielectric, we apply the fundamental concept that the field **E**

arises from all the charges present. In this instance we must include the free charge on the plates and the induced charge on the
surfaces of the dielectric, since the volume density of charge is
zero. Figure 4.7(c) shows the charge distributions. The magnitude
of the field **E** at an interior point Q may be regarded as the sum of
two components; that is,

$$E = E_0 - E_i = \frac{\sigma}{\varepsilon_0} - \frac{\sigma_i}{\varepsilon_0} \qquad (4.17)$$

where E_0 denotes the contribution from the free charges and E_i
is the oppositely directed contribution originating from the induced charge. In this special case we see why the externally applied field is reduced by virtue of the field created by the polarized dielectric itself. Here the symmetry of the charge distribution
on the plates is not affected by the presence of the slab, and the
polarization vector **P** is everywhere constant in magnitude and
normal to the faces of the slab. In accordance with (4.11) we can
write

$$P = \sigma_i \qquad (4.18)$$

With the aid of (4.18) we rewrite (4.17) in the form

$$\sigma = \varepsilon_0 E + P \qquad (4.19)$$

The right-hand member of (4.19) contains the magnitudes of the
fundamental vector **E** and of the polarization vector **P**. The
former arises from the total charge (free and induced) while the
latter arises from the induced charge. At this point we can introduce an auxiliary vector quantity **D**, such that

$$\mathbf{D} \equiv \varepsilon_0 \mathbf{E} + \mathbf{P} \qquad (4.20)$$

D is called the *electric displacement*. Figure 4.7(d) gives a geometrical relation among the three quantities at the point Q.

The treatment of the polarized state in terms of induced surface densities is inconvenient, since in experiments it is the free
charge on conductors that is readily controlled. In this special
case, where the boundaries of the dielectric are everywhere perpendicular to the direction of the field existing in the absence of
the dielectric, the field of **D** is determined by the free charge distribution on the conductors. In fact, from (4.19) and (4.20)

$$D = \sigma \qquad (4.21)$$

That is, the magnitude of the displacement vector is set equal to
the surface density of free charge or charge placed on conductors.

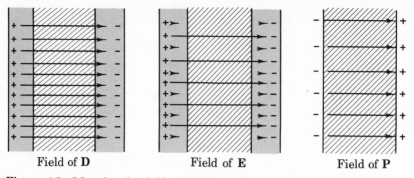

Field of **D**   Field of **E**   Field of **P**

Figure 4.8 Mapping the fields of **D**, **E**, and **P**. Dielectric slab with plane faces perpendicular to the field vectors.

Figure 4.8 shows a mapping of the fields of **D**, **E**, and **P**. In the following section we shall deduce the general property of the electric displacement **D**.

4.6   **The General Property of the Vector D**

In the preceding illustration, the plane boundaries of the dielectric were everywhere normal to the electric field present initially in the absence of the slab. The field of **D** was produced by the distribution of free charges on the metal plates and was not altered by the presence of the dielectric. In general, the field of **D** is modified by the presence of boundaries between dielectrics, and it is just in this connection that the auxiliary vector **D** plays a useful part. This displacement vector has an important characteristic: The surface integral of the normal component of the electric displacement over any closed surface is equal to the *free* (not the induced) charge located within the volume bounded by the surface. This property of **D** is demonstrated by starting with Gauss's law for the electric field as applied to polarized dielectrics, namely

$$\int_S \varepsilon_0 \mathbf{E} \cdot d\mathbf{A} = Q_T = Q + Q_i \qquad (4.22)$$

in which Q_T is the total charge, or the sum of the free charge Q and the induced charge Q_i. But by (4.15) the induced charge remaining within the gaussian surface is given in terms of the polarization vector **P** by the relation

$$\int_S \mathbf{P} \cdot d\mathbf{A} = -Q_i \qquad (4.23)$$

Adding (4.22) and (4.23), we obtain

$$\int_S (\varepsilon_0 \mathbf{E} + \mathbf{P}) \cdot d\mathbf{A} = Q \qquad (4.24)$$

where Q is the free charge within the surface S. We now define $\mathbf{D}$ by the relation

$$\mathbf{D} \equiv \varepsilon_0 \mathbf{E} + \mathbf{P} \qquad (4.25)$$

which, on substitution in (4.24), yields

$$\int_S \mathbf{D} \cdot d\mathbf{A} = Q \qquad (4.26)$$

The presence of polarized matter does not affect this result, which expresses the important property that the surface integral of $\mathbf{D}$ is equal to the *conduction* charge enclosed by the surface over which the integration is carried out. The form of (4.26) suggests that $\mathbf{D}$ may be evaluated by the use of an appropriate gaussian surface lying partly or wholly within the dielectric or including boundaries between conductors and dielectrics. In ordinary dielectrics (see Section 4.7) the three vectors appearing in (4.25) have the same direction. In anisotropic media, where $\mathbf{P}$ and $\mathbf{E}$ have different directions, $\mathbf{D}$ is defined as the vector sum. In the example of the parallel-plate capacitor, the three vectors were parallel to one another and also normal to the boundaries. The free charge may be distributed continuously throughout the interior of the volume, or it may be spread over boundaries, or it may be present as a set of discrete charges. The unit of $\mathbf{D}$ is the same as that of $\mathbf{P}$, namely coulombs per square meter. The vector $\mathbf{E}$ is expressed in newtons per coulomb. Since the unit of ε_0, the permittivity of free space, is coulomb^2/newton-meter^2, the product $\varepsilon_0 \mathbf{E}$ is again expressed in coulombs per square meter.

4.7   Relations between Field Vectors in Ordinary Dielectrics

When we say that a dielectric is ordinary, we mean that it is homogeneous, isotropic, and linear. The last qualification implies that there is a linear relationship between the polarization $\mathbf{P}$ and the electric intensity $\mathbf{E}$. Linearity may be expected if the dipole moment induced due to the separation of charge and the average moment resulting from a process of alignment are proportional to

the strength of the applied field. This simple dependence is justi-
fied experimentally for low values of the field. The assumption of
linearity may not be valid if the external field is sufficiently high
to produce a state of saturation in which all dipoles are aligned
parallel to the field.

Symbolically, the proportionality between P and E is expressed
by

$$P = \eta E \tag{4.27}$$

where η is called the *electric susceptibility*. The units of η are the
same as those of ε_0, namely coulomb^2/newton-meter^2. With the
aid of the defining relation for $\mathbf{D}$ given in (4.25), the quantity $\mathbf{P}$
can be eliminated. Thus

$$D = \varepsilon_0 E + P = (\varepsilon_0 + \eta)E \tag{4.28}$$

Upon introducing the additional substitution

$$\varepsilon = (\varepsilon_0 + \eta) \tag{4.29}$$

the dependence in (4.28) becomes

$$D = \varepsilon E \tag{4.30}$$

where ε is referred to as the permittivity of the medium. The dimensionless ratio of ε to ε_0 is called the dielectric constant or dielectric coefficient and is denoted by k. Thus, utilizing (4.29), we
obtain

$$k \equiv \frac{\varepsilon}{\varepsilon_0} = 1 + \frac{\eta}{\varepsilon_0} \tag{4.31}$$

The dielectric constant k is to be identified with C/C_0, the ratio
of capacitances introduced previously (Section 4.1). The values
of k for solids range from about 2 for Parowax to about 7 for
porcelain. In liquid dielectrics, the value of k may range from 2 for
petroleum oil to around 80 for water. In certain colloidal suspen-
sions of particles with large dipole moments, k may possess a value
of the order of 1000.

Referring to (4.29) and (4.31), we see that dielectric properties
may be described by k, by ε, or by η. In a region devoid of matter,
where no polarizable material exists, η and P are zero. From (4.31)
it follows that for free space $k = 1$ and $\varepsilon = \varepsilon_0$.

4.8   Boundary Conditions

When two dielectrics of arbitrary shape are polarized in a given
field, the vectors **D** and **E** may make any angle with the surface
separating the two media, and at the boundary there may be
sudden changes in the magnitudes and directions of these vectors.
To determine the changes that occur at the boundary, we make
use of two basic relations of the electrostatic field. The first is
Gauss's law for **D** as expressed in (4.26). The second is the conservative character of the electrostatic field **E** which is expressed in
the vanishing of the line integral of **E** around a closed path. See
(3.47). As we have seen before, no work is done in taking a charge
around a closed path.

$\vec{E} \cdot d\vec{l} = 0$

Figure 4.9 shows a portion of the boundary between two dielectrics of dielectric constants k_1 and k_2. Consider a short cylindrical
gaussian surface whose flat ends have an area A and whose curved

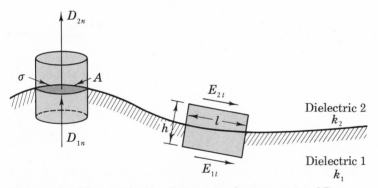

Figure 4.9   The continuity of the normal components of **D**
and the tangential component of **E**.

surface is normal to the boundary. Let the components of **D** normal to the boundary be denoted by D_{1n} and D_{2n} in dielectrics 1
and 2 respectively. By making the area of the curved surface small
relative to the area of the flat end, we can make the outward flux
of **D** from the cylindrical surface arbitrarily small. Furthermore,
we can make the end areas sufficiently small so that D_{1n} and D_{2n}
do not vary over them. Then, by (4.26), the net outward flux of
D over the surface is

$$(D_{2n} - D_{1n})A = \sigma A \qquad (4.32)$$

where σ is the *free* charge density which might be present at the interface. In the absence of such a charge, (4.32) reduces to

$$D_{2n} = D_{1n} \qquad (4.33)$$

which states that the normal component of **D** is continuous across the boundary provided there are no conduction charges at the interface.

The boundary condition on **E** is deduced by applying the circuital law to a closed rectangular loop portions of which lie in each medium (see Fig. 4.9). For this path $l \gg h$, and l is made short enough so that E_{1t} and E_{2t}, the tangential components of **E** in dielectrics 1 and 2 respectively, do not vary over l. Writing out the line integral, we obtain

$$E_{1t}l - E_{2t}l = 0 \qquad (4.34)$$

In writing (4.34) we assumed that the contributions to the line integral from the normal components of **E** become vanishingly small as h is allowed to go to zero. Relation (4.34) yields

$$E_{1t} = E_{2t} \qquad (4.35)$$

Hence the tangential component of the electric intensity is continuous across the boundary.

To deduce the boundary condition involving **P**, we integrate over the gaussian surface used to determine the behavior of **D** at the boundary. In terms of the normal component of **P**,

$$-P_{2n} - P_{1n} = -\sigma_i \qquad (4.36)$$

where σ_i is the net polarization charge density at the surface of separation.

At the interface between a conductor and a dielectric, we can deduce the following relations: Since E_t is zero in the conductor, it is also zero in the dielectric. While E_n is also zero in the conductor, it is not zero in the dielectric. Similarly, D_n is zero in the conductor, but in the dielectric $D_n = \sigma$, where σ is the free charge density on the surface of the conductor. E_n in the dielectric is D_n/ε or $\sigma/k\varepsilon_0$. By appropriate substitutions in $D_n = (\varepsilon_0 E_n + P_n)$, we obtain $P_n = \sigma_i = \sigma(k - 1)/k$. The induced density of charge σ_i is zero for $k = 1$ and approaches σ as k increases.

Figure 4.10 shows the various vectors at an interface between two dielectrics or between a conductor and a dielectric. Since we are dealing with linear isotropic dielectrics, **D** and **E** are parallel. Vectors **D** and **E** are expressed in different units; the diagrams must be regarded as schematic representations.

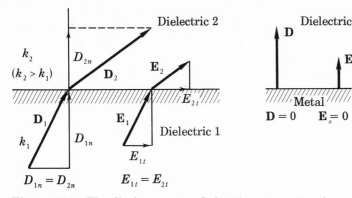

Figure 4.10 The displacement and electric vectors at an interface between two dielectrics and between a conductor and a dielectric.

4.9   Permanent Polarization

Recent studies have been made of crystalline dielectrics which exhibit a permanent electric dipole moment—that is, even in the absence of an externally applied field, the material behaves as though it were polarized. Rochelle salts, potassium dihydrogen phosphate, and barium titanate are typical examples of this group of so-called *ferroelectric* crystals. The name is appropriate because the electrical properties of these crystals are analogous to the magnetic properties of such ferromagnetic materials as iron, cobalt, and nickel.

The polarized state of a ferroelectric substance is fairly stable and can last for a long time. Consider a slab of permanently polarized material located in the field produced by a pair of parallel conducting plates. Let a weak field be applied to the slab in a direction opposite to that of its natural polarization. If the strength of the applied field E is gradually increased, P, the polarization of the specimen, will be gradually reduced and will become zero for a particular value of the reversed electric field. If the field is increased further, the polarization will reverse and will eventually attain a saturation value. If the direction of E is reversed and its magnitude brought back to zero, the specimen will retain its polarization even if $E = 0$. The complete curve showing the magnitudes of E vs P is given in Fig. 4.11. A curve of this sort is called a hysteresis loop. The term hysteresis means "lagging behind," and here P lags behind E. Such a dielectric does not possess linear properties (P is not proportional to E); in fact, P is a double-valued function of E. The two polarized states at $E = 0$ represent permanent polarizations retained by the specimen during a cyclic variation of E. The reversed field of magnitude E_c must be exceeded in order for P to be established in the opposite direction.

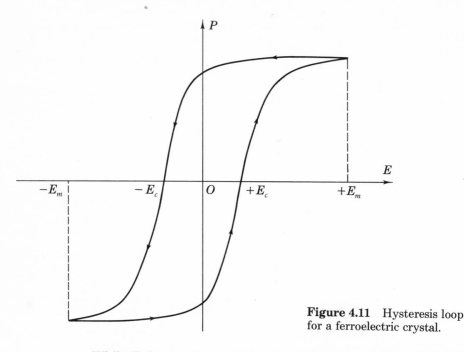

Figure 4.11   Hysteresis loop for a ferroelectric crystal.

While E changes from zero to E_m, free charge will be furnished to the plates by the source of potential difference. This free charge will almost equal the bound charge appearing on the surface of the slab whose dielectric constant is high. A similar situation is also present in the case of an ordinary dielectric. If E is changed from $+E_m$ to $-E_m$, the polarization of the specimen is reversed. During this process free charge of opposite sign will be transferred to the plates through the external circuit. For instance, electrons will be transferred to the plate which was positively charged initially, and the number of electrons transferred will be sufficient to neutralize the positive charge already on the plate and also to match the new positive bound charge appearing on the slab. If the conducting plates are connected together, the electrons on the negative plate will not return to the positive plate but will remain on the negative plate, because they are held in place by the positive bound charge on the permanently polarized slab.

Now if the source of potential is reintroduced with the same polarity as before (negative terminal to negatively charged plate), practically no charge will flow through the external circuit. This behavior differs from that of ordinary dielectrics, which do not possess permanent polarization; with such materials free charges do not remain on the conducting plates when they are shorted and there is always a flow of charge when the external emf is introduced.

It follows that we can determine the direction of polarization of a ferroelectric slab between two plates by applying an external field. If the applied field is in the direction of the original polarization, there will be little flow of charge in the external circuit; if the direction of the applied field is opposite to the direction of the original polarization, there will be a change in the polarization and an attendant transfer of charge through the circuit. A ferroelectric crystal placed between two metal plates is, in the absence of a field, capable of retaining its state of polarization in one direction or the other. It may be used as an element in a memory device.

4.10   Illustrative Examples

Example 1. Two large parallel metallic plates are separated by two sheets of dielectric material of permittivity ε_1 and ε_2 respectively (see Fig. 4.12). The plates carry equal and opposite charges, and the thicknesses of the dielectric sheets are t_1 and t_2. The electric field at any point in dielectric 1 is E_1 and in dielectric 2 is E_2. Find (1) the displacement in each dielectric, (2) the surface density of free charge, (3) the polarization charge per unit area on the surface of each dielec-

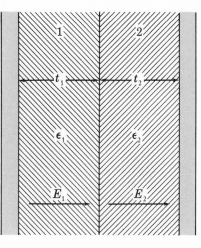

Figure 4.12 Two charged conducting plates separated by two different dielectrics.

tric, (4) the component of electric field due to induced charges, (5) the potential difference between the plates, and (6) the electric susceptibility of each dielectric.

The fields are normal to the conducting plates as well as to the boundaries of the dielectric.

(1) $D_1 = \varepsilon_1 E_1$ and $D_2 = \varepsilon_2 E_2$.

(2) Since there are no conduction charges on the intersurface between the sheets, $D_1 = D_2$, the surface density of free charge may be obtained from either $\sigma = D_1$ or $\sigma = D_2$. Note that if $\varepsilon_2 > \varepsilon_1$, then $E_1 > E_2$—that is, the field in the dielectric of higher permittivity is weaker.

(3) To find the polarization we use the defining relation for **D** and make use of the results obtained above. Thus

$$P_1 = D_1 - \varepsilon_0 E_1 = D_1 - \frac{\varepsilon_0 D_1}{\varepsilon_1} = \sigma\left(1 - \frac{1}{k_1}\right)$$

and
$$P_2 = D_2 - \varepsilon_0 E_2 = D_2 - \frac{\varepsilon_0 D_2}{\varepsilon_2} = \sigma\left(1 - \frac{1}{k_2}\right)$$

where k_1 and k_2 are the dielectric constants respectively of the two sheets.

Since P_1 and P_2 are also normal to the surfaces of the dielectrics, the induced charge densities at the dielectric surfaces adjacent to the metal plates are

$$\sigma_{1i} = P_1 = \sigma\left(1 - \frac{1}{k_1}\right) \quad \text{and} \quad \sigma_{2i} = P_2 = \sigma\left(1 - \frac{1}{k_2}\right)$$

At the interface between the dielectrics the net induced charge is

$$\sigma_{1i} - \sigma_{2i} = \sigma\left(\frac{1}{k_2} - \frac{1}{k_1}\right)$$

(4) $$E_{1i} = \frac{\sigma_{1i}}{\varepsilon_0} \quad \text{and} \quad E_{2i} = \frac{\sigma_{2i}}{\varepsilon_0}$$

These components are oppositely directed to the field $E_0 = \sigma/\varepsilon_0$ existing between the plates prior to the insertion of the sheets. Also the actual electric field may be found from

$$E_1 = E_0 - E_{1i} = \frac{(\sigma - \sigma_{1i})}{\varepsilon_0} = \frac{\sigma}{\varepsilon_0 k_1} = \frac{\sigma}{\varepsilon_1}$$

This result is consistent with the relation in (1) above. Similarly, $E_2 = \sigma/\varepsilon_2$.

(5) The potential difference V between the conducting plates is

$$V = E_2 t_2 + E_1 t_1 = \frac{\sigma}{\varepsilon_0} \left(\frac{t_1}{k_1} + \frac{t_2}{k_2} \right)$$

(6) The susceptibility η is obtained from the definition of ε—that is,

$$\varepsilon_1 = \varepsilon_0 + \eta_1 \qquad \text{and} \qquad \varepsilon_2 = \varepsilon_0 + \eta_2$$

Example 2. A conducting sphere of radius a carrying a charge $+Q$ is placed concentrically within a spherical cavity of radius b. The cavity is located in an extensive homogeneous, isotropic dielectric of dielectric constant k_2.

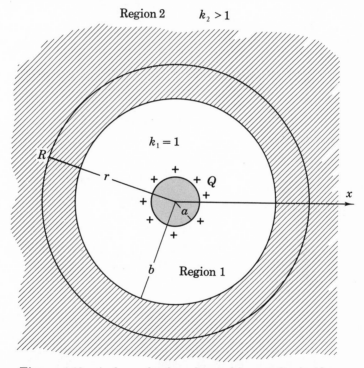

Figure 4.13   A charged sphere located in a cavity inside an extensive dielectric.

(1) Obtain expressions for **D**, **E**, and **P** at any point within the dielectric at a distance r from the center of the cavity ($r > b$).

(2) Repeat for a point within the cavity ($a < r < b$).

(3) Calculate the sum of the induced charge and the free charge Q.

(4) Obtain expressions for the potential at any point in the dielectric and also at a point in the cavity. The zero of potential is taken at $r = \infty$.

(5) What is the volume density of charge due to polarization?

Solution: Refer to Fig. 4.13. We note that the field has radial symmetry. Let the subscripts 1 and 2 denote quantities in the empty cavity (region 1) and in the dielectric (region 2). Through R, a point in region 2, pass a concentric spherical gaussian surface of radius r. Then, by Gauss's law, for **D**

$$D_2 = \frac{Q}{4\pi r^2} \qquad (r > b)$$

$$E_2 = \frac{D_2}{\varepsilon_0 k_2} = \frac{Q}{4\pi\varepsilon_0 k_2 r^2} \qquad (r > b)$$

$$P_2 = D_2 - \varepsilon_0 E_2 = \frac{Q}{4\pi r^2}\left(\frac{k_2 - 1}{k_2}\right) \qquad (r > b)$$

In the cavity (region 1), $k_1 = 1$. From the boundary condition, $D_{2n} = D_{1n}$. Since **D** is normal to the cavity surface,

$$D_1 = D_2 = \frac{Q}{4\pi r^2} \qquad (a < r < b)$$

and, since $k_1 = 1$,

$$E_1 = \frac{D_1}{\varepsilon_0 k_1} = \frac{Q}{4\pi\varepsilon_0 r^2} \qquad (a < r < b)$$

$$P_1 = D_1 - \varepsilon_0 E_1 = 0$$

as it should be, since the cavity is free from matter.

The surface density of induced charge on the cavity wall is given by

$$\sigma_i = -P_n = -P_2\bigg|_{r=b} = -\frac{Q}{4\pi b^2} \cdot \frac{(k_2 - 1)}{k_2}$$

Let the total charge induced on the inner surface of the cavity be represented by Q_i. Then

$$Q_i = 4\pi b^2 \sigma_i = -Q(k_2 - 1)/k_2$$

The induced charge is of the opposite sign and is less than the free charge, but it approaches the free charge as the value of k_2 increases. If we add Q and Q_i, we obtain Q/k_2. The field of **E** in region 2 may be calculated from Gauss's law for **E** by using the sum of the free and bound charges within the gaussian surface.

To find V_2, the potential at a point within region 2, we integrate E_2. Thus, using x as the variable of integration, we get

$$V_2 = -\int_\infty^r E_2\, dx = -\frac{Q}{4\pi\varepsilon_0 k_2} \int_\infty^r \frac{dx}{x^2} = \frac{Q}{4\pi\varepsilon_0 k_2} \cdot \frac{1}{r}$$

$$(b < r < \infty)$$

To find V_1, the potential at a point in the cavity (region 1), we must integrate E_2 from $x = \infty$ to $x = b$, and E_1 from $x = b$ to $x = r$ where $a < r < b$. Thus

$$V_1 = \frac{Q}{4\pi\varepsilon_0 k_2} \cdot \frac{1}{b} + \int_b^r -E_1\, dx = \frac{Q}{4\pi\varepsilon_0} \left(\frac{1}{r} - \frac{k_2 - 1}{k_2} \cdot \frac{1}{b} \right)$$

$$(a < r < b)$$

At the boundary of the cavity

$$V_1 \bigg|_{r=b} = \frac{Q}{4\pi\varepsilon_0 k_2} \cdot \frac{1}{b} = V_2 \bigg|_{r=b}$$

as it should.

The volume density of induced charge is to be evaluated from the differential form

$$\rho_i = -\left(\frac{\partial P_x}{\partial x} + \frac{\partial P_y}{\partial y} + \frac{\partial P_z}{\partial z} \right)$$

where P_x, P_y, and P_z refer to the rectangular components of $\mathbf{P}$ in region 2. Now

$$P_x = P_2 \frac{x}{r} = \frac{Cx}{r^3}$$

where

$$C = \frac{Q(k_2 - 1)}{4\pi k_2}$$

and

$$\frac{\partial P_x}{\partial x} = \frac{C}{r^5} (r^2 - 3x^2)$$

Similarly $\dfrac{\partial P_y}{\partial y} = \dfrac{C}{r^5} (r^2 - 3y^2)$ and $\dfrac{\partial P_z}{\partial z} = \dfrac{C}{r^5} (r^2 - 3z^2)$

On adding the partial derivatives, we find for ρ_i

$$\rho_i = -\frac{C}{r^5} \left[3r^2 - 3(x^2 + y^2 + z^2) \right] \equiv 0$$

4.11   Summary

As before, we shall now collect the various relations describing the properties of the field in connection with the study of dielectrics.

In integral form:

$$\int_{\substack{\text{closed} \\ \text{surface}}} \mathbf{D} \cdot d\mathbf{A} = Q \tag{4.37}$$

$$\int_{\substack{\text{closed} \\ \text{surface}}} \mathbf{P} \cdot d\mathbf{A} = -Q_i \tag{4.38}$$

$$\varepsilon_0 \int_{\substack{\text{closed} \\ \text{surface}}} \mathbf{E} \cdot d\mathbf{A} = Q_T \tag{4.39}$$

In differential form:

$$\nabla \cdot \mathbf{D} = \rho \tag{4.40}$$

$$\nabla \cdot \mathbf{P} = -\rho_i \tag{4.41}$$

$$\varepsilon_0 \nabla \cdot \mathbf{E} = \rho + \rho_i \tag{4.42}$$

$$\nabla \times \mathbf{E} = 0 \tag{4.43}$$

It should be emphasized that $\mathbf{D} = \varepsilon \mathbf{E}$ given in (4.30) is not a fundamental relation but only an attempt to describe approximately the dielectric property of the medium. The linear relationship may break down, and the permittivity may depend on the time rate of change of $\mathbf{E}$. The introduction of the constitutive relation is a convenience. The fundamental relations given in (4.42) and (4.43) are always valid, and fields in dielectrics may be described in terms of all the charges, bound or free.

Dielectrics: Problems

4.1   Start with the definition $\mathbf{D} = \varepsilon_0 \mathbf{E} + \mathbf{P}$, and the more special relation $\mathbf{D} = \varepsilon_0 k\,\mathbf{E}$. Express the polarization vector $\mathbf{P}$ in terms of the electric vector $\mathbf{E}$ and appropriate constants. Test your result, to see that $\mathbf{P} \to 0$ in free space.

4.2 A plane boundary separates two isotropic, homogeneous dielectric media. Assuming that no free charges exist at the interface, apply the boundary condition on the vector **D** and calculate the magnitude of E_{2n}, the component of **E** normal to the interface in medium 2, if E_{1n}, the corresponding component in medium 1, has the value $6 \times 10^{+3}$ new/coul.

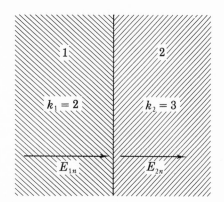

4.3 The polarization of a piece of sulfur has the magnitude of 4×10^{-6} coul/m^2. From handbook data calculate the number of atoms per cubic meter and the dipole moment of a sulfur atom. Recalling that the charge of each sign is the atomic number times the electronic charge, calculate the distance l between the centers of positive and negative charge.

4.4 A cavity in the form of a pillbox is cut within a dielectric slab located between two parallel charged conducting plates. The flat faces of the pillbox are perpendicular to the field. The dielectric constant of the slab k. What is the electric field inside the cavity? Express your answer in terms of
(a) the field vector **D** in the dielectric,
(b) the field vectors **P** and **E** existing in the dielectric.

4.5 The field in a cavity cut in a dielectric depends both on the shape and the orientation of the cavity. Show that $\mathbf{E}_0$, the field in the center of a long, thin needle-like slot, is equal to the average field **E** present in the dielectric.

4.6 (a) The distance between the plates of a parallel-plate capacitor is 5 mm. The plates are in free space. A potential difference of 2250 v is applied to the terminals of the capacitor. What is the surface density of charge? Take $\varepsilon_0 = 9 \times 10^{-12}$mks units.
(b) The charged capacitor described in (a) is disconnected from the source of potential difference and is insulated so that the charge on each plate remains unchanged. A dielectric slab 2 mm in thickness is inserted between the plates so that the faces of the slab are parallel to those of the plates. The dielectric coefficient of the slab is 3. What is the potential difference between the plates of the capacitor after the insertion of the dielectric?

4.7 By applying the boundary conditions on the field vectors **D** and **E**, obtain an expression for the surface polarization charge σ_i at the boundary between two dielectrics of dielectric constants k_1 and k_2. Assuming that no free charge resides at the interface, show that

$$\sigma_i = \varepsilon_0 E_{1n}\left(1 - \frac{k_1}{k_2}\right)$$

where E_{1n} is the component of **E** in dielectric 1 normal to the interface.

4.8   The dielectric constant k of the material between the plates of a large parallel-plate condenser varies continuously from one plate to the other in accordance with the relation

$$k = \left(1 + \frac{4}{d}x\right)$$

where d is the separation of the plates and x is the perpendicular distance from one of the plates to any point in the dielectric.

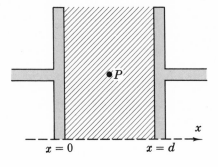

(a) If σ, the surface density of free charge on one of the plates, is 54×10^{-12} coul/m², what is the magnitude of the electric field at the point P halfway between the plates? $\varepsilon_0 = 9 \times 10^{-12}$ mks units.

(b) If the separation d is equal to 3.6 mm, calculate the capacitance of the condenser per unit area.

4.9   Two sheets of dielectric materials A and B, whose thicknesses are 4 mm and 5 mm respectively, fill the region between two large conducting plates. The dielectric coefficient of A is 3; that of B is 6. The electric intensity at any point in A is given by 2×10^4 v/m and in B by 1×10^4 v/m.

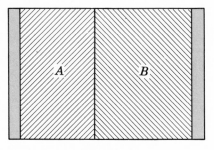

(a) What is the difference in potential between the conducting plates?

(b) What is the surface density of free charge on the plates? Take the permittivity of free space to be 9×10^{-12} mks units.

4.10   The dielectric constant k of the material between the plates of a parallel-plate capacitor varies linearly with x, the perpendicular distance from one of the plates. The relation is represented by

$$k = \left(A + \frac{B}{d}x\right)$$

where d is the separation between the plates and where A and B are constants, with $A > 1$. What is the volume density of polarization charges?

4.11   Two parallel metal plates are separated by a distance d. The space between the plates is partially filled with a dielectric slab whose thickness t is less than the separation d. The dielectric constant of the slab is k. The boundary faces of the slab are parallel to, and have the same area as those of the metal plates. Neglect edge effects and express the capacitance of the arrangement in terms of k, t, d, and C_0. The latter is the capacitance when the medium between the plates is free space.

Chapter 5.
Charges in Motion

5.1   Electric Current and Current Density

In the preceding chapters we have dealt only with the equilibrium state of charge distributions. Experimentally, however, it can be demonstrated that a charge can be transferred from a charged body to an uncharged one. In this process the equilibrium is disturbed, and a transient state exists as long as the charge is in motion. Once the flow has ceased, equilibrium is again established. The movement of charge can exist in a great variety of physical situations. It may be steady in a given direction, or it may vary periodically with reversal of direction, or it may be intermittent. It may be accompanied by the emission of light, by the development of heat, or by chemical and magnetic effects. An electric current is said to exist when there is a flow of charge through empty space or through a material medium.

From the atomic viewpoint, an electric current is identified with a stream of charged particles or ions, such as electrons, negatively or positively charged atoms, or atomic groups. In the highly evacuated region within a television picture tube, the current is composed primarily of electrons. In the gaseous discharge of the familiar fluorescent light tube, electrons and gaseous ions are involved in the conduction process. In electrolytes, the slow movement of positive and negative ions is responsible for the transport of charge, while in good conductors it is the slow drift of so-called free electrons which constitutes the current.

On the laboratory scale an electric current is considered as a continuous flow of charge, despite the discrete nature of the charged carriers. Such a concept is defensible provided a sufficiently large number of ions participate in the transport of charge.

In presenting a quantitative definition of current it is necessary to imagine a surface of area A across which there is a flow of charge. The electric current i is defined as the time rate at which charge crosses the area A. In symbols

$$i \equiv \frac{dq}{dt} \tag{5.1}$$

The quantity in (5.1) is the instantaneous rate given by the $\lim_{\Delta t \to 0} \Delta q / \Delta t$, where Δq is the charge which crosses A in the time interval Δt. In general, the current is a function of the time, and the charge Q which has crossed A in the time interval $t = T_1$ to $t = T_2$ is calculated from

$$Q = \int_{T_1}^{T_2} i \, dt \tag{5.2}$$

The average value of this current over the same time interval is

$$i_{\text{avg}} = \frac{Q}{(T_2 - T_1)} \tag{5.3}$$

In many physical situations involving extensive media, the time rate of flow of charge per unit area varies in magnitude and direction at different points in the stream. We shall take as a model the flow in a region in which there is one type of ion of charge $+q$. The number of ions per unit volume (that is, the ion concentration) will be denoted by N. The ions possess thermal motions, but owing to the randomness of such motions, on the average, no net charge is transported across a given area. In our model we shall imagine that the ions have a common drift velocity $\mathbf{v}$, which has been acquired by the action of an electric field $\mathbf{E}$. In Fig. 5.1, v_n represents the component of the drift velocity normal to an element of area A. In the time interval dt, each ion will move a distance $\mathbf{v} \, dt$. From the diagram it is seen that in this time the charge located in a volume $A v_n \, dt$ will cross the area A. Now the charge in this volume is $N q v_n A \, dt$, and the current through A will therefore be

$$i = \frac{dQ}{dt} = N q v_n A \tag{5.4}$$

But $v_n = v \cos \theta$, where θ is the angle between the vector $\mathbf{v}$ and

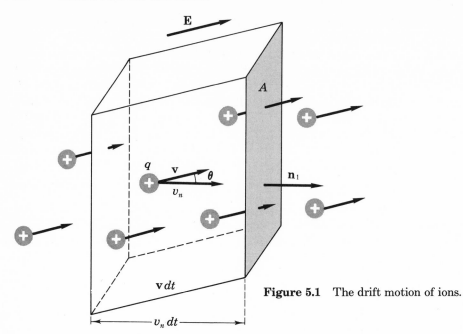

Figure 5.1   The drift motion of ions.

the unit vector $\mathbf{n}_1$ normal to A. Hence (5.4) may be written as

$$i = Nq\mathbf{v} \cdot \mathbf{n}_1 A \tag{5.5}$$

Whereas the current i is a scalar, the quantity $Nq\mathbf{v}$ is a vector. Denoting this vector by $\mathbf{j}$, we write

$$\mathbf{j} = Nq\mathbf{v} \tag{5.6}$$

The vector quantity $\mathbf{j}$ is called the *current density*. It has the dimensions of current per unit area. In our approach $\mathbf{j}$ defines the average current density over the area A. In general the current is not uniformly distributed over A. In such a case we need to consider an element of area dA and define the current density as a quantity which varies from point to point in magnitude and direction. Then di, the contribution to the current through dA, is given by

$$di = \mathbf{j} \cdot \mathbf{n}_1 \, dA \tag{5.7}$$

and the current through an open surface A (Fig. 5.2) of any size is expressed by the integral

$$i = \int_A \mathbf{j} \cdot \mathbf{n}_1 \, dA \tag{5.8}$$

In passing, we note that (5.8) can be written in the following equivalent forms

$$i = \int_A \mathbf{j} \cdot d\mathbf{A} = \int_A j \cos \theta \, dA = \int_A j_n \, dA \qquad (5.9)$$

In the first integral, $d\mathbf{A}$ is a vector in the direction of the normal of magnitude dA. In the remaining integrals, $j_n = j \cos \theta$ represents the component of the current density normal to the element of area.

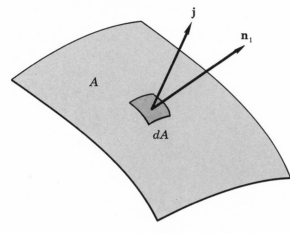

Figure 5.2   Calculation of current crossing area A.

If free charges of both signs act as carriers, as in electrolytes and in gaseous conduction, the velocities of the negative and positive ions are directed oppositely under a given field direction (Fig. 5.3). In general, the two ions have different concentrations, N_1 and N_2, and also different charges, q_1 and q_2. The net charge which crosses A in the time dt is

$$dq = A \, dt \, (N_1 q_1 v_{1n} + N_2 q_2 v_{2n}) \qquad (5.10)$$

But charges of unlike sign move in opposite directions, so the terms in the parentheses in (5.10) have the same sign. In this case the expression for the current density becomes

$$\mathbf{j} = N_1 q_1 \mathbf{v}_1 + N_2 q_2 \mathbf{v}_2 \qquad (5.11)$$

In metals, the mobile ion is the electron. In this case the model presented in Fig. 5.1 would be applicable if, for the given direction of the applied field, the sense of the drift velocity vector were reversed. We have seen that under a given field both negative and positive ions may participate in the conduction process. Therefore some convention must be adopted in associating the current den-

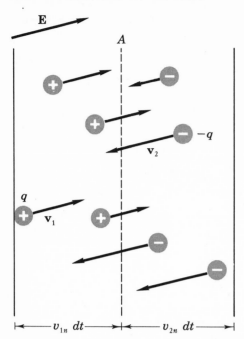

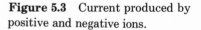

Figure 5.3 Current produced by positive and negative ions.

sity with the motion of a particular type of free ion. It is common to refer to the direction of the current density as though all carriers were positively charged ions.

The mks unit of current is the ampere, and the unit of current density is amperes per square meter. A more complete definition of the unit of current will be given in Chapter 7.

In the subsequent discussion, we shall make use of a relation between flow of charge in a volume and flow confined to a filamentary medium such as a slender wire of length dl and of transverse dimensions which are much smaller than dl. In this case it may be assumed that j is uniform over A, the cross-sectional area of the filament, and that j is parallel to dl. The current i in the filament is jA. Upon multiplying each of these quantities by dl, we may write

$$i \, dl = jA \, dl = j \, dV \qquad (5.12)$$

where dV is the volume of the element associated with the length dl. According to (5.6), $j = Nqv$. So (5.12) may be cast in the alternate form

$$i \, dl = Nqv \, dV \qquad (5.13)$$

In (5.13) $i \, dl$ is referred to as a current element.

5.2   Equation of Continuity

Consider a *closed* surface S (Fig. 5.4) situated in the interior of a conducting medium such as a metal bar. Let there be a steady (not time-varying) current in the medium. At any point within the conductor $\mathbf{j}$ can be used to describe the flow. The rate of passage of charge through an area dA is $\mathbf{j} \cdot d\mathbf{A}$, and its integral over S represents the net current entering or leaving the volume enclosed by S. However, in the special case of steady flow there can be no increase or decrease of charge within S and the *net* current is zero. Hence

$$\int_S \mathbf{j} \cdot d\mathbf{A} = 0 \tag{5.14}$$

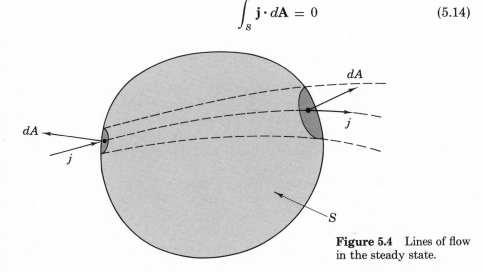

Figure 5.4   Lines of flow in the steady state.

Next consider a charge q placed on a conductor insulated from ground. At a later instant the charged body is connected to ground by means of a wire. After the connection has been made, there will be a current in the wire. In this case the current is not steady but depends on the time. As shown in Fig. 5.5, S again represents the closed hypothetical surface. But now, i, the net current outward over S, is not zero; instead, it is equal to the rate of decrease of charge enclosed within S. Hence, the current, or the surface integral of $\mathbf{j}$ over S, is written as

$$\int_S \mathbf{j} \cdot d\mathbf{A} = - \frac{dq}{dt} \tag{5.15}$$

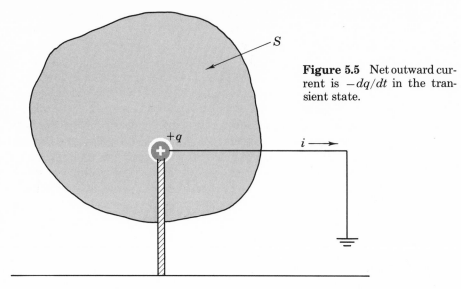

Figure 5.5 Net outward current is $-dq/dt$ in the transient state.

This relation is known as the *equation of continuity* and is based on the law of conservation of charge, which states that no net charge can be created or destroyed within S. In the steady state a certain amount of charge enters over a portion of the closed surface S, and an equal amount leaves over the remainder of the surface. This means that the charge within S does not change with the time, and (5.15) reverts to (5.14). The equation of continuity prescribes the pattern of the lines of flow. These are lines whose tangents specify the direction of the current density vector. In the steady state, lines of flow cannot start or end in the medium where charge is flowing and hence are represented by closed curves.

5.3   Metallic Conduction

In order to explain the transfer of charge in a particular physical situation we must account for the origin of the charge carriers and their motions under the action of forces. As an example, we shall present a crude model to describe the conduction process in metals. The classical approach to be offered here gives an essentially correct picture, although the details of the argument are oversimplified. Actually, the problem requires wave mechanical treatment.

In the electronic configuration of an isolated atom certain electrons form closed shells, whereas others belong to incomplete outer shells and are collectively referred to as valence electrons. For example, an isolated neutral atom of copper has 29 extranuclear electrons, 28 of which are distributed in the K, L, and M shells while the 29th is the valence electron. When free atoms are brought together to form the crystalline state, the inner-shell electrons remain more or less tightly bound to their cores, but the valence electrons behave as though they were nearly free, in the sense that their potential or binding energy is small relative to their kinetic energy.

We shall consider the action of an electric field on a collection of free electrons. In the absence of an externally applied field, the average velocity of an assemblage of electrons is zero, since we picture these particles to be in random thermal motion. When an external field is applied, the electron velocities are modified. Superimposed upon their thermal motions the electrons acquire a component of velocity referred to as the drift velocity. It is the drift component of velocity which constitutes the electric current. The electrons suffer collisions with one another and with atomic cores, and the new velocity of each particle after each collision is independent of the velocity it had before the collision. If the applied field is E, each electron acquires an acceleration in a direction opposite to that of the field. If there were no other forces, the electron would be accelerated indefinitely under the action of the field. Because of the collisions that occur, we must introduce a resistive or a frictional type of damping force proportional to the drift velocity. The equation of motion is then written as

$$m\frac{dv}{dt} + \frac{mv}{\tau} = Eq \qquad (5.16)$$

where m and q are the electronic mass and charge, and v is the drift velocity superimposed upon the thermal velocities. The coefficient of v in the resistive term is the damping constant (force per unit velocity). It contains a characteristic time τ, the meaning of which will be clarified as we discuss the solution of (5.16). The differential equation in (5.16) can be solved by separating variables. Upon rearrangement we obtain

$$\frac{dv}{(v - c)} = -\frac{dt}{\tau} \qquad (5.17)$$

where

$$c \equiv \frac{Eq\tau}{m}$$

At the time $t = 0$, the drift velocity $v = 0$. With this initial condition the integration yields

$$v = c\,(1 - e^{-t/\tau}) \tag{5.18}$$

which shows how the drift velocity behaves with the time. For $t \gg \tau$, v approaches a terminal value v_f given by the constant c; that is,

$$v_f = c = (q\tau/m)E \tag{5.19}$$

From (5.18) we see that the parameter τ, called the relaxation time, is a characteristic time during which the drift velocity v reaches the value of $(1 - 1/e)v_f$; or in time τ, v attains the value $v = 0.62\,v_f$. A long relaxation time means a weak frictional force. From (5.16) it appears that the drift velocity of the conduction electron increases with a constant acceleration qE/m. If τ is very short, the frictional force is large, but v attains 62 per cent of v_f in a correspondingly short time. For the purposes of this calculation, τ may be interpreted as the time during which the electron does not suffer a collision and the applied field is free to accelerate it.

When the value of v_f in (5.19) is used as the drift velocity in (5.6), the expression for the current density in a metallic conductor becomes

$$j = (Nq^2\tau/m)E \tag{5.20}$$

or

$$j = \sigma E \tag{5.21}$$

where

$$\sigma \equiv Nq^2\tau/m \tag{5.22}$$

The result in (5.21) indicates that the current density is proportional to the field and is recognized as Ohm's law. The proportionality constant σ in (5.21) is the conductivity of the metal. Such a dependence is valid only in the case of a small group of materials known as metallic conductors. For instance, the flow of electrons in the space between the electrodes of a vacuum tube cannot be described by a linear law such as that given in (5.21). In this situation the motion of an electron is governed by the electric (and other) forces acting on the particle.

If the medium is isotropic, the flow of charge is in the direction of the field. In vectorial form (5.21) may be written as

$$\mathbf{j} = \sigma\mathbf{E} \tag{5.23}$$

or as

$$\mathbf{E} = \rho\mathbf{j} \tag{5.24}$$

where ρ, defined as $1/\sigma$, is known as the resistivity of the medium.

If the medium is homogeneous, the parameters ρ and σ are independent of position within the medium and are constants. However, the magnitude of the parameters is temperature-dependent. So when citing numerical values, it is necessary to specify the temperature.

Consider a cylindrical conductor of length L and cross-sectional area A. If V is the potential difference between faces 1 and 2 [see Fig. 5.6(a)], then the strength of the electric field E is equal to V/L. The current density j is parallel to the axis of the cylinder and perpendicular to A. It has the magnitude (I/A) if j is independent of position within the area A and if I is the current in the conductor. Substituting in (5.21), we obtain

$$V = IR \tag{5.25}$$

where R, defined by

$$R = \frac{L}{\sigma A} = \rho \frac{L}{A} \tag{5.26}$$

is the resistance of the particular cylindrical conductor when the flow of charge is parallel to the axis of the cylinder. The dependence expressed by $V = IR$ is also known as Ohm's law. It is of practical importance in the study of circuits containing metallic conductors.

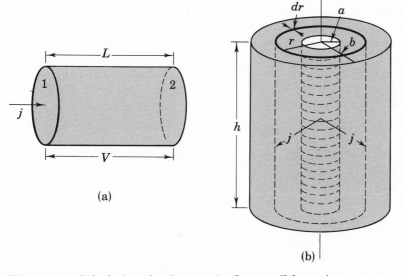

(a)

(b)

Figure 5.6   Calculation of resistance: (a) flow parallel to axis of cylinder; (b) flow normal to axis of hollow tube with thick walls.

The expression for resistance assumes a different form if the flow of charge is radial—that is, if it is normal to the axis of the cylinder. Consider a thick-walled cylindrical tube (inner radius a and outer radius b), as shown in Fig. 5.6(b). The area normal to flow is $2\pi rh$. By (5.26), dR, the resistance of an elementary cylindrical shell of height h and thickness dr, is

$$dR = \frac{dr}{\sigma 2\pi rh}$$

The resistance of the tube to radial flow is obtained by integrating the above expression as indicated below:

$$R = \frac{1}{2\pi\sigma h}\int_a^b \frac{dr}{r} = \frac{1}{2\pi\sigma h}\ln\left(\frac{b}{a}\right) \qquad (5.27)$$

The unit of resistance is the ohm (volt per ampere). As can be seen from (5.25), a conductor has a resistance of 1 ohm when the potential difference across the ends of the conductor is 1 v and the current in the conductor is 1 amp. Also from (5.26) it is seen that the resistivity ρ has the dimensions of ohm-meter and the conductivity σ has the dimensions of ohm^{-1}-meter^{-1}.

The conductivity σ is a readily measurable quantity, and its experimental value makes it possible to evaluate τ for a particular metal. From Avogadro's number, from the gram atomic weight, and from the density we can find the concentration of Cu atoms. This is also the concentration of electrons, since, in Cu, we may assume that there is one valence electron per atom. Therefore

$$N = \frac{(6.03 \times 10^{23} \text{ atoms/mole})}{63.5 \text{ g/mole}} \times 8.90 \times 10^6 \text{ g/m}^3$$

$$= 8.46 \times 10^{28} \text{ atoms/m}^3$$

The electronic constants are

$$m = 9.10 \times 10^{-31} \text{ kg} \qquad q = -1.60 \times 10^{-19} \text{ coul}$$

and the conductivity of Cu at room temperature is

$$\sigma = 5.88 \times 10^7 \text{ } (\Omega\text{-m})^{-1}$$

From (5.22)

$$\tau = \frac{m\sigma}{Nq^2} = \frac{9.10 \times 10^{-31} \times 5.88 \times 10^7}{8.46 \times 10^{28} \times (1.60)^2 \times 10^{-38}} = 2.48 \times 10^{-14} \text{ sec}$$

This means that in a time interval of about 3×10^{-14} sec the steady-state velocity would be attained in the presence of a field in a good conductor like copper. This observation justifies the selection of v_f as the appropriate drift velocity to be used in connection with the transport of charge in the steady state.

The magnitude of the drift velocity can be estimated from (5.6). Let the steady current in a copper conductor 1 cm in diameter be 100 amp distributed uniformly over the cross section. The current density in this case is 1.28×10^6 amp/m². Using the values of N and q from above, we obtain

$$v = \frac{j}{Nq} = \frac{1.28 \times 10^6}{8.46 \times 10^{28} \times 1.60 \times 10^{-19}} = 9.55 \times 10^{-5} \text{ m/sec}$$

or about 0.01 cm/sec. Hence the drift velocity in conductors is quite small.

5.4   Direct-Current Circuits

The simplest electrical circuit consists of two types of elements. One element, referred to as an electromotive force (abbreviated as emf), is a device which can maintain an electric field in a conductor and thus give rise to a current. The second element consists of thin metallic conductors or connecting wires. In Chapter 8 we shall present a careful formulation of the meaning of the term emf. For the present it will suffice to note the following physical properties of this circuit element:

(1) An emf is a source of power which converts some form of energy into electrical energy. For example, a battery is a seat of emf which converts chemical energy into electrical energy. A mechanical generator is a source of emf which transforms mechanical energy into electrical energy.

(2) The process of energy conversion is reversible. The chemical reactions in a storage battery are capable of doing work on charges which in turn impart their energy to resistive elements in the circuit with the attendant production of heat energy. In addition, the circuit may contain a device, such as a motor, which is capable of producing a mechanical torque due to the passage of charge through it. The conversion of electrical energy into heat is an irreversible process. On the other hand it is possible to restore the internal chemical energy of a battery by the so-called charging process. This is done by the use of an auxiliary emf which can maintain a flow of charge through the battery in a direction opposite to that which is present while the battery itself

is delivering power. Similar reversible energy transformations exist in the case of a motor or a mechanical generator.

(3) The terminals of the seat of emf carry charges of opposite sign. In fact, the function of a seat of emf is to separate charge and to maintain the separation.

Diagrammatically, an emf is represented by symbols such as $-|\!|^{+}$ or $\stackrel{+}{-}\!\bigcirc\!\stackrel{-}{-}$. The magnitude of the emf is defined as work done per unit charge transported through the seat. If a charge dq passes through the seat in an element of time dt, and if dW is the amount of work done on the charge, then the emf $\mathcal{E}$ is equal to

$$\mathcal{E} = \frac{dW}{dq} \qquad (5.28)$$

This expression reduces to $\mathcal{E} = W/q$ if the rate is constant. The unit of emf is either the volt or one joule per coulomb. Thus potential difference and emf are measured in the same unit.

The time rate of energy transformation, or the electrical power developed by the emf, is deduced from the definition in (5.28). The power P is measured by

$$P = \frac{dW}{dt} = \mathcal{E}\frac{dq}{dt} = \mathcal{E}i \qquad (5.29)$$

The unit of electrical power is the watt, which is equivalent to one joule per second.

As was explained in Section 5.3, between collisions the electron acquires kinetic energy from the field. At each impact the electron transfers energy to an atom of the solid structure, and the vibrational motion of the atom gains in amplitude. This mechanism accounts for the production of heat when charge passes through connecting wires or other elements which possess resistance. In diagrams, it is customary to indicate the presence of resistance by the symbol $-\!\wedge\!\wedge\!\wedge\!-$. A circuit element of this nature is called a *resistor*.

The electrical power delivered to any portion of a circuit may be measured by the product Vi, where V is the potential difference across the portion and i is the current. If V and i are functions of the time, the product represents the instantaneous power. The proof of this statement is as follows: If dW is the energy imparted to the portion of the circuit in question, then

$$dW = V\,dq \qquad (5.30)$$

where dq is the charge transported through the portion in the time dt. In terms of the current i, $dq = i\,dt$, and the power delivered is expressed by

$$\frac{dW}{dt} = V\frac{dq}{dt} = Vi \tag{5.31}$$

This result is valid generally and does not depend on the specific nature of the contents included within a particular portion of the circuit. In Section 5.6 we shall see that V, the terminal potential difference, may depend on the current and on such parameters as $\mathcal{E}$ and R.

In the particular case where the portion of the circuit contains only a resistance R, then $V = iR$ and the power P appearing as heat in the resistor may be written as

$$P = Vi = i^2R \tag{5.32}$$

provided the value of R is independent of the current in the resistor. The above relation is known as Joule's law, which states that the rate of heat production varies as the square of the current.

5.5 The Circuit Equation

Figure 5.7 is a diagram of a single closed circuit consisting of an emf $\mathcal{E}$ and a resistor R. The points x and z are the terminals of the source of emf. The source possesses an internal ohmic resistance r. This could be either the resistance of the solution within a battery or the resistance of the armature wires in a generator. In the diagram the resistance of all cönductors external to the

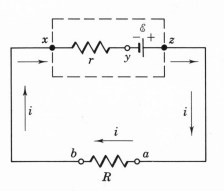

Figure 5.7 A single-loop circuit.

seat is lumped and is shown as a single quantity R. The arrows indicate the sense of circulation of positive charge.

This circuit contains a single emf, and the circulation is clockwise out of terminal z, through the external resistance, and back to terminal x. The signs associated with $\mathcal{E}$ are independent of the sense of the current. In passing from x to y with the current, we encounter a potential drop—that is, point x is higher in potential than point y. In going from point y to point z there always exists a potential rise equal to $\mathcal{E}$.

If we agree to designate potential rises as positive and potential drops as negative, the terminal potential difference $(V_z - V_x)$ can be written as $V_{zx} = -ir + \mathcal{E}$. Similarly, $(V_b - V_a) = V_{ba} = -iR$. Although the emf $\mathcal{E}$ arises from nonstatic forces, the effect of the seat may be replaced by an electrostatic potential difference of magnitude $\mathcal{E}$, the terminal with excess positive charge being at the higher potential. Without making any detailed analysis, we can state that, although there is a steady current in the circuit, the potential distribution is such as to obey the circuital law of the electrostatic field. Consequently, the sum of the potential differences $V_{zx} + V_{ba}$ should equal zero. This principle forms the basis of the circuit equation

$$V_{zx} + V_{ba} = -ir + \mathcal{E} - iR = 0 \qquad (5.33)$$

It follows directly that the current in the single-loop circuit may be written as

$$i = \frac{\mathcal{E}}{(R + r)} \qquad (5.34)$$

The same result can be derived by equating the rate of heat development in the entire circuit to the rate at which the emf supplies energy to the circuit. In symbols,

$$\mathcal{E}i = i^2 R + i^2 r \qquad (5.35)$$

This result is identical to that found in (5.34).

5.6   Potential Difference Across Portions of a Circuit

Consider portions of a circuit represented by the three diagrams in Fig. 5.8. For each arrangement we shall write the potential dif-

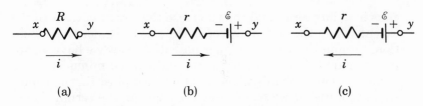

Figure 5.8   Potential difference across portions of a circuit.

ference $(V_y - V_x) \equiv V_{yx}$, with due regard for the sign convention adopted in Section 5.5. (Rise, $+$; drop, $-$.)

In Fig. 5.8(a),

$$V_{yx} = -iR$$

This is the potential difference or voltage across a purely resistive
element. The negative sign means that there is a potential drop as
we proceed from terminal x to terminal y with the current.

In Fig. 5.8(b),

$$V_{yx} = -ir + \mathcal{E}$$

Here the battery is doing work and is being discharged. In passing from x to y we first encounter a drop of ir and then a rise of
$\mathcal{E}$. The expression for V_{yx} is a measure of the terminal potential
difference of a seat of emf. Under discharge conditions, V_{yx} is
less than $\mathcal{E}$.

Finally, in Fig. 5.8(c),

$$V_{yx} = +ir + \mathcal{E}$$

Here work is being done on the seat of emf—that is, the battery
is being charged by an auxiliary emf located elsewhere in the
circuit. In passing from x to y against the current, we encounter a rise of ir followed by a rise of $\mathcal{E}$, as before. Here V_{yx} exceeds $\mathcal{E}$.

Exclusive of the potential drop associated with the internal
resistance, there is always a rise in potential as we pass through
the seat of emf from the negative to the positive charge concentration. Had we gone from y to x, the signs of all terms in
the above formulas would be reversed—that is, $V_{xy} = -V_{yx}$.

In Fig. 5.8(c) the point y is always at the higher potential,
while in (b) the potential of point y can be either higher or lower
than that of x, depending on the magnitude of the current. If
there are no other emfs in the circuit, point y will always be at
the higher potential. However, it is possible to place auxiliary

emfs in aiding series and thus increase the circuit current to the extent where the *ir* drop exceeds the rise $\mathcal{E}$. Under this condition, terminal x is at the higher potential. Now we have an apparent paradox: the battery terminal marked minus is at the higher potential than the terminal marked plus. But no confusion need arise if we recall that the signs on the terminals are uniquely determined by the chemical make-up of the battery, while the potential difference across the terminals includes the internal drop or rise in voltage as well as the emf $\mathcal{E}$.

In the limiting case where $i \to 0$, then $V_{yx} \to \mathcal{E}$ in the portions containing an emf. Thus we may regard the emf as the terminal potential difference when the circuit current is zero—that is, when the circuit is open.

Now, by applying the content of the preceding discussion, let us determine the current in the single-loop circuit whose diagram is shown in Fig. 5.9. The polarity and the magnitude of each emf and its internal resistance are indicated on the diagram. The resistance of the circuit external to the seats of emf is 5 Ω. (The Greek capital letter omega Ω is used as an abbreviation for the ohm, the unit of resistance.) In measuring potentials it is convenient to use, as a reference level, a zero of potential. We designate this reference level by the symbol $\perp\!\!\!\perp$ to suggest that the circuit is "grounded" at this point. Accordingly, the potential of point z is arbitrarily taken as zero. We assume that positive charge circulates in the clockwise sense. Starting at point z, we proceed clockwise along the circuit and write down the potential differences across successive elements in a systematic way, subject to the sign convention (potential rises, + ; drops, −). We thus obtain the circuit equation

$$-5i - i + \mathcal{E}_1 - \mathcal{E}_2 - 2i = 0$$

whence $\qquad\qquad\qquad i = -0.50 \text{ amp}$

The negative sign signifies that the circuit current is actually counterclockwise. As we proceed from z, the zero of potential, toward the point x, there is 2.5 v rise in potential. The potential further rises by 0.5 v across the 1 Ω resistor, and by an additional amount of 6.0 v across the seat. We have now reached point y, which is 9.0 v higher than "ground." From y to z there is a drop of 10 v and a rise of 1.0 v, making a total drop of 9.0 v. Thus z, which is at the zero of potential, is 9.0 v below y, as it should be. (Redraw the diagram with the correct sense of circulation. Or determine the rise or fall in potential by including the minus sign associated with the current.)

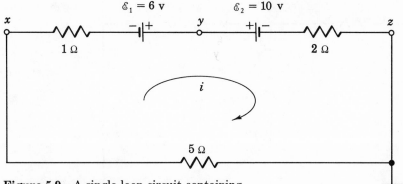

Figure 5.9 A single-loop circuit containing two emfs in opposing series.

The terminal potential difference across the battery with an emf of 6.0 v is 6.5 v, indicating that this battery is being charged at the rate of 6.5 × 0.50, or 3.25 w. Of this amount, 0.25 w appears as heat, while the remainder, 3.0 w, is converted into chemical energy. Similarly, in the second battery, chemical energy is converted at the rate of 5.0 w, and the power evolved as heat is 0.5 w. Throughout the circuit heat is evolved at the rate of $(0.50)^2 \times 8$, or 2.0 w. The power supplied to the circuit is 10×0.5, or 5.0 w. The difference $(5.0 - 2.0)$, or 3.0 w, represents power conversion into chemical energy, as we have already found.

5.7   Direct-Current Networks

A network is a system of circuit elements and seats of emf which form a number of closed conducting paths. In the present treatment we shall include only constant emfs and only circuit elements that consist of ohmic resistors. Under equilibrium conditions, steady unidirectional currents exist in various branches of the network. There are several methods for determining the values of these currents. For our purposes we shall formulate two rules (Kirchhoff's laws), which are extensions of the methods presented in the preceding sections.

Consider the network shown in Fig. 5.10. The points labeled ①, ②, ③, and ④ constitute junctions. (A junction is said to exist where three or more conductors meet.) In this example, three conductors meet at each junction.

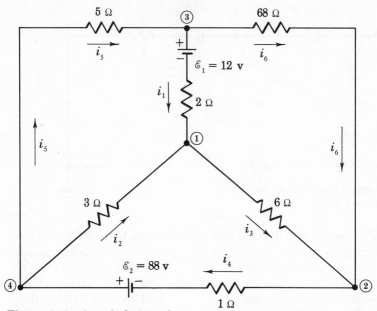

Figure 5.10   A typical network.

There are six branch currents—i_1, i_2, i_3, i_4, i_5, and i_6. The senses of these currents are assumed arbitrarily to be those indicated by the arrows. Consider the junction or branch point ① shown in Fig. 5.11. Surround the junction by a closed imaginary surface. Since the currents have reached the steady state, the charge entering this surface per unit time must equal the charge flowing out of the surface per unit time. This is a consequence of the continuity equation for the steady-state flow as expressed in (5.14) and leads to the statement of Rule 1:

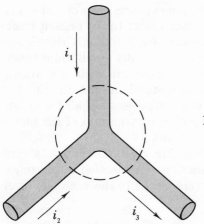

Figure 5.11   Illustration of branch point rule.

Rule 1. The sum of the various currents into a junction is equal to the sum of currents away from the junction. Or, the algebraic sum of currents meeting at a junction is zero.

It follows that at junction ① the branch currents satisfy the relation

$$i_1 + i_2 = i_3 \tag{5.36}$$

Similarly, the application of Rule 1 yields the following relations between the currents at junctions ②, ③, and ④, respectively:

$$i_3 + i_6 = i_4 \tag{5.37}$$

$$i_1 + i_6 = i_5 \tag{5.38}$$

$$i_2 + i_5 = i_4 \tag{5.39}$$

Note that only three of these four equations are independent. This can be seen by substituting the value of i_3 from (5.37) in (5.36). Upon combining the result with (5.38), we obtain (5.39). In this network there are four junctions, and the use of Rule 1 yields only three independent relations. It is generally true that if the number of junctions is m, there are $(m - 1)$ independent junction equations.

The second rule is a restatement of the principle presented in (5.33):

Rule 2. The sum of potential rises and drops taken around any closed conducting path is zero. Or, the algebraic sum of potential differences taken sequentially around a closed loop is equal to zero.

In applying this rule, we must trace each loop in a clockwise (or counterclockwise) sense continuously until we have covered at least once all potential rises and drops associated with the various network elements. We continue to designate rises as positive and drops as negative and adhere faithfully to the assumed positive senses of the branch currents.

In the systematic tracing of loops it is important to realize that as many independent relations are necessary as there are unknowns. In the problem under study, the number is six. We already have noted that (5.36), (5.37), and (5.38) represent three independent relations. Hence three more must be formulated by the application of Rule 2.

Starting at junction ④ and proceeding in a clockwise sense, we obtain

$$-5i_5 - 12 - 2i_1 + 3i_2 = 0 \tag{5.40}$$

Similarly, starting first at junction ③ and then at junction ②, we write the loop equations

$$-68i_6 + 6i_3 + 2i_1 + 12 = 0 \qquad (5.41)$$

$$-i_4 + 88 - 3i_2 - 6i_3 = 0 \qquad (5.42)$$

In tracing these three loops, we have traversed every branch at least once. No new information will be gained if we trace the periphery of the network. Such an attempt would give

$$-5i_5 - 68i_6 - i_4 + 88 = 0 \qquad (5.43)$$

which is not an independent relation, since we can obtain (5.43) by adding (5.40) to (5.41) and combining the sum with (5.42). However, this procedure serves as a check on the correctness of the various formulations.

The simultaneous solution of six equations exclusive of (5.39) and (5.43) yields the following numerical values for the six currents involved: $i_1 = 1.0$ amp, $i_2 = 8.0$ amp, $i_3 = 9.0$ amp, $i_4 = 10.0$ amp, $i_5 = 2.0$ amp, $i_6 = 1.0$ amp. The algebraic steps are likely to be laborious unless the elimination of unknowns is planned carefully. For example, it might be advisable to eliminate i_4, i_5, and i_6 by combining the junction relations with the loop equations. The resulting equalities will involve only i_1, i_2, and i_3. The simultaneous system of six equations may also be solved by means of determinants. This scheme is also laborious but provides a systematic approach.

From the numerical results, we see that the signs associated with the branch currents are all positive. This means that the arrows shown in Fig. 5.10 represent the correct senses for the currents. (This outcome is not an accident, but was planned by the author.)

In other network problems, the currents may be given while the resistances and emfs appear as unknowns. If sufficient information is available, the requisite independent relations can be formulated by applying the junction and loop relations.

5.8   Grouping of Resistances

A number of resistances R_1, R_2, R_3, . . . , R_N are connected in series as shown in Fig. 5.12. If a constant voltage V_{xy} is applied to the terminals of the combination, the current in each resistance will have the same value i. In addition,

$$V_{xy} = V_1 + V_2 + V_3 + \cdots + V_N$$

where V_1, V_2, V_3, $\ldots$, V_N are the voltages across the individual resistors and are given by

$$V_1 = iR_1, \qquad V_2 = iR_2, \qquad V_3 = iR_3, \qquad \cdots, V_N = iR_N$$

Let R denote the single resistance which when placed between the points x and y will have the same current i in it for the same impressed potential difference V_{xy}. Hence

$$V_{xy} = iR = iR_1 + iR_2 + iR_3 + \cdots + iR_N$$

and the single resistance that is equivalent to the series combination is seen to be

$$R = R_1 + R_2 + R_3 + \cdots + R_N$$

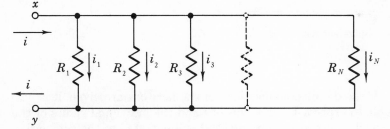

Figure 5.12   Resistors connected in series.

If three or more resistances are connected in parallel as in Fig. 5.13, the potential difference across each resistance is equal to the potential difference V_{xy} applied to the combination, i.e.,

$$V_{xy} = V_1 = V_2 = V_3 = \cdots = V_N$$

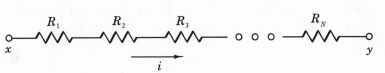

Figure 5.13   Resistors connected in parallel.

But the current entering at x (or leaving at y) must be equal to the sum of all the branch currents. Thus

$$i = i_1 + i_2 + i_3 + \cdots + i_N$$

or
$$\frac{V_{xy}}{R} = \frac{V_1}{R_1} + \frac{V_2}{R_2} + \frac{V_3}{R_3} + \cdots + \frac{V_N}{R_N}$$

where R represents the single resistance equivalent to the parallel combination of N resistances. It follows that

$$\frac{1}{R} = \frac{1}{R_1} + \frac{1}{R_2} + \frac{1}{R_3} + \cdots + \frac{1}{R_N} \qquad (5.45)$$

In the series connection, the equivalent resistance is the sum of the individual resistances. In the parallel connection, the reciprocal of the equivalent resistance is equal to the sum of the reciprocals of the individual resistances, and the equivalent resistance is smaller in value than the smallest resistance present in any one branch.

The equivalent resistance of any network composed only of resistive elements can be computed in a similar way. Assume that a potential difference V_{xy} is applied to the two-terminal network, and that the current entering or leaving the network is i. Then the equivalent resistance R_{eq} is defined by

$$R_{eq} \equiv \frac{V_{xy}}{i} \qquad (5.46)$$

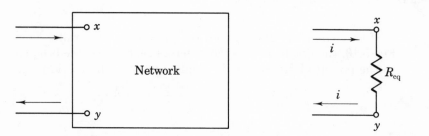

Figure 5.14   Equivalent resistance of a network.

If the detailed connections of the network are given, it is possible to express V_{xy} in terms of i and the individual values of the branch resistances. The method is illustrated in the calculation of R_{eq} of a skeleton cube made up of 12 wires, each of resistance r. R_{eq} is to be calculated for the case where the terminals x and y are at the ends of a cube diagonal. If the current entering at one corner is i, then

$$V_{xy} = iR_{eq} = i_1 r + i_2 r + i_3 r$$

where the branch currents are identified in Fig. 5.15.

But a consideration of this highly symmetrical arrangement indicates that $i_1 = i/3$ and that $i_2 = i_1/2 = i/6$, and that $i_3 = i/3$. Upon substitution of these values in the equation for the voltage drop along the particular path, we find

$$iR_{eq} = r\left(\frac{i}{3} + \frac{i}{6} + \frac{i}{3}\right) = \frac{5}{6}ri$$

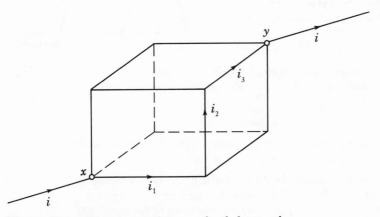

Figure 5.15 Equivalent resistance of a skeleton cube.

That is, $R_{eq} = 5r/6$. The equivalent resistance depends on the choice of terminals. If the cube edges have different resistances, the problem can still be solved by the application of Kirchhoff's rules. The algebraic manipulations are considerably more involved.

Charges in Motion: **Problems**

5.1 The current in a certain circuit decays according to the relation

$$i = \frac{e^{-t}}{1000} \text{ amp}$$

where t is the time expressed in seconds and e is the base of natural logarithms. Calculate the charge displaced past any point in this circuit during the interval $t = 0$ to $t = 1$ sec.

5.2 A device known as a rectifier modifies an alternating current (sine wave form) in such a way that there are two positive pulses per cycle, each pulse having a sine wave form and the same amplitude as the original current. Calculate the average value of each current over a time interval equal to one period of the original current.

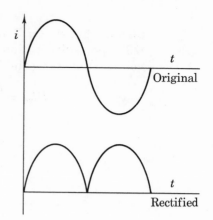

5.3 The charge on an insulated conductor flows to ground through a wire. The charge q remaining on the conductor at any time t is given by

$$q = 10^{-6}e^{-t/20}$$

where q is in coulombs and t is in seconds. What is the current in the wire at $t = 0$ and $t = 10$ sec?

5.4 What must be the magnitude of the electric intensity in a nichrome wire if the current density in the wire is to be 1.28×10^6 amp/m²? This is the current density in a copper conductor of diameter 0.01 m when the current in the conductor is 100 amp. The conductivity of copper is 5.88×10^7 $(\Omega\text{-m})^{-1}$, while that of nichrome is 1.00×10^6 $(\Omega\text{-m})^{-1}$.

5.5 Two long metal cylinders (radii b and a, with $b > a$) are mounted coaxially. A potential V is applied to the cylinders and a medium of conductivity σ fills the space between them. Calculate the electric current per unit length of conductor. Assume the medium obeys Ohm's law.

5.6 In each of the following cases determine the potential difference between the points x and y and state which point is at the higher potential.

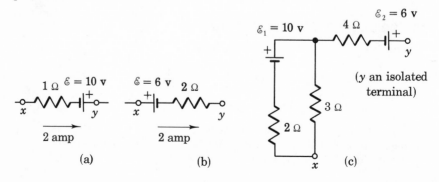

5.7 In the accompanying circuit diagram *A* and *B* represent two d-c generators which have equal emfs of 100 v. The resistances shown are the internal resistances of the generators. When operated in parallel as shown, the combined power furnished to the load *L* is 3750 w. What are the magnitudes of the currents i_A, i_B, and i_L?

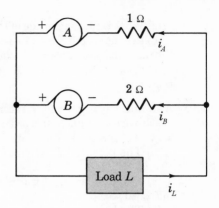

5.8 In the accompanying circuit diagram the 2 Ω and 1 Ω resistors represent the internal resistances of the generator *G* and the battery *B*. With the switch *S* in the open position as shown, the generator current is 8 amp.

(a) What is the emf of the generator?

(b) When the switch *S* is closed, the terminal potential difference of the generator exceeds the emf of the battery by 15 v. What is the current in the battery when the switch is closed? Does the battery absorb or deliver electrical energy?

(c) What is the current in the 12 Ω resistor when the switch is in the closed position?

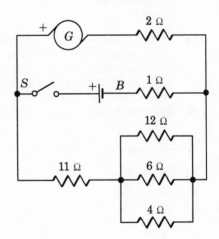

5.9 In the accompanying circuit diagram all the batteries have negligible internal resistances and the point *D* is grounded—that is, $V_D = 0$. With the switch *S* in the open position as shown, the potentials at the points *A*, *B*, and *C* are given by:

$$V_A = +10 \text{ v}, \qquad V_B = +8 \text{ v},$$
$$V_C = +26 \text{ v}$$

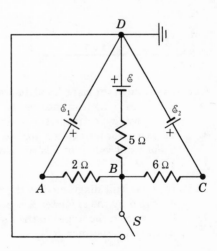

(a) What is the magnitude of the emf $\mathcal{E}$ located in the branch BD?

(b) Let the switch S be closed so that the point B is also grounded. What are the potentials at the points A and C?

(c) What is the current in $\mathcal{E}_2$ when the switch is in the closed position?

5.10   A storage battery (emf 6 v, int. res. 0.5 Ω) is charged by a current i which varies in time in accordance with the relation $i = t/6$ amp, where t is in seconds. Calculate:

(a) The potential difference across the battery at the time $t = 10$ sec.

(b) The total energy furnished to the battery in the time $t = 0$ to $t = 10$ sec.

(c) The heat produced in the battery in the time $t = 0$ to $t = 10$ sec.

5.11   In the left-hand circuit diagram below, the points x and y represent the terminals of a d-c generator whose emf is constant and equal to 120 v and whose internal resistance is 3 Ω. The generator supplies power to the battery (emf 40 v, int. res. negligible) and the variable resistance R. For what value of R is the power furnished by the generator to the battery and the external resistance a maximum?

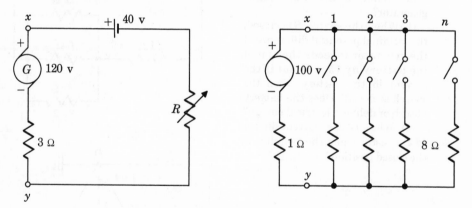

5.12   As shown in the right-hand diagram above, a d-c generator (emf 100 v, int. res. 1 Ω) furnishes power to a resistive load which may be varied by connecting in succession n individual 8 Ω resistors across the generator terminals x and y.

For what values of n is the power delivered to the load equal to 1600 w?

5.13   In the circuit diagramed at the top of page 127 (left), the current indicated by the ammeter A is not changed when both switches are thrown from the upper to the lower position. Find the value of the unknown resistance R.

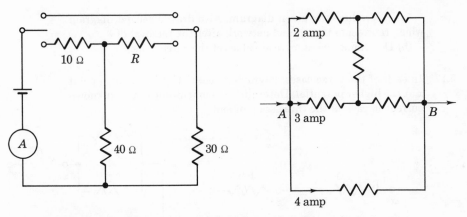

5.14 For the circuit shown above (right), determine the equivalent resistance of the network between the points A and B if $V_{AB} = 108$ v.

5.15 In the circuit represented by the accompanying diagram, currents of equal magnitude in the direction shown by the arrows are present in the two batteries whose emfs, $\mathcal{E}_1$ and $\mathcal{E}_2$, are unknown and whose internal resistances are 1 Ω and 2 Ω respectively. A third battery, whose terminals are designated by the points A and B, has an emf of 4 v and an internal resistance of 3 Ω.

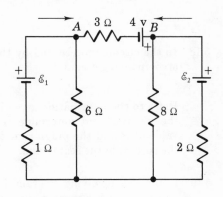

If the potential difference between the points A and B is 4 v with point B higher,

   (a) What is the current in the branch AB?
   (b) What are the magnitudes of the unknown emfs $\mathcal{E}_1$ and $\mathcal{E}_2$?

5.16 The three batteries shown in the diagram have constant emfs $\mathcal{E}_1$, $\mathcal{E}_2$, and $\mathcal{E}_3$ and negligible internal resistances. For the network shown, the currents through the batteries with emf $\mathcal{E}_1$ and $\mathcal{E}_2$ are 1 and 2 amp respectively in the indicated directions.

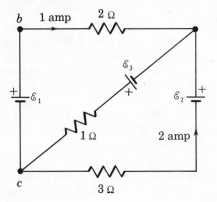

When the battery with emf $\mathcal{E}_1$ is removed from the circuit and the point b is connected to c, the current in the 2 Ω resistor becomes zero.

(a) Reproduce the given diagram. Also draw a second diagram which represents the altered network after the removal of $\mathcal{E}_1$.

(b) Determine the numerical values of the three emfs.

5.17   In each of the three cases diagramed below, $V_{xy} = 8$ v, with point x at the higher potential. Determine the magnitude of the unknown current in each of the three seats of emf.

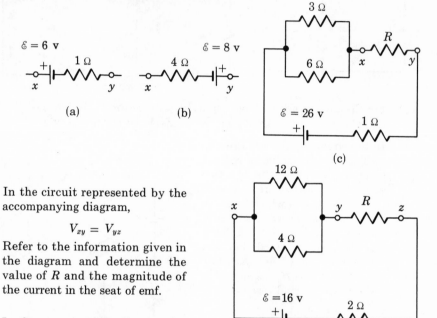

$\mathcal{E} = 6$ v

1 Ω

x y

(a)

$\mathcal{E} = 8$ v

4 Ω

x y

(b)

3 Ω

R

6 Ω x y

$\mathcal{E} = 26$ v

1 Ω

(c)

5.18   In the circuit represented by the accompanying diagram,

$$V_{xy} = V_{yz}$$

Refer to the information given in the diagram and determine the value of R and the magnitude of the current in the seat of emf.

12 Ω

x y R z

4 Ω

$\mathcal{E} = 16$ v

2 Ω

5.19   In the accompanying diagram the points a and b represent the terminals of a d-c generator (emf 120 v, int. res. 2 Ω). The generator supplies power to a battery and to a variable resistance R. The points x and y represent the terminals of the battery (emf 40 v, int. res. 1 Ω). The variable resistance is so adjusted that the power delivered to the battery equals that delivered to R.

What is the magnitude of the current in the circuit for this adjustment?

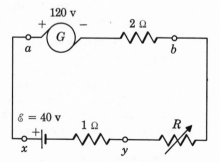

120 v

$+$ $-$ 2 Ω

G

a b

$\mathcal{E} = 40$ v   1 Ω R

x y

5.20   A battery has a constant emf of 12 v and negligible internal resistance. An external resistor whose magnitude may be varied continuously is connected to the battery. The current in the circuit varies in time in accordance with the relation $i = (3 + 2t^2)$ amp, where t is the time in seconds.

(a) Calculate the charge displaced through the battery in the time interval $t = 1$ to $t = 4$ sec.

(b) From the result of (a), determine the average value of the above current over the time interval specified.

(c) How much work is done by the battery per coulomb of electricity displaced through it?

5.21 Observations made separately on each of two filament lamps indicate that over a certain range of voltages the current in each lamp may be represented by

$$i_1 = (0.4 + 0.004V) \qquad \text{and} \qquad i_2 = (0.1 + 0.005V)$$

where V is the potential difference across the lamp. What current will these lamps take when connected in series across 105 v, and what will be the drop across each lamp?

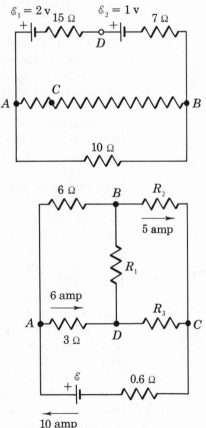

5.22 In the circuit shown, ACB is a uniform straight wire 60 cm long. The current in the 10 Ω resistance is 0.08 amp. The resistances shown in the branch ADB include the internal resistances of the cells.

(a) Find the current in the cell whose emf is 2 v.

(b) Calculate the resistance of the wire ACB.

(c) What must be the length of the portion AC in order that the potential difference between the points C and D shall be zero?

5.23 In the diagram shown, the magnitude of the potential drop between A and C is equal to 54 v.

(a) Determine the values of the resistances R_1, R_2, and R_3.

(b) What is the value of the emf $\mathcal{E}$?

(c) What is the equivalent resistance of the five resistances in the network from A to C?

Chapter 6.
Magnetic Fields of Steady Currents

6.1   **Law of Magnetic Force**

We shall now turn to the study of mechanical forces that are
produced by charges in uniform motion—that is, by steady currents. Strictly, we shall consider the case where there is neither
acceleration of charge nor time variation of current. However,
our discussion will also be applicable to cases where the currents
are changing slowly in time. The moving charges may be located
in free space, or they may appear as streams of ions in solutions,
in gases, or in the interior of conductors. For example, when
steady currents are present in each of two isolated circuits whose
neighboring portions consist of long parallel conductors, attractive or repulsive interactions are developed. A stream of charged
particles such as electrons or protons is subjected to a force of similar nature when the stream is located in the vicinity of a circuit
in which a current is present. The force referred to in these cases
is velocity-dependent and therefore is different from electrostatic
forces. The velocity dependence necessitates the specification of
a reference frame for the description of the motion. More advanced treatment reveals that any *inertial* frame is satisfactory,
and that electric and magnetic effects are dependent. The connection between electric and magnetic fields is embodied in Maxwell's equations, presented in Chapter 14.

Oersted observed in 1820 that a magnetic needle experienced
a force in the presence of a current. Eventually the term magnetic force was used to describe not only the force between pieces
of magnetized matter but also the force on a magnet or a current

due to the presence of other magnets or currents. Today we at-
tribute the origin of such a force to some type of motion of charge
—either translatory, as in the case of a current in a wire, or circu-
latory, as in the case of the orbital motions of electrons. The law
of magnetic force was formulated by Ampère, who during the
years 1820–1825 carried out a series of ingenious experiments with
currents in conductors.

The law of force action between currents is more complex than
Coulomb's law, because a number of directed quantities are required to specify the force. Following Ampère, it is customary to
state the law as an interaction between elementary portions of
two closed rigid circuits. The force or torque on one of the rigid circuits is then evaluated by integrating over both of the circuits.
The results of this procedure agree with experimentally observed
forces or torques. In the actual verification we deal with the currents in circuits of known geometrical shapes or with trajectories
of discrete charges in the neighborhood of known current distributions.

Now we shall state the law of force in its differential form. In
Fig. 6.1, $d\mathbf{l}_1$ and $d\mathbf{l}_2$ are elements of two closed isolated circuits
located in free space. The circuits are to be regarded as filamen-
tary—that is, the transverse dimension of conductors is to be neglected. The magnitudes of the steady currents in circuits 1 and 2
will be denoted by i_1 and i_2. The magnitude of the mechanical
force on $d\mathbf{l}_1$ depends on (1) the length of $d\mathbf{l}_1$, (2) the length of $d\mathbf{l}_2$,

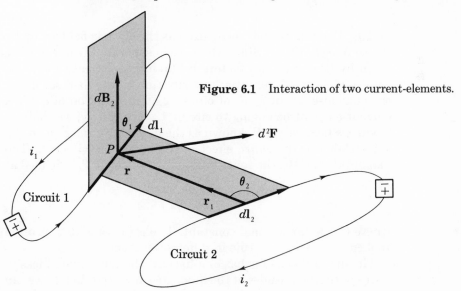

Figure 6.1 Interaction of two current-elements.

(3) the magnitudes of i_1 and i_2, (4) the displacement $\mathbf{r}$ between the circuit-elements, and (5) the sines of the angles θ_1 and θ_2. In agreement with experiment, the magnitude is represented by

$$d^2F_1 = C\frac{(i_1\, dl_1 \sin\,\theta_1)(i_2\, dl_2 \sin\,\theta_2)}{r^2} \tag{6.1}$$

The second-order differential on the left-hand side implies that $\mathbf{F}_1$, the force on circuit 1, is to be obtained by a double vector integration: once over circuit 2 and then over circuit 1. The quantity $i\,d\mathbf{l}$ is called a *current-element*. The expression (6.1) indicates that the force varies directly as the product of the two current-elements and inversely as the square of the distance between them. However, the force is *not* along $\mathbf{r}$. The angular variations are best described in a vectorial formulation to be introduced subsequently. The vectors involved in describing the law of force are shown in Fig. 6.1.

In electrostatics, it is advantageous to utilize the concept of a field of force. In that connection Coulomb's law

$$\frac{1}{4\pi\varepsilon_0} \cdot \frac{q_1 q_2}{r^2}$$

for the force between two point charges was split into two factors, namely

$$\frac{1}{4\pi\varepsilon_0}\frac{q_1}{r^2}$$

and q_2. The first term is recognized as the electric field set up by the source charge q_1. Similarly, we can separate the law of force given by (6.1) into two factors by taking the quantity $(Ci_2\, dl_2 \sin\,\theta_2)/r^2$ as the differential contribution to the field set up by the current-element $i_2\, dl_2$ of circuit 2 at the location of $i_1\, dl_1$, a current-element belonging to circuit 1. Accordingly, we shall introduce a field vector $\mathbf{B}$, known as the *magnetic induction*, at the point P due to the *entire* effect of the current in circuit 2. The magnitude of $d\,\mathbf{B}_2$, the contribution to the field at P, is defined as

$$dB_2 = C\frac{i_2\, dl_2 \sin\,\theta_2}{r^2} \tag{6.2}$$

where C is a dimensional constant. The expression (6.2) is often spoken of as Ampère's rule in differential form.

The discussion so far has emphasized the underlying ideas in terms of the magnitudes of the quantities involved. Before we can apply (6.2) to specific problems, we must understand the vectorial properties of these quantities.

First, $d\mathbf{l}_2$ is treated as a vector whose direction coincides with that of the current i_2. The distance $\mathbf{r}$ is denoted as a vector drawn from the element $i_2\,d\mathbf{l}_2$ to the field point P. The vector $d\mathbf{B}_2$ is described conveniently by the cross product

$$d\mathbf{B}_2 = Ci_2\frac{d\mathbf{l}_2 \times \mathbf{r}_1}{r^2} \tag{6.3}$$

where $\mathbf{r}_1$ is a unit vector along $\mathbf{r}$. As shown in Fig. 6.2, $d\mathbf{B}_2$ is perpendicular to the plane determined by $d\mathbf{l}_2$ and $\mathbf{r}$. To determine the sense of $d\mathbf{B}_2$, apply the following rule: Rotate $d\mathbf{l}_2$ through the angle θ_2 (the smaller of the two angles between $d\mathbf{l}_2$ and $\mathbf{r}$) to bring $d\mathbf{l}_2$ into alignment with $\mathbf{r}$. The direction of ad-

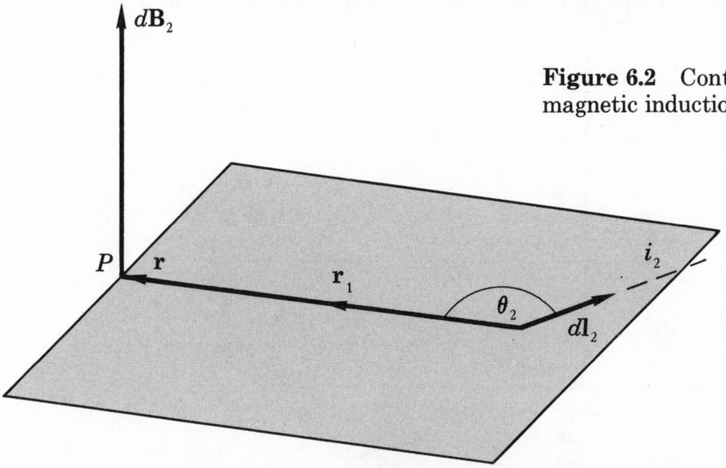

Figure 6.2   Contributions to the magnetic induction at P.

vance of a right-handed screw under a similar rotation fixes the sense of $d\mathbf{B}_2$. To find the magnetic induction $\mathbf{B}_2$ at P due to the current in circuit 2, we must integrate the right-hand side of (6.3) over circuit 2. This means that we must sum vectorially at the point P contributions from various circuit-elements distributed over the particular geometrical form of circuit 2. Formally,

$$\mathbf{B}_2 = Ci_2\int\limits_{\text{circuit 2}} \frac{d\mathbf{l}_2 \times \mathbf{r}_1}{r^2} \tag{6.4}$$

To carry out the integration we resolve $d\mathbf{B}_2$ into its rectangular components at P, then integrate to obtain the x, y, and z components of the resultant. For circuits of other symmetry, cylindrical or spherical coordinates may advantageously be used.

Once the magnitude and direction of $\mathbf{B}_2$ are known at any point of circuit 1 such as the point P, the total force $\mathbf{F}_1$ on circuit 1 is found by integration over circuit 1. The magnitude of $d\mathbf{F}_1$, the force on $i_1 \, d\mathbf{l}_1$ due to the magnetic induction $\mathbf{B}_2$ produced by the whole of circuit 2, can be expressed as

$$dF_1 = i_1 \, dl_1 \, B_2 \sin \theta_1 \qquad (6.5)$$

This follows from (6.1) after $\mathbf{B}_2$ has been determined as a function of the coordinates used to specify $d\mathbf{l}_1$. In vector notation, (6.5) assumes the form

$$d\mathbf{F}_1 = i_1 \, d\mathbf{l}_1 \times \mathbf{B}_2 \qquad (6.6)$$

where $d\mathbf{F}_1$ is perpendicular to the plane determined by $d\mathbf{l}_1$ and $\mathbf{B}_2$, and the sense of $d\mathbf{F}_1$ is determined by the vector rule. As before, rotate $d\mathbf{l}_1$ into $\mathbf{B}_2$ through angle θ_1 (not more than

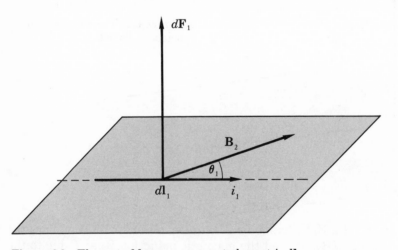

Figure 6.3   Element of force on a current-element $i_1 \, d\mathbf{l}_1$ arising from a magnetic induction $\mathbf{B}_2$.

$180°$). The sense of $d\mathbf{F}_1$ is fixed by the direction of advance of a similarly rotated right-handed screw. The total force on circuit 1 is found by integrating $d\mathbf{F}_1$ around the circuit. Thus

$$\mathbf{F}_1 = i_1 \int_{\text{circuit 1}} d\mathbf{l}_1 \times \mathbf{B}_2 \qquad (6.7)$$

The force action between two currents has thus been subdivided into two steps. The first step is to determine the *magnetic induction* produced by one of the currents (i_2) at any point in space [see (6.4)]. The second step is to calculate the force exerted on the other current (i_1) by the field $\mathbf{B}_2$ [see (6.7)]. We can now regard the calculation of either $\mathbf{B}$ or of $\mathbf{F}$ as a distinct operation without recourse to the interactions between individual elements of particular circuits. Consequently, the subscripts can be omitted in the preceding formulas. The contribution to the magnitude of the magnetic induction as given by (6.2) is now written as

$$dB = \left(\frac{\mu_0}{4\pi}\right) \frac{i\,dl \sin (d\mathbf{l}, \mathbf{r})}{r^2} \qquad (6.8)$$

The constant C, which appears in (6.2), is replaced in (6.8) by ($\mu_0/4\pi$) where the dimensional constant μ_0, called the *permeability of free space* has the assigned value of $4\pi \times 10^{-7}$ new/amp^2. (We shall have more to say elsewhere about the introduction of this constant.) The quantity $(d\mathbf{l}, \mathbf{r})$ stands for the angle between the positive directions of $d\mathbf{l}$ and $\mathbf{r}$. Similarly, for the element of force as given in (6.5), we now write

$$dF = i\,dl\,B \sin (d\mathbf{l}, \mathbf{B}) \qquad (6.9)$$

where $(d\mathbf{l}, \mathbf{B})$ denotes the angle between $d\mathbf{l}$ and $\mathbf{B}$. Relation (6.9) embodies the significant result that the magnetic force on a current-element of fixed length depends only on the current and not on the type of charge which constitutes the current.

We conclude this section with a few additional remarks. The form of the law given in (6.1) must be regarded as a means to an end. The differential element of force cannot be tested experimentally, since it deals with a current-element which cannot be realized. It must be accepted as a starting point. Experimentally, we can observe only the interaction between complete circuits. In these instances, the integration of (6.1) yields correct results.

The differential form is in violation of the third law of motion. This can be verified in the special case in which one current-element is located on the x-axis and the second one on the y-axis. However, the force on a complete circuit obeys the law of action and reaction.

In the next section we shall arrive at the properties of the magnetic induction by way of a slightly different approach. Then we shall develop expressions for the field produced by a discrete charge in motion and for the force on an individual charge moving in a magnetic field. The remainder of the chapter will be devoted to various examples concerned with the force and torque experienced by currents or moving charges located in an induction field.

Galvani (1737–98) noted the muscular response of a frog's leg when the leg was connected to the terminals of an electrostatic machine. He also observed the muscular spasms that occurred when the body of a frog was made to complete the conducting path between two dissimilar metal plates. (The frog is still the testing ground of the budding zoology student and his scalpel!) At the turn of the nineteenth century Volta (1745–1827) discovered the principle of the chemical battery by assembling a pile of alternate strips of zinc and copper separated by blotting paper soaked in brine. Such were the humble beginnings of the science of current electricity.

Magnetic phenomena are among the oldest known properties of matter. Historical records assert that the Greeks and the Romans knew that lodestone or magnetite (a mineral composed of the oxides of iron) could attract bits of iron or other pieces of lodestone. Even today, however, these phenomena are only imperfectly understood.

Once convenient sources of electric current had become available, Oersted (in 1820) discovered a significant relationship between magnetism and current electricity. He found that a magnetic needle would orient itself at right angles to a long straight conductor in which there was a current. Soon thereafter, Biot and Savart developed a formula to serve as a measure of the field produced by a current element. [See (7.2).]

As a result of a series of brilliant experiments with closed circuits, André Marie Ampère (1775–1836) succeeded in systematizing the law of magnetic force between current-bearing conductors. [See (6.1).] (Ampère assumed, incorrectly, that the force between two current-elements was *along* a line joining the elements. Even today an ill-informed student occasionally commits this grave error!) Still, amazingly, Ampère obtained correct results for the force exerted by one circuit on another, and he pointed out clearly the relation between currents and magnetic effects. He even suggested that permanent magnetism could arise from atomic currents circulating within matter itself.

The foundations of electrodynamics were laid in the first quarter of the nineteenth century. The crowning achievements came with Faraday's discovery of electromagnetic induction (1831) and Maxwell's introduction of the concept of displacement current (1862).

6.2   An Alternate Approach to the Definition of B

In the preceding section, we defined the vector **B** in terms of the current distribution which served as a known source of the field of **B**. In this section we shall define **B** without specific knowledge about its source. (An analogous procedure was followed in the definition of the electric field **E**, which was introduced to describe the force on charges.) In the conceptual experiment to be described, we shall assume that the presence of a magnetic field brings about changes in the properties of a region of space. The changes are such that a moving charge or an electric current becomes subject to a force. We shall explore the properties of such a region by introducing into the field a test current-element $i\,d\mathbf{l}$.

Exploration reveals certain properties of the force $d\mathbf{F}$ as exerted on $d\mathbf{l}$ at a fixed point P in the space. The experimenter is free to vary the magnitude of i, the length of $d\mathbf{l}$, and the orientation of $d\mathbf{l}$. A change in each of these variables leads to the following observations: (1) $dF \propto i$. (2) $dF \propto dl$. (3) As dl is oriented along different directions, we find the remarkable feature that there is *one* (and only one) direction for which the force on dl vanishes. We shall label this direction as the zero-force direction. (4) $dF \propto \sin\theta$, where θ is the angle between the zero-force direction and $d\mathbf{l}$. (5) $d\mathbf{F}$ is perpendicular to the plane defined by the zero-force direction and $d\mathbf{l}$. (6) The sense of the force is reversed when the sense of the current in $d\mathbf{l}$ is reversed. When $\theta = 90°$, the force will be maximum, and this particular orientation of $d\mathbf{l}$ may be utilized to define the magnitude of **B** at the field point P, whose coordinates are (x, y, z). Thus, for known values of i, dl, and $(dF)_{\max}$, B is specified by

$$B(x, y, z) \equiv \frac{(dF)_{\max}}{i\,dl} \tag{6.10}$$

It follows from the results of this conceptual experiment that at every point in space we can define a vector whose direction is the zero-force direction and whose magnitude is given by the maximum force per unit current-element as in (6.10). In the mks system **B** is expressed in weber/m^2. (The origin of the name of this unit will be made clear in Chapter 7.) From (6.10) the dimensions of B are seen to be newtons per ampere-meter.

6.3   **Force on a Discrete Charge in Motion**

From the expression for the force on a current-element located in a magnetic field, we can obtain a measure of the force on an individual particle of charge q moving in the field. In the preceding chapter we found that a steady current i could be equated to $NqvA$, where v was the drift velocity, A the cross-sectional area of the conductor, and N the ion concentration. Upon substitution of the content of i in (6.9) after rearrangement, we have

$$\frac{dF}{NA \; dl} = qvB \sin (d\mathbf{l}, \mathbf{B})$$

But $dF/(NA \; dl)$ is the force on dl divided by the number of ions in the volume $A \; dl$, or simply the force on an individual ion. Denoting this force by the symbol f, we have

$$f = qvB \sin (\mathbf{v}, \mathbf{B}) \tag{6.11}$$

since the angle $(\mathbf{v}, \mathbf{B})$ is the same as the angle $(d\mathbf{l}, \mathbf{B})$. In vector representation

$$\mathbf{f} = q\mathbf{v} \times \mathbf{B} \tag{6.12}$$

The three vectors in (6.12) are shown in Fig. 6.4. The expression in (6.12) is often referred to as the *Lorentz force*. More generally, the Lorentz force is interpreted to mean the electromagnetic force on a moving charge q, including the force arising from the **E**-field. The total force on a particle may be written as

$$\mathbf{f} = q(\mathbf{E} + \mathbf{v} \times \mathbf{B}) \tag{6.13}$$

Figure 6.4   The Lorentz force.

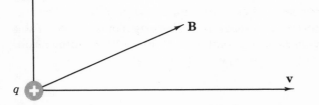

6.4   Magnetic Induction Due to a Single Moving Charge

The contribution to the induction at a field point due to a single particle of charge q and velocity $\mathbf{v}$ may also be deduced from (6.8) by inserting the value of i, as was done in the preceding section. Upon substitution and rearrangement, (6.8) assumes the form

$$\frac{dB}{NA \, dl} = \left(\frac{\mu_0}{4\pi}\right) \frac{qv \sin (d\mathbf{l}, \mathbf{r})}{r^2}$$

But the ratio in the left-hand member represents the contribution to dB from a single charged particle. The ratio is the field $\mathbf{b}$ arising from the motion of a discrete charge q. Hence, since $\mathbf{v}$ is parallel to $d\mathbf{l}$, the magnitude of $\mathbf{b}$ is given by

$$b = \left(\frac{\mu_0}{4\pi}\right) \frac{qv \sin (d\mathbf{l}, \mathbf{r})}{r^2}$$

or, in vector notation,

$$\mathbf{b} = \left(\frac{\mu_0}{4\pi}\right) \frac{q\mathbf{v} \times \mathbf{r}_1}{r^2} \tag{6.14}$$

The diagram in Fig. 6.5 illustrates the vectors involved.

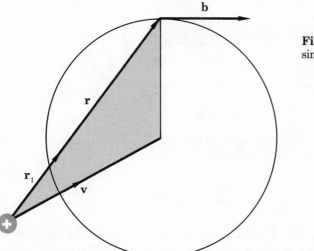

Figure 6.5   Field due to a single charge in motion.

6.5   **Force and Torque on Conductors in Which There Is a Steady Current**

To illustrate the method for calculating the magnetic force, we shall select conductors of simple geometrical shapes. Further, we shall regard the conductors as rigid and filamentary. The magnetic force, which acts on the charge carriers within the conductor, will be transmitted to the crystal lattice of the material itself. Hence the conductor as a whole becomes subject to a force.

1. *Straight conductor of length L.* Figure 6.6 represents a straight, long conductor which forms a portion of a closed circuit in which there is a steady current i. The conductor is located on the x-axis with one end at $x = a$. At all points of the x-axis, the induction has only one component, parallel to the y-axis and of magnitude $B_y = C'/x$, where C' is a constant. It is required to find (a) the force on the conductor, and (b) the torque about the y-axis.

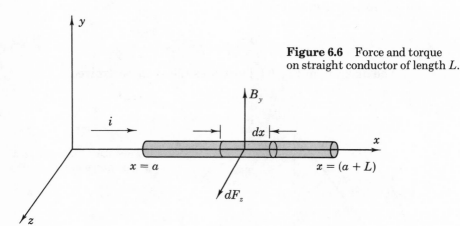

Figure 6.6   Force and torque on straight conductor of length L.

We apply the relation (6.9), noting that $dl = dx$, $\sin (d\mathbf{l}, \mathbf{B}) = 1$, and $B = C'/x$. The force on dx is in the z direction, and its magnitude is

$$dF_z = \frac{C'i\,dx}{x}$$

As we move along the x-axis, the magnitude of the element of force diminishes, but its direction remains parallel to the z-axis.

Hence F_z, the total force on the length L, is found by evaluating the integral

$$F_z = C'i \int_a^{a+L} \frac{dx}{x} = C'i \ln\left(\frac{a+L}{a}\right)$$

The element of torque dT about the y-axis is $x\, dF_z$. Hence the torque on L is given by

$$T = C'i \int_a^{a+L} dx = C'iL$$

2. *Semicircle of diameter 2a.* **B** *normal to plane of circle.* Let a uniform magnetic induction **B** be applied along the $+z$ direction. The sense of **B** is indicated by the symbol $\odot$. The dot suggests that the tip of the arrow, which prescribes the direction of **B**, is about to emerge from the plane of the diagram. The symbol $\otimes$ is used to indicate the opposite direction—i.e., the tail of the arrow is about to enter the plane. The semicircle is located in the x,y plane, with its center at the origin (Fig. 6.7). The force on an

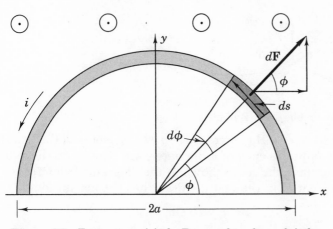

Figure 6.7   Force on semicircle. **B** normal to plane of circle.

element of arc length ds is directed radially away from the center for the indicated sense of i. Its magnitude is $dF = i\, ds\, B = iaB\, d\phi$. Resolve $d\mathbf{F}$ into x and y components. Inspection shows that the integral of the x component vanishes. The force along the y direction is obtained from

$$F_y = \int_0^{\pi} dF \sin\phi = iaB \int_0^{\pi} \sin\phi\, d\phi = 2aiB \quad (6.15)$$

Hence, the force exerted on the semicircle is the same as the force on a straight conductor of length equal to the diameter $2a$, carrying the same current and in the same **B**-field.

3. *Circular loop of diameter 2a.* **B** *in plane of loop.* Consult Fig. 6.8. The loop lies in the x,y plane, with its center at the origin. The uniform induction **B** is parallel to the y-axis. For the

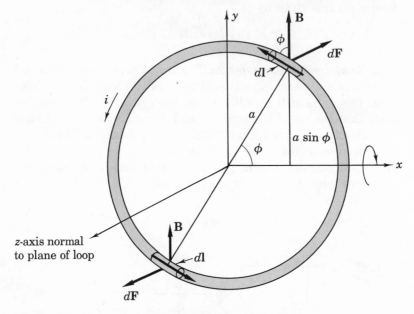

Figure 6.8 Torque on circular loop. **B** in plane of loop.

indicated sense of i, the forces $d\mathbf{F}$, on two elements dl ($= a\, d\phi$) located at opposite ends of a diameter, are parallel to the z direction and have the sense shown in the diagram. The force $d\mathbf{F}$ on the element dl in the first quadrant has the magnitude

$$dF = iaB \sin \phi\, d\phi$$

The force $d\mathbf{F}$ produces a torque $d\mathbf{T}$ about the x-axis. The magnitude of $d\mathbf{T}$ is

$$dT = (dF)a \sin \phi = ia^2B \sin^2 \phi\, d\phi$$

and the torque on the entire loop may be found from

$$T = ia^2B \int_0^{2\pi} \sin^2 \phi\, d\phi = i\pi a^2B = iAB \qquad (6.16)$$

where A is the area of the loop. We state without proof that the expression for T is valid for a plane closed circuit of any shape.

4. *Torque on a circular loop.* **B** *at angle* α *with normal to loop.* If **B** is inclined to the normal, we may resolve **B** into two components: $B \sin \alpha$ in the plane of the loop, and $B \cos \alpha$ normal to the ring. (See Fig. 6.9.) The normal component $B \cos \alpha$ gives rise to zero net translatory force, as may be seen by referring to Fig. 6.7 and the accompanying analysis. The component $B \sin \alpha$ produces a torque about the x-axis whose magnitude is given by (6.16), provided we substitute $B \sin \alpha$ for B. Therefore

$$T = iAB \sin \alpha \qquad (6.17)$$

The vectorial representation for the torque on the loop follows directly from (6.17) if the area A is denoted by a vector **A** along the positive normal to the loop. The positive sense of the normal is conventionally defined as follows: If we associate the sense of circulation of charge with the direction of rotation of a right-handed screw, then the direction of advance of the screw defines the sense of the positive normal. Then

$$\mathbf{T} = i\mathbf{A} \times \mathbf{B} \qquad (6.18)$$

The vector torque **T** is perpendicular to the plane determined by **A** and **B** and is such as to rotate **A** to bring it into alignment with **B**. The torque is maximum when **B** lies in the plane of the loop ($\alpha = 90°$) and is zero when **B** is parallel to the normal. The effect of the torque **T** due to the magnetic force is to rotate the loop about the x-axis (Fig. 6.9) if the loop is free to turn and

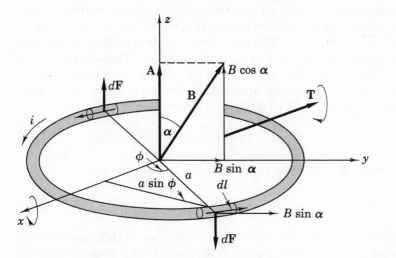

Figure 6.9 Torque on circular loop.
B at an angle to plane of loop.

to orient the loop so that its axis **A** is parallel to **B**. The vector **T** is directed along the negative x-axis.

A more general calculation for the torque on a plane rigid loop of any shape gives the same result. Hence the expression in (6.18) is valid in general. We shall have occasion to use the result in describing the magnetic properties of matter.

6.6   ## Force on a Charged Particle Moving in a Magnetic Field

Expressions (6.8) and (6.9) were obtained strictly from experiments with steady currents. However, they also hold even if the currents change in time, provided the changes are not large during the time necessary for a disturbance to traverse the dimensions of the circuits that are usually found in the laboratory. In the case of alternating currents, the formulas may be used with negligible error up to frequencies in the range of 10^8 cycles/sec. Similarly, the force given by $q\mathbf{v} \times \mathbf{B}$ holds strictly for the case where the charge moves with steady velocity. However, the relation is valid even when there is a small acceleration of the charge—that is, when **v** changes slowly. An accelerated charge emits radiant energy, and additional forces come into play.

As an illustration of the behavior of an ion in a magnetic field, let us assume that a positive ion (charge q, mass m) from a source S is accelerated by the application of an electric field and passes through an aperture into a region in which there is a uniform magnetic induction **B** directed out of the plane, as shown in Fig. 6.10. The ion enters the field of **B** normally and is subject to a force **f** at right angles to **v**. Therefore no work is done on the ion, and the magnitude of its velocity and its kinetic energy remain unchanged. However, the ion has an acceleration v^2/R. The equation of the motion is

$$\frac{mv^2}{R} = qvB \tag{6.19}$$

Solving (6.19) for the ratio of charge to mass, we get

$$\frac{q}{m} = \frac{v}{BR} \tag{6.20}$$

For a given type of ion the left-hand side of this equation is a fixed characteristic quantity. Moreover, the magnitudes of v and B on the right-hand side are constant. Hence, the trajec-

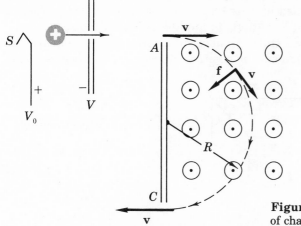

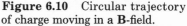

Figure 6.10 Circular trajectory of charge moving in a **B**-field.

tory of the ion is a circle of radius R. The ion, entering at A, will return to C and emerge into a field-free space. Experimentally, the distance $AC = 2R$ may be measured. The speed v may be computed from the law of conservation of energy

$$\tfrac{1}{2}mv^2 + Vq = \tfrac{1}{2}mv_0^2 + V_0q \qquad\qquad (6.21)$$

where the total energy (kinetic plus potential) of the ion at the aperture is equated to its total energy at the source. In (6.21) the potential and initial velocity at the source are represented by V_0 and v_0 respectively. V and v give the corresponding quantities at the aperture. The scheme may be used to determine q/m for different atomic species and makes it possible to evaluate isotopic masses. The expression $\tfrac{1}{2}mv^2$ for the kinetic energy holds only for nonrelativistic speeds.

It is worthwhile to point out again that in the relation $\mathbf{f} = q\mathbf{v} \times \mathbf{B}$ as used in (6.19), $\mathbf{f}$ is always perpendicular to $\mathbf{v}$—that is, the magnetic force $\mathbf{f}$ does no work. It merely serves as a constraint.

6.7   Hall Effect

When a conductor in the form of a ribbon is placed in a magnetic field whose direction is transverse to the current in the ribbon, there appears an electrostatic field whose direction is perpendicular both to the magnetic field and to the direction of the flow of charge. Figure 6.11(a) shows a situation in which the current is assumed to arise from the flow of electrons in the $-x$ direction. When a field B_y is applied in the $+y$ direction, the Lorentz force will cause an accumulation of negative charge on the upper surface and of positive charge on the lower surface.

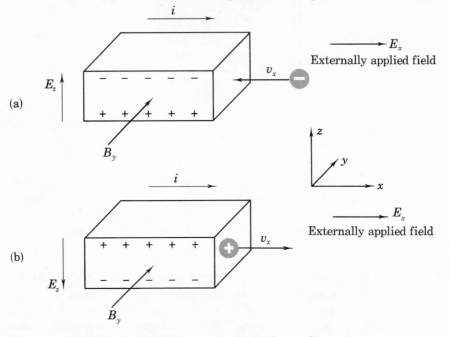

Figure 6.11   Hall effect. (a) Electrons moving in the $-x$ direction. (b) Positive charge carriers moving in the $+x$ direction.

When equilibrium is established, the electrostatic field E_z will just balance the effect of the magnetic force, and charges will flow in the x direction. However, there will be a potential difference across the ribbon. This potential difference is known as the Hall voltage. Figure 6.11(b) shows a state of affairs in which the current is to the right as before, but now the current is due to the transfer of positive charge. In this case, the electric field E_z is directed in the $-z$ direction, although B_y is unchanged.

The Hall electric field may be deduced from the condition that the net force on a charge is zero in the z direction—that is,

$$F_z = 0 = q v_x B_y - q E_z \qquad (6.22)$$

Whence

$$E_z = v_x B_y = j_x B_y / N q \qquad (6.23)$$

where j_x is the current density given by Nqv_x. From (6.23) it is seen that E_z is directly proportional to B_y, and that if $q = -e$ the sense of E_z is reversed with the same directions of j_x and B_y. This provides a means for deciding whether the sign of the charge carrier is negative or positive. In addition, the ratio $(E_z/j_xB_y) = 1/Nq$. We recall that N is the carrier concentration, and from observations of the Hall effect we could arrive at the free-electron concentration in a particular metal.

6.8   The e/m Ratio for Electrons

The deflection of electrons in a magnetic field has led to the determination of the value of the charge-to-mass ratio of the electron. From (6.20) this ratio is given by v/BR, where B is perpendicular to v. With appropriate geometrical arrangements we can measure the radius R of the circular deflection. We can determine the induction B from known current distributions. And at low electron energies we can deduce the velocity v from the accelerating potentials [see (6.21)].

The measurement of the velocity can also be carried out by using the method of crossed electric and magnetic fields. In Fig. 6.12, let **E** denote the electric field between two oppositely charged parallel plates. A uniform magnetic induction **B**, directed along the z-axis, is present over the evacuated region in

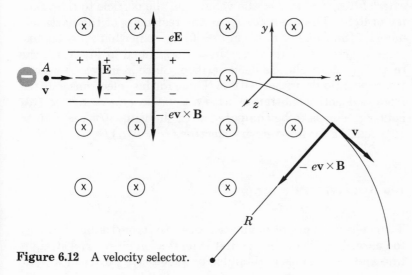

Figure 6.12   A velocity selector.

which the apparatus is located. An electron entering at A along the x-axis with a velocity v is subject to an electric force $-e\mathbf{E}$ and a magnetic force $-e\mathbf{v} \times \mathbf{B}$. If the electric force is made to balance the magnetic force, the electron will emerge undeflected from the region of the plates.

For this adjustment, the net force on the electron is zero, and we must satisfy the condition

$$F_y = Ee - evB = 0$$

or
$$v = E/B \qquad (6.24)$$

Hence, electrons of this particular velocity will travel in a straight path through the electric field. Upon emergence into the field of $\mathbf{B}$ alone, the electron will move in a circular trajectory of radius R and center C. Combining the result in (6.24) with relation (6.20), we obtain for the mass of the electron

$$m = \frac{eB^2R}{E} \qquad (6.25)$$

The use of (6.24) and (6.25) makes it possible to measure the velocity v and the mass m.

The special theory of relativity predicts that mass should vary with velocity in accordance with

$$m = \frac{m_0}{\sqrt{1 - v^2/c^2}} \qquad (6.26)$$

where v/c is the ratio of the velocity of the particle to the velocity of light. The quantity m_0 is the rest-mass of the particle—namely, the value of m when $v = 0$. By somewhat more sophisticated arrangements than those diagramed in Fig. 6.12, the relativistic formula has been verified. Since m increases with v, the e/m ratio decreases with v. Thus, for fast electrons emitted from radioactive substances with $v = 0.69c$, $e/m = 1.28 \times 10^{11}$ coul/kg. This is to be compared with the value $e/m_0 = 1.76 \times 10^{11}$ coul/kg for low-velocity electrons ($v/c \ll 1$).

6.9   Ion Accelerators

Two general types of device are used to impart kinetic energy to charged particles. In the first type the ion moves in a straight line and receives a single pulse or successive pulses of kinetic energy. The gain in kinetic energy is the result of work done on the ion by an electric field. In the second type the charged particle is given periodic pulses of energy.

1. *Van de Graaff generator.* The Van de Graff electrostatic generator is an example of a linear accelerator in which the charged particle is given one "shot" of energy. Figure 6.13 shows the workings of the machine in bare outline. A large spherical conductor S is insulated from ground by the supporting column C. An auxiliary generator G "sprays" electrons on a belt which is driven at high speed over pulleys marked P. As the belt passes the point E, it picks up electrons and transports them to the point F, where they are removed. The collector F not only removes electrons but also introduces additional positive charge onto the belt. In this manner a large amount of charge can be accumulated on S, which attains a high negative potential. Through the introduction of various refinements, the upper limit of the potential attained by S may reach about 10 million volts. A source of negative ions (not shown in the diagram) placed inside the sphere S near the top of the insulating column furnishes the particles which are accelerated by the high potential and are driven down the column to strike a target at its base. The polarity of the accelerator can be reversed. Conse-

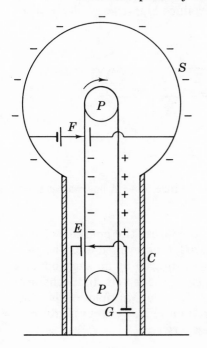

Figure 6.13 A Van de Graaff generator.

quently, positively charged particles may also be accelerated. Electrons, protons, deuterons, and alpha particles (helium nuclei) are the particles commonly employed in the Van de Graaff generator.

2. *Linear accelerator.* We describe briefly another variety of linear accelerator. Consider an ion which approaches the short cylindrical tube T_1 shown in Fig. 6.14. The ion is accelerated toward T_1. As it emerges from T_1 into the space between T_1 and a second, longer tube T_2, it is again accelerated. As the ion travels along the axis of the system, successive accelerations are imparted to it in the gaps between tubes. If the energy of the ion is to increase, the field in the gap between the tubes must be phased appropriately so that the ion is accelerated while it is in the gap. For instance, if the particle is a positive ion, the potential of T_2 must be negative as the ion emerges from T_1. The length of the successive tubes is made longer so that the ion spends the same amount of time traversing each tube. A high-frequency alternating potential is applied to alternate tubes T_2, T_4, . . . so that these tubes are at a high negative potential with respect to T_1, T_3, . . . as the ion emerges from T_1, T_3, ... The time of passage through each tube must be made equal to half the period of the alternating power supply. Linear accelerators of this type have been used to produce high-energy electrons or protons.

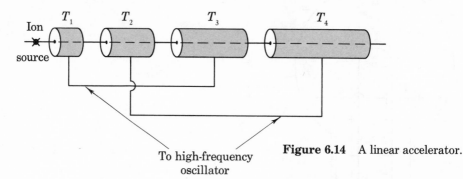

To high-frequency
oscillator

Figure 6.14   A linear accelerator.

In practice, it is convenient to express the energies of particles in multiples of the *electron-volt* (abbreviated ev). The electron-volt is the amount of energy acquired by an electron as it passes through a potential difference of one volt. In mechanical units it is equivalent to 1.60×10^{-19} joule. Multiples of the electron-volt (ev), such as Mev (10^6 ev) and Bev (10^9 ev), are commonly used in measuring particle energies.

3. *The Cyclotron.* In the second type of accelerator the particle is confined to a circular orbit by the application of a **B**-field
and is given periodic pulses of energy by the action of a suitable
electric field. Depending on the nature of the particle to be accelerated, this group is further divided into several varieties, of
which the cyclic accelerator shown schematically in Fig. 6.15 is
an example. The cyclotron consists of two hollow metallic electrodes in the form of semicylinders connected to a source of radio frequency (RF) voltage. The electrodes are called "dees,"
since they resemble the letter "D" in shape. The diagram represents a median section of the acceleration chamber. S is a
source of ions (protons, deuterons, or alphas) located at the center of the chamber. The chamber is evacuated, and a uniform
magnetic field (directed away from the reader normally to the
dees) is maintained by a magnet whose pole pieces lie above and
below the plane of the diagram.

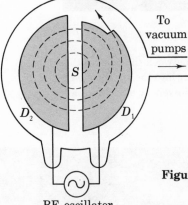

To
vacuum
pumps

S

D_2 D_1

Figure 6.15   The acceleration chamber of a cyclotron.

RF oscillator

Suppose that at some instant the potential of D_1 has reached
a maximum negative value. A positive ion starting from S will
be accelerated toward D_1 by the electric field which exists primarily between D_1 and D_2. The interior of the electrodes is free
from electric fields. As the ion enters the interior of D_1, the magnetic field present over the space occupied by the electrodes
causes the ion to move in a circular path. Upon completing the
semicircular trajectory, the ion re-enters the space between the
electrodes. The period of the alternating field is such that, at
this time, D_2 is at maximum negative potential. Consequently
the positive ion is again accelerated. Now the velocity of the ion
is increased and its path in D_2 has a larger radius.

A 60-in. cyclotron. (ABOVE) The vacuum chamber between the poles of the magnet. (BELOW) A 15-Mev deuteron beam emerging into the air. (See page 151.) (Courtesy Lawrence Radiation Laboratory, University of California.)

We shall show presently that the time of the ion's traversal through the dee is independent of the radius of its path, so that upon emergence into the acceleration gap the polarity of applied voltage is again appropriate for increasing the energy of the ion. This process continues, and the ion spirals in circles of increasing radii. Eventually it is brought out of the chamber and allowed to strike a suitable target.

The motion of the ion is described by (6.19), which is valid at relativistic speeds. The tangential velocity v is related to the angular velocity ω by $v = \omega R$. Upon substitution in (6.19) we get

$$\omega = qB/m \tag{6.27}$$

which states that the angular velocity is independent of the radius but dependent on q/m and B.

The time τ needed to traverse a semicircle of length πR is

$$\tau = \frac{\pi R}{v} = \frac{\pi}{\omega} = \frac{\pi m}{qB} \tag{6.28}$$

Thus τ is independent of the radius of the semicircle provided that m, the mass of the ion, does not differ much from the rest-mass m_0.

Under this restriction, we obtain T, the kinetic energy of the ion, from

$$T = \frac{1}{2} m_0 v^2 = \frac{1}{2} \frac{B^2 q^2 R^2}{m_0} \tag{6.29}$$

by substituting the value $v = BqR/m_0$ derived from (6.19). The result is valid for an orbit of radius R, where v is the tangential velocity of the ion in this orbit. Equation (6.29) indicates that the kinetic energy is proportional to the square of the radius for a given type of ion moving in a constant field **B**.

Returning to the so-called *cyclotron resonance* condition given in (6.27), we see that, if m is the relativistic mass given by (6.26), then ω is not constant but decreases with an increase in the velocity of the ion. To maintain the proper phase of the accelerating electric field, either the oscillator frequency must be decreased with time or else the magnetic field must be increased. In the frequency-modulated cyclotron (the synchrocyclotron), the oscillator frequency is varied periodically. In the electron synchrotron, the frequency of the electric field is kept constant, but the **B**-field is allowed to increase in time.

The cyclotron is not a suitable device for accelerating electrons. In relativistic mechanics the kinetic energy of a particle varies with its mass, in accordance with

$$T = (m - m_0)c^2 \tag{6.30}$$

where c is the speed of light and m_0 is the rest-mass of the particle. From (6.30) we find that

$$m = m_0\left(1 + \frac{T}{m_0c^2}\right)$$

When the relativistic mass is introduced in the cyclotron resonance condition, the result is

$$\omega = \frac{qB}{m} = \frac{qB}{m_0(1 + T/m_0c^2)} \tag{6.31}$$

The quantity m_0c^2 is the rest-energy of the particle. For an electron, $m_0c^2 = 0.51$ Mev. If ω is to change by 1 per cent, then $T/m_0c^2 = 0.01$; whence $T = 5100$ ev. Hence the ordinary cyclotron cannot be used to obtain high-energy electrons. On the other hand, for a proton the rest-energy is 931 Mev. Therefore protons may be accelerated to about 9.3 Mev before ω is lowered by 1 per cent.

Magnetic Fields of Steady Currents: Problems

6.1 In a demonstration of the deflection of ions in a magnetic field, electrons (mass m, charge $q = -e$) enter the magnetic field through a small hole with an initial speed v directed along the $+z$-axis.

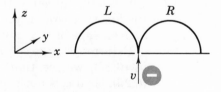

(a) Which circular path (L or R) represents the correct trajectory if the magnetic induction vector $\mathbf{B}$ is directed along the $+y$-axis (normally into the paper)?

(b) Derive an expression for the radius of the orbit. Express the result in terms of v, B, e, and m.

6.2 The rod AC, 0.25 m in length, lies in the horizontal (x,y) plane, and is free to turn about the vertical z-axis which passes through O, the midpoint and the center of gravity of the rod.

For any angular position ϕ, measured from the y-axis, the entire length of the rod is located in a uniform magnetic induction of 0.60 weber/m² directed along the *y*-axis. A current of 30 amp is maintained in the rod, whose weight is 2.25 new.

What is the value of ϕ at which the magnetic force is just equal to the gravitational force? What must be the sense of the current (*C* to *A*, or *A* to *C*) to achieve this condition of balance?

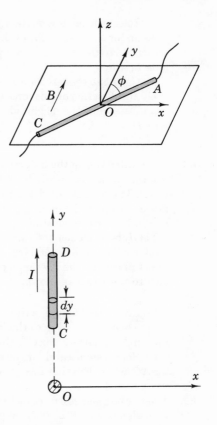

6.3 A long, thin wire is coincident with the *z*-axis. A steady current is maintained in the wire in the positive *z* direction (outward from the *x,y* plane). As a result, at all points of the *x,y* plane there is a magnetic induction **B** whose magnitude is given by k/r weber/m², where k is a constant, and r is the radial distance in meters from the origin *O* to any field point.

In the diagram, *CD* is a straight conductor of length *L* meters located on the *y*-axis so that *OC* = *CD*. The current in *CD* is *I* amp in the direction shown.

(a) Select the coordinate *y* as the variable and write an expression for *dF*, the magnitude of the force (due to **B**) on the element of length *dy*. Specify the direction of this force.

(b) Calculate the resultant force on *CD*. Specify the units of your answer.

6.4 At all points of the *x,y* plane the magnetic induction vector has the constant magnitude of *B* weber/m² and is directed along the positive *y*-axis.

In the accompanying diagram, *AC* represents a rigid wire in the form of a quadrant of a circle with center at the origin *O* and a radius of *R* m; *CD* is a straight wire along the *y*-axis of length equal to the radius *R*. A constant current of 1 amp in the direction shown is present in each conductor.

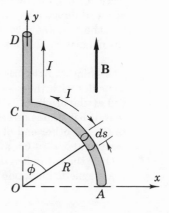

(a) Select the angle ϕ as the variable and write the differential expression for the magnitude of the mechanical force on an element of arc ds due to the induction **B**. Specify precisely the direction of this force in words.

(b) Calculate the resultant force on the length AC and specify precisely the direction of this force in words.

(c) Determine the magnitude of the force on the straight conductor CD.

6.5   In a limited region the induction **B** is directed radially away from the origin. The magnitude of **B** at a distance r from O is given by $B = k/r^2$, where k is a constant.

Let dy be an element of a straight rigid conductor AC carrying current i placed in the x,y plane parallel to the y-axis as shown.

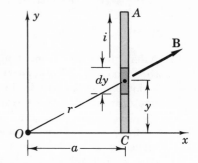

(a) Copy the diagram, write down the magnitude of $d\mathbf{F}$, the force on an element $i\,dy$, due to the induction **B**. Express $d\mathbf{F}$ in terms of the single variable y. Specify the direction of $d\mathbf{F}$.

(b) Set up an integral for the magnetic force on the entire conductor AC, whose length is L, and evaluate the integral.

6.6   There is no magnetic force on a current element $i\,\Delta\mathbf{l} = 0.24$ amp-m when placed at the origin O along the line OR in the x,y plane. When the same current element is placed at O, with the current along the positive z direction, the element experiences a force $\Delta\mathbf{F}$ in the x,y plane, of magnitude equal to 0.36 new and directed as shown. Calculate the x, y, and z components of the magnetic induction at O.

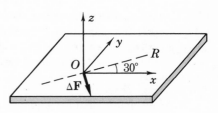

6.7   The thin, straight, rigid wire OC coincides with the x-axis with one end at the origin O. A steady current of 6.0 amp is directed from O to C. The other end of the wire is located at $x = +0.5$ m.

Over the entire length OC, there is a magnetic induction **B** directed

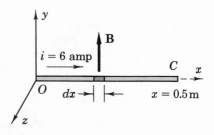

along the y-axis. When x is expressed in meters, the magnitude of **B** is given by

$$B = (1 + 3x^2) \quad \text{weber/m}^2$$

(a) What is the magnitude of the force $d\mathbf{F}$ exerted on the current element $i\,dx$?

(b) Give the units and direction of $d\mathbf{F}$.

(c) What is the magnitude of the torque $d\mathbf{L}$ exerted on the element dx about the y-axis?

(d) What is the magnitude of the torque $d\mathbf{L}$ exerted on the element dx about the z-axis?

(e) Calculate the force on the entire length OC due to the magnetic induction B.

6.8   A steady current of 5 amp is maintained between the center and the rim of a thin copper disk. A uniform magnetic induction **B**, of magnitude equal to 0.40 weber/m² and directed parallel to the axis of the disk, is present over the entire face of the disk.

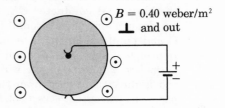

$B = 0.40$ weber/m²
⊥ and out

(a) For the sense of the induction vector **B** and the polarity of the battery shown, does the risk rotate in the clockwise or the counterclockwise direction?

(b) The radius of the disk is 11 cm. What is the torque about the axis of rotation exerted on a radial element of length 2 cm with its center located at a distance of 5 cm from the axis?

6.9   A self-luminous streamer discharge produced within a partially evacuated tube is seen to rotate about the axis of a solenoid (z-axis). At a radial distance of 0.040 m from the axis, the axial component of the magnetic induction is 0.080 weber/m² and the radial component is 0.25 weber/m². What is the magnitude of the torque about the z-axis on a positive ion (charge 1.60×10^{-19} coul, mass 13.3×10^{-27} kg.) if the ion is located at a distance of 0.040 m from the axis and is moving in the $+z$ direction with a speed of 2.0×10^3 m/sec? Draw a set of cartesian axes, and on it indicate the directions of all vectors used in the calculation and the direction of the force on the ion.

6.10 A rigid conductor 2 m long coincides with the x-axis with its midpoint at the origin. (See figure at top of page 158.) The current in it is 3.0 amp in the positive x direction. The boundaries of the field are so shaped that the magnetic induction at points on the x-axis is directed parallel to the y-axis, and its magnitude is described by

$$B_y = 0.50 \, (1 - 10x^2) \quad \text{weber/m}^2$$

between $x = -0.30$ m and $x = +0.30$ m. Elsewhere, $B = 0$.

(a) What are the magnitude and direction of the force $d\mathbf{F}$ exerted on an element dx of the conductor, as shown in the diagram?

(b) Calculate the force on the conductor due to the magnetic induction specified. State the units of the result.

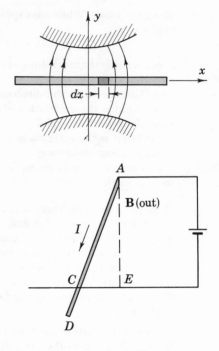

6.11 A wire AD 12 cm long is free to rotate about an axis through A. The wire makes frictionless contact with the horizontal conductor CE. A current of 1 amp is sent from A to C, and a uniform magnetic induction of 0.1 weber/m² is applied normal to the plane of the wires and is directed upward from the page. The plane ACE is vertical. It is found that at equilibrium the length AC is equal to 10 cm. Under equilibrium conditions,

(a) Calculate the torque on AC about A due to the magnetic field of 0.1 weber/m².

(b) Calculate the distance CE if the copper wire weighs 0.02 new. Consider only the torques due to the weight and to the magnetic field of 0.1 weber/m².

6.12 A thin disk of dielectric material has a uniform surface charge density $+\sigma$. The disk rotates about its axis at the rate of ω radian/sec. What is the magnetic induction at a point on the axis at a distance x from the center of the disk whose radius is a?

6.13 The equilateral triangle ACD represents a rigid conductor. The current in each side is 10 amp in the sense shown.

(a) Find the magnitude and direction of the force on each side if there is a uniform flux density $\mathbf{B}$ of magnitude 0.20 weber/m² in the space occupied by the conductor. $\mathbf{B}$ is perpendicular to and directed outward from the plane of the triangle whose side is 0.05 m.

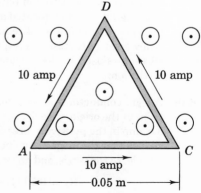

(b) Repeat part (a) if **B** has the same magnitude but is directed parallel to the side AC.

(c) What is the net force on ACD for the field direction described in parts (a) and (b)?

6.14   A coil of 50 turns is wound on the periphery of a rectangular wooden frame $ACDE$. The frame is hinged rigidly so that it can rotate about the z-axis. The current in each wire is 2.0 amp directed from A to C. There is a uniform magnetic field of induction equal to 0.15 weber/m² parallel to the $+y$-axis. Write an expression for the torque on the rectangle as a function of the angle ϕ. Length of side $AC = 0.40$ m; of side $CD = 0.50$ m. For what value of ϕ is the torque a maximum?

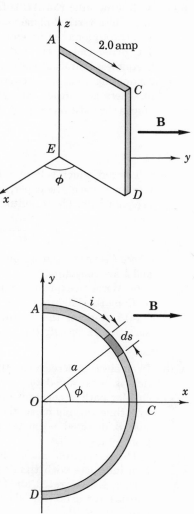

6.15   A rigid semicircular conductor ACD of radius a m is situated in the x,y plane with its center at the origin O, the diameter AD coinciding with the y-axis. A uniform magnetic induction of B weber/m² directed along the positive x-axis is present over the region occupied by the conductor.

(a) Copy the diagram and write the magnitude of the force $d\mathbf{F}$ exerted on ds, an element of the conductor which carries a steady current of i amp in the clockwise sense. Specify the direction and units of $d\mathbf{F}$.

(b) What is the torque on ds about the y-axis? Express your answer in terms of the single variable ϕ.

(c) Set up an integral for the torque on the entire semicircle ACD due to the induction **B** and evaluate the integral.

6.16   In a certain cyclotron the radius of the last orbit is 0.75 m. What magnetic induction must be applied if protons are to be accelerated to a final energy of 10 Mev? What is the cyclotron resonance frequency?

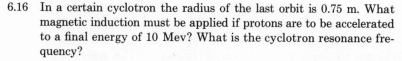

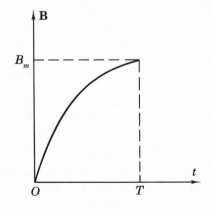

6.17   A thin metallic rod AC is free to rotate in a vertical plane about an axis through one of its ends at A. The other end of the rod makes frictionless contact along a circular conducting track of radius $AC = L$ m. There is a steady current of I amp in the rod directed from A to C.

The rod, which is located in a horizontal magnetic field directed into the plane of the paper, makes an angle θ with the vertical when in equilibrium. The magnitude of the induction **B** is given by

$$B = \frac{k}{(a + l \sin \theta)} \quad \text{weber/m}^2$$

where l is the distance from A to any elem⸍ dl of the rod, and a and k are constants.

(a) Write an expression for $d\mathbf{F}$, the force on the element of length dl. Copy the diagram and on it show the vector $d\mathbf{F}$.

(b) Determine the magnitude of the force on the rod due to the induction **B**. Specify the units of your answer.

6.18   In an electron accelerator, the particle is constrained to move in a circular path of constant radius R by a time-varying magnetic induction **B** directed normally to the plane of the orbit.

The momentum mv of the electron increases with time t as the particle is accelerated, and the centripetal force on the electron is given by mv^2/R.

If the magnetic induction **B** varies with the time in accordance with

$$B = B_m \sin\left(\frac{\pi t}{2T}\right)$$

over the interval $t = 0$ to $t = T$, obtain an expression which gives the electron momentum at any instant t during this time interval.

Chapter 7.
Sources and Properties
of Magnetic Induction

7.1   **Magnetic Field Arising from Simple
        Current Distributions**

In this section we shall apply Ampère's rule, which was given in
(6.3) and (6.8), to obtain formulas for the values of **B** due to the
current in filamentary circuits of simple shape. We shall assume
that the circuits are located in a vacuum. The magnetic effects
of matter surrounding the circuits will be described in Chapter 9.

    1. *Long, straight conductor.* Regard the conductor as a portion
of a closed circuit in which there is a steady current i. As shown
in Fig. 7.1, the conductor coincides with the y-axis and the field
point P is located on the x-axis at a distance a from the conductor. The contribution $d\mathbf{B}$ to the field at P coming from $i\,d\mathbf{l}$ is
equal to

$$d\mathbf{B} = \left(\frac{\mu_0}{4\pi}\right)\frac{i\,d\mathbf{l} \times \mathbf{r}_1}{r^2} \tag{7.1}$$

The sense of $d\mathbf{B}$ is normal to the x,y plane and away from the
reader. Since all contributions from various portions of the conductor are parallel, B is obtained by a scalar integration of (7.1)
directly. The cross product involves the angle θ between $d\mathbf{l}$ and
the unit vector $\mathbf{r}_1$. Since $dl = dy$, for the magnitude of $d\mathbf{B}$, we
can write

$$dB = \left(\frac{\mu_0}{4\pi}\right)\frac{i\,dy\,\sin\theta}{r^2} \tag{7.2}$$

161

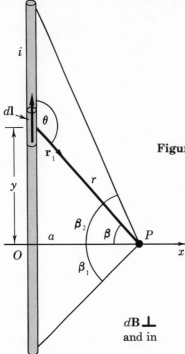

Figure 7.1   Field due to current in straight conductor.

$dB\perp$
and in

Either y or the angle β may be selected for the variable of integration. Selecting the angle β, we have $y = a \tan \beta$, with the convention that positive values of y correspond to positive values of β. Then $r = a \sec \beta$; $dy = a \sec^2 \beta \, d\beta$; and (7.2) assumes the form

$$dB = \frac{\mu_0 i}{4\pi a} \cos \beta \, d\beta \tag{7.3}$$

If the ends of the conductor are specified by the angles β_1 and β_2, the magnitude of **B** at P is given by the integral

$$B = \frac{\mu_0 i}{4\pi a} \int_{\beta_1}^{\beta_2} \cos \beta \, d\beta = \frac{\mu_0 i}{4\pi a} (\sin \beta_2 - \sin \beta_1) \tag{7.4}$$

If the straight conductor is infinitely long, $\sin \beta_2 = 1$, $\sin \beta_1 = -1$, and

$$B = \frac{\mu_0 i}{2\pi a} \tag{7.5}$$

2. *Circular loop—axial point.* Next we consider the field on the axis of a circular turn of wire of radius a and carrying a current i.

As shown in Fig. 7.2(a) the field point P is at a distance y from the plane of the loop. As before, the unit vector $\mathbf{r}_1$ is drawn away from the element $d\mathbf{l}$ toward P. The cross product $d\mathbf{l} \times \mathbf{r}_1$ in (6.3) yields a vector $d\mathbf{B}$ normal to the plane determined by $d\mathbf{l}$ and $\mathbf{r}_1$.

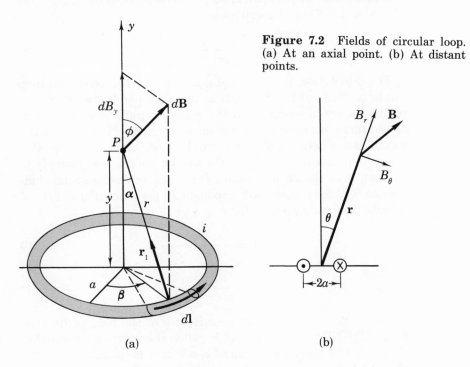

Figure 7.2 Fields of circular loop. (a) At an axial point. (b) At distant points.

(a)　　　　　　　　　　　(b)

The sense of $d\mathbf{B}$ corresponds to a counterclockwise circulation of charge as the loop is observed from P. The contributions $d\mathbf{B}$ from various elements $d\mathbf{l}$ will have the same magnitude

$$dB = \frac{\mu_0 i}{4\pi} \frac{dl}{r^2} \tag{7.6}$$

but will be inclined at an angle ϕ to the axis. In integrating over the loop, the component of $d\mathbf{B}$ normal to the axis will add up to zero, as can be seen from the symmetry. The axial components $dB_y = dB \cos \phi$ are directed along the y-axis. Thus the field B_y at P is obtained by integrating dB_y after substituting $\cos \phi = \sin \alpha = a/r$ and $dl = a \, d\beta$.
Thus

$$B_y = \frac{\mu_0 i a^2}{4\pi r^3} \int_0^{2\pi} d\beta = \frac{\mu_0 i a^2}{2r^3} = \frac{\mu_0 i a^2}{2(a^2 + y^2)^{3/2}} \tag{7.7}$$

At the center of the loop, $y = 0$, and B assumes the value

$$B_y = \frac{\mu_0 i a^2}{4\pi r^3} \int_0^{2\pi} d\beta = \frac{\mu_0 i a^2}{2a^3} = \frac{\mu_0 i}{2a} \tag{7.8}$$

The area of the loop, which is πa^2, shall be denoted by A. In terms of this area (7.7) can be written as

$$B_y = \frac{\mu_0 i A}{2\pi (a^2 + y^2)^{3/2}} \tag{7.9}$$

The calculation of the field at points not on the axis of the loop can be carried out by the application of Ampère's law. The computations are laborious, and the results cannot be expressed in closed form in terms of elementary functions. However, in the special case where the distance r to the field point is much greater than the radius of the loop a, the results are relatively simple to express. If at the off-axis point, $\mathbf{B}$ is resolved into a radial component B_r and a transverse component B_θ perpendicular to $\mathbf{r}$, then calculations indicate that for $r \gg a$

$$B_r = \frac{2\mu_0 i A}{4\pi} \frac{\cos\theta}{r^3} \tag{7.10}$$

$$B_\theta = \frac{\mu_0 i A}{4\pi} \frac{\sin\theta}{r^3} \tag{7.11}$$

where r and θ are the polar coordinates of the field point. [See Fig. 7.2(b).] The quantity $\mu_0 i A$ is called the *magnetic moment of the loop*. The magnetic moment is a vector perpendicular to the plane of the loop. In vector notation it is defined by

$$\mathbf{m} = \mu_0 i \mathbf{A} \tag{7.12}$$

The expressions for the **B**-field around a current loop as given by (7.10) and (7.11) are identical in form with the corresponding components of the electric intensity **E** in the field of an electric dipole, again at distances which are large relative to the dimensions of the dipole. [See (4.3) and (4.4).] We shall have occasion to refer to the concept of magnetic dipoles in our study of the magnetic properties of matter.

3. *Solenoid.* We shall now use the result appearing in (7.7) to deduce an expression for the field at a point on the axis of a solenoid. (A solenoid is a helical winding on a cylindrical surface.) Actually, we shall consider the field of the solenoidal winding to be the same as the field of a series of coaxial, closely spaced, circular turns of the same radius. Figure 7.3 gives a cross-sectional

view. The field point P is chosen at the origin. The symbols $\odot$ and $\otimes$ indicate the sense of the current in the winding toward and away from the reader respectively. If n is the number of turns per unit length, the number of turns in a length dx is $n\,dx$.

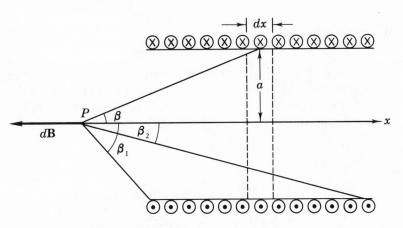

Figure 7.3   Field on axis of solenoid.

The magnitude of the contribution $d\mathbf{B}$ at P due to a length dx of the solenoid of radius a is

$$dB = \frac{\mu_0 i a^2 n\,dx}{2(a^2 + x^2)^{3/2}} \qquad (7.13)$$

from the result in (7.7), which gives the axial field of a steady current i in a single circular turn of radius a. The sense of advance of a right-handed screw rotated with the current specifies the direction of $d\mathbf{B}$. For the purposes of integration, it is convenient to select the angle β as the variable. Thus

$$x = a \cot \beta, \qquad dx = -a \csc^2 \beta\,d\beta$$

Hence,

$$B = -\frac{\mu_0 n i}{2} \int_{\beta_1}^{\beta_2} \sin \beta\,d\beta = \frac{\mu_0 n i}{2}(\cos \beta_2 - \cos \beta_1) \qquad (7.14)$$

where the limits of integration are specified by the limiting values of β. For a point at the center of a solenoid whose length is much greater than its radius, $\cos \beta_1 = -1$; $\cos \beta_2 = 1$; and (7.14) reduces to

$$B = \mu_0 n i \qquad (7.15)$$

Similarly, for an axial point at the end closest to the origin, $\cos \beta_1 = 0$; $\cos \beta_2 = 1$; and

$$B = \frac{\mu_0 ni}{2} \tag{7.16}$$

7.2   Magnetic Flux

As shown in Fig. 7.4, the field of **B** can be mapped by curves (lines of induction) so drawn that at a given point of the field the tangent to the curve has the direction of the vector **B**. Thus, the lines of induction around a long straight conductor are concen-

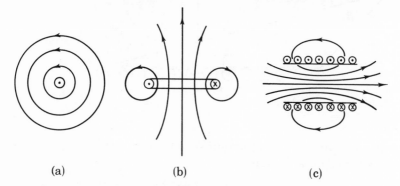

| (a) | (b) | (c) |

Figure 7.4   Lines of induction surrounding (a) a straight conductor; (b) a circular loop; and (c) a solenoid.

tric circles, and the **B**-field surrounding a circular turn and a solenoidal coil consists of closed lines. By a procedure similar to that adopted in describing the flux of the **E**-field, we can consider an element of area dA in the field (see Fig. 7.5) and define $d\Phi$ as the element of the flux of **B** crossing this area. Thus

$$d\Phi = \mathbf{B} \cdot d\mathbf{A} = B \cos \theta \, dA = B_n \, dA \tag{7.17}$$

where θ is the angle between **B** and $d\mathbf{A}$, and B_n is the component of **B** normal to dA. The flux of **B** crossing a surface of area S is now given by the surface integral

$$\Phi = \int_S \mathbf{B} \cdot d\mathbf{A} = \int_S B \cos \theta \, dA \tag{7.18}$$

While lines of **B** describe the direction of the induction at every point in the field, we can extend the usefulness of the geometri-

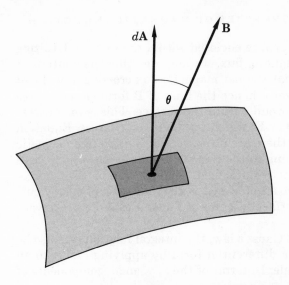

Figure 7.5 Flux of the **B**-field.

cal representation by associating the magnitude of **B** with the number of lines per unit area. In this sense, the magnetic flux may be thought of as the total number of lines crossing an area. In the mks system, the unit of flux is the *weber*. The definition in (7.17) explains the origin of the name assigned to the unit of **B** (weber per square meter).

7.3   Properties of the Vector Field of B

We shall describe the nature of the magnetic induction by stating two fundamental relations obeyed by the vector field of **B**. Although these generalizations are deduced from the differential form of Ampère's law, the proofs are somewhat involved and will not be offered here. The mathematical statements that will be presented are integral representations dealing with the surface and line integrals of the magnetic induction.

First property. The surface integral of the magnetic induction vector **B** over a closed surface is always zero. In symbols,

$$\int_{\substack{\text{closed} \\ \text{surface}}} \mathbf{B} \cdot d\mathbf{A} = 0 \qquad (7.19)$$

This relation is radically different from Gauss's law for the field of **E**. For electrostatics the corresponding integral is equal to

167

$1/\varepsilon_0$ times the net charge enclosed within the surface. Utilizing the concept of magnetic flux, we may describe the content of (7.19) by saying that the net magnetic flux crossing any closed surface is *always* zero; hence the lines of **B** form closed curves and cannot start or end within the surface. This is in contrast with the lines of **D** or **E**, which terminate on charges. Equation (7.19) implies that there are no sources of **B** or no free magnetic charges corresponding to the free electrical charges which serve as sources of the electrostatic field. Another example of a source-free vector field was encountered in the discussion of steady currents where the surface integral of **j** over a closed surface vanishes identically.

As in the case of Gauss's law, the integral relation can also be transformed into a differential form by applying (7.19) to an elementary rectangle. In terms of the x, y, and z components of **B**, the result is

$$\nabla \cdot \mathbf{B} = \frac{\partial B_x}{\partial x} + \frac{\partial B_y}{\partial y} + \frac{\partial B_z}{\partial z} = 0 \qquad (7.20)$$

(Refer to Sections 3.5 and 3.6 for the derivational details.)

Second property. The line integral of the magnetic induction around a closed path is equal to μ_0 times the net current that crosses any area bounded by the path of integration. In symbols,

$$\oint \mathbf{B} \cdot d\mathbf{l} = \mu_0 i \qquad (7.21)$$

This relation shows once again the difference between the field of **B** and the electrostatic field **E**. In the latter case, the line integral over a closed path vanishes identically. The formula in (7.21) is known as *Ampère's circuital law*. It may be used to evaluate B in special instances where, because of symmetry, the magnitude of **B** is constant along a path of integration.

We shall now verify the circuital law in the special case of a long filamentary current normal to the x,y plane. Let the conductor cross the plane at the origin, as shown in Fig. 7.6(a). By direct integration we have already shown that $B = \mu_0 i/2\pi r$, where r is the distance from the origin to any field point P. Also, the direction of **B** is normal to the radius r_1. For the path of integration we shall choose the closed figure $ACDEA$ formed by two circular arcs of radii r_1 and r_2 and parts of radial distances, as shown. A contribution to the line integral is obtained by taking the product of an element of path length and the component of **B** tangential to the element. Such contributions along AC and DE are given by $B_1\,dl = B_1 r_1\,d\theta$ and by $B_2\,dl = B_2 r_2\,d\theta$. Furthermore, the component of **B** along the radial direction is zero. A counterclockwise tracing of the path will be taken as

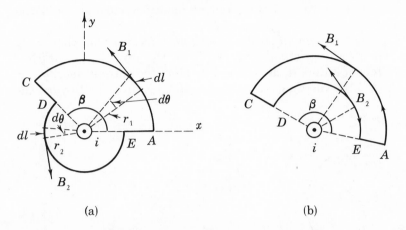

(a)   (b)

Figure 7.6   Verification of the circuital law. (a) Path encloses current i. (b) No current enclosed by path.

positive. This convention corresponds to the rotation of a right-handed screw whose advance is parallel to the current (toward the reader). The line integral over $ACDE$ may be written as

$$\int_0^\beta B_1 r_1\,d\theta + \int_\beta^{2\pi} B_2 r_2\,d\theta = \frac{\mu_0 i}{2\pi}\Big(\beta - 0 + 2\pi - \beta\Big) = \mu_0 i$$

which verifies the circuital law. If the chosen path $ACDE$, as shown in Fig. 7.6(b), does not encircle the current, traversal over AC will be in the counterclockwise sense, traversal over DE will be in the clockwise sense, and the contribution to the line integral over AC will just cancel that from DE. This result is also in accord with (7.21), which predicts that the line integral will vanish when no current is encircled.

The circuital law as presented is valid for steady or, at most, slowly varying currents in free space. Actually, it may also be used when the currents are located in nonmagnetic materials such as copper. However, the law requires modification in the presence of magnetic materials such as iron.

7.4   Applications of the Circuital Law

The use of the circuital law will now be illustrated by computing the magnitude of **B** for two symmetrical current configurations.

1. *Infinitely long conducting cylinder.* Assume that the steady current i is distributed uniformly over the cross section which is a circle of radius R, as in Fig. 7.7. Then the current density $j = i/(\pi R^2)$. In the diagram, assume that **j** is directed toward the

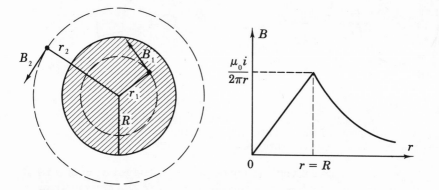

Figure 7.7 Application of the circuital law. Calculation of **B** due to a current in a long cylindrical conductor.

reader. By symmetry, **B** lies in a plane normal to the axis of the cylinder. **B** is tangent to a circular path about the axis and has the same magnitude at all points of the path. For a path of radius r_1 lying within the body of the conductor, the circuital law becomes

$$2\pi r_1 B_1 = \mu_0 \pi r_1^2 j$$

or
$$B_1 = \frac{\mu_0 i}{2\pi R^2} r_1 \tag{7.22}$$

Similarly, for a path outside the surface of the conductor,

$$2\pi r_2 B_2 = \mu_0 i$$

or
$$B_2 = \frac{\mu_0 i}{2\pi r_2} \tag{7.23}$$

Hence the magnetic induction increases linearly from zero on the axis to a maximum value at the surface of the conductor, and then decreases inversely with the distance from the axis as we pass to external points. As a consequence of the result in (7.23), for field points outside the conductor, the current may be considered as concentrated on the axis of the conductor. At the surface, $r_1 = r_2 = R$, and $B_1 = B_2$. (See the plot in Fig. 7.7.)

    2. *Toroidal winding.* The circuital law can be used to calculate **B** inside a toroidal winding. The current in the winding is i, and the coil has N closely wound turns. Figure 7.8 represents a midsection of the toroid. The sense of the current in the winding is indicated symbolically by $\odot$ and $\otimes$ (current toward and away from the reader respectively). The symmetry again suggests the use of circular paths P_1, P_2, and P_3 centered about the axis. The current encircled by path P_1 is zero; that encircled by

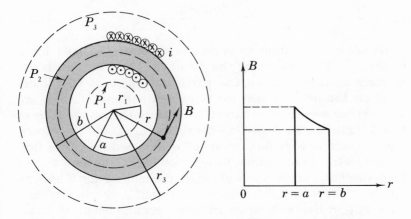

Figure 7.8   Application of the circuital law. Calculation of **B** arising from the current in a toroidal winding.

path P_2 is Ni; and that encircled by path P_3 is again zero, since P_3 encloses two equal and opposite currents. For $r < a$, $2\pi r_1 B_1 = 0$. Hence $B_1 = 0$. For the region between the inner and outer radii

$$B = \frac{\mu_0 Ni}{2\pi r} \qquad (a < r < b) \tag{7.24}$$

Finally, for $r > b$, $2\pi r_2 B_2 = \mu_0(Ni - Ni)$, so that $B_2 = 0$. Consequently, for the ideal toroid the **B**-field is zero everywhere except in the interior of the winding, where it falls off inversely with the distance from the center. The plot of B vs r is shown in Fig. 7.8.

7.5   Force Between Parallel Straight Elements.
The Definition of the Ampere and the Coulomb

For the special case of two parallel current-elements, the expression for force given by (6.1) reduces to

$$d^2F = C\frac{(i_1\,dl_1)(i_2\,dl_2)}{r^2} \qquad (7.25)$$

The corresponding expression for the magnetic force f between two discrete charges q_1 and q_2 separated by a distance r and moving along straight parallel paths with speeds v_1 and v_2 can also be deduced from (6.12) and (6.14). The result is

$$f = C\frac{(q_1v_1)(q_2v_2)}{r^2} \qquad (7.26)$$

We are now in a position to discuss the matter of units. From (7.25) or (7.26) we see that the constant C has the dimensions of force/current². Hence the particular value of C will depend on the units chosen for force and current. If these are given, then we can determine C by experiment, on the basis of (7.25). Actually, current-elements do not exist, and the experiments would have to be carried out with closed circuits of simple geometry. For instance, integration of (7.25) over a pair of long, straight, parallel wires of adjacent circuits 1 and 2 leads to $i_2B_1l_2$ for the force F_2 on length l_2 of circuit 2. But in this case, $B_1 = 2Ci_1/r$. Hence the attractive force per unit length of circuit 2 is given by

$$\frac{F_2}{l_2} = \frac{2Ci_1i_2}{r} \qquad (7.27)$$

In modern practice, the measurement of forces is carried out by means of a "current balance" which consists of a pair of coils— a small coil suspended over a large one. The force between the coils can be determined with high precision.

Alternately, an exact arbitrary value is assigned to C and experimental measurements are then used to define the unit of current. This is the procedure that is actually adopted in the so-called rationalized mks system of units, where C is identically set equal to 10^{-7} new/amp². In terms of a preceding substitution— that of (6.8)—

$$C \equiv \frac{\mu_0}{4\pi} \equiv 10^{-7} \text{ new/amp}^2 \qquad (7.28)$$

The ratio $1/4\pi$ is introduced for the purpose of "ratio-olizing"— or, for the sake of euphony, rationalizing. Its presence simplifies the appearance of the fundamental field equations that will be presented later. From (7.28) we see that

$$\mu_0 \equiv 4\pi \times 10^{-7} \text{ new/amp}^2 \qquad (7.29)$$

The units of μ_0, the permeability of free space, may also be expressed as weber per amp-meter or as henry per meter (to be shown later).

On the basis of the preceding discussion, the absolute ampere, or the mks unit of current, may be defined in the following way, with the aid of (7.27) and (7.28): The current in each of two straight, infinitely long, parallel conductors one meter apart and located in free space is equal to one ampere when the magnetic interaction force per meter of length is exactly 2×10^{-7} new.

The coulomb, or the unit of charge, is defined in terms of the ampere. The coulomb is the charge that crosses a section of a conductor in one second when there is an unvarying current of one ampere in the conductor. In principle, the coulomb may be defined from (7.26) by first assigning to C the arbitrary value of 10^{-7}. This procedure, however, is of no practical value in any process of standardization.

Sources and Properties of Magnetic Induction: Problems

7.1 A steady current of I amp is maintained in the conducting path $ACDE$. Starting with the expression for the magnetic induction due to a current element, calculate the magnitude of the induction vector **B** at the point P. The field point P is located at the center of the circular arc CD of radius R m subtending an angle of 120° at P. AC and DE are straight conductors along radial directions. What is the direction of the vector **B**?

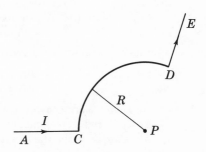

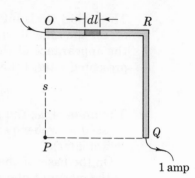

7.2   Follow the steps below and calculate the magnetic induction at the
point P due to a steady current of
1 amp in the path of ORQ. In the
diagram, $OPQR$ is a square s m on
a side. The current is maintained
in the conductors OR and RQ,
which coincide with two sides of
the square.

(a) Reproduce side OR (including element dl) and the point P in
a diagram. Write down the magnitude of the contribution $d\mathbf{B}$ to
the field at P due to the current in dl. Attach proper units to each
factor and designate on the diagram all quantities involved.

(b) State the direction of $d\mathbf{B}$ in words.

(c) Set up an integral for the magnitude of $\mathbf{B}$ at the point P due
only to the current in OR. Express the integral in a single variable
and carry out the integration.

(d) Using the result of (c), write an expression for the magnitude
of the field at P due to the current in both OR and RQ.

7.3   Two infinitely long, straight wires,
each carrying a current of 10 amp,
lie in the x,y plane. Each wire
makes an angle $\phi = 30°$ with the
y-axis, and the direction of the
current in each wire is shown in
the diagram. Find the magnitude
of the magnetic induction at point
$x = 1$ m, $y = 0$, $z = 0$. The magnetic induction outside a long
straight wire, at a distance r m
from the axis of the wire, is given
by $\mu_0 i/2\pi r$, where i is the current
and $\mu_0 = 4\pi \times 10^{-7}$ mks units.

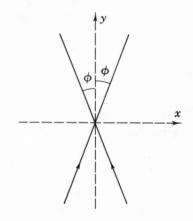

7.4   Consider two time-varying magnetic fields described by

$$B_x = B \sin \omega t$$
and
$$B_y = B \cos \omega t$$

where B and ω are constants and where B_x and B_y denote respectively the x and y components of the induction at the origin of the
coordinates. Describe the resultant field (magnitude and direction)
as a function of the time.

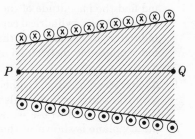

7.5 The diagram shows a cross-sectional view of a large number (N) of long, thin, straight wires which are spaced closely in the x,y plane, forming a single layer w m in width. Each wire is parallel to the y-axis and carries a current of I amp out of the x,z plane (i.e., the plane of the paper).

    (a) Starting with the expression

$$B = \frac{\mu_0 i}{2\pi r}$$

which represents the value of the magnetic induction due to an infinitely long, slender wire, write an expression for the magnitude of $d\mathbf{B}$, the contribution to the magnetic induction at P due to the current in an element of width dx located at x m from the origin at O. The point P is located on the z-axis at a distance of a m from the x,y plane and is equidistant from the edges of the layer.

    (b) Calculate the magnitude of $\mathbf{B}$ due to the current in the entire layer of width w.

7.6 The magnetic induction at an axial point x m from the plane of a circular turn of radius a m has the magnitude

$$B = \frac{\mu_0 i a^2}{2(a^2 + x^2)^{3/2}}$$

where i is the current and $\mu_0 = 4\pi \times 10^{-7}$ mks units.

    Starting with the above expression, compute the magnetic induction at the point P in the figure, which gives a cross-sectional view of N circular turns spaced closely on the surface of a cone of axis PQ. The radius of the largest turn is $2c$ m; that of the smallest turn is c m, and $PQ = c \sqrt{3}$ m.

7.7 The steady current in a long conducting cylinder is I amp. The current is distributed uniformly over the cross section shown in the diagram at the top of page 176.

The magnetic induction **B**, at a point P, r m from the axis at O, lies in the plane of the diagram and is perpendicular to the radial distance r. The magnitude of **B** is represented by

$$B = Cr^n \quad \text{weber/m}^2$$

where C is a constant and n the exponent of r.

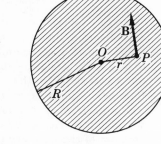

(a) Apply the circuital law

$$\oint \mathbf{B} \cdot d\mathbf{l} = \mu_0 \sum i$$

and determine the values of C and n for the case shown in the diagram, where the point P is inside the conductor ($r < R$).

(b) Repeat the calculations to determine the values of C and n for the case where P is outside the conductor ($r > R$).

(c) What is the direction of the current density for the specified direction of **B**?

7.8   Apply the circuital law

$$\oint \mathbf{B} \cdot d\mathbf{l} = \mu_0 \sum i$$

and find the magnitude of the magnetic induction at a point *inside* a long, straight, cylindrical copper conductor of circular cross section and radius R. Assume that the current I in the conductor is steady and is uniformly distributed over the cross section.

7.9   A long, straight wire is coincident with the z-axis, which is also the axis of the toroid whose section in the x,y plane is shown in the diagram by the shaded area. The current in the wire is equal to 5 amp and is along the positive z-axis—that is, outward from the plane of the diagram. The toroid is uniformly wound with 500 turns and the current in the winding is 10 ma. (See diagram for directions.) The medium surrounding the conductors and in the interior of the toroid is air.

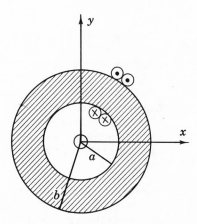

(a) Determine the magnitude of the magnetic induction **B** at three points on the *x*-axis specified by $x = 5$ cm, $x = 10$ cm, and $x = 15$ cm. Inner radius of toroid $a = 9$ cm; outer radius $b = 12$ cm; $\mu_0 = 4\pi \times 10^{-7}$ h/m.

(b) Draw a graph showing how *B* varies with distance along the *x*-axis. Your graph should include the interval $x = 5$ to $x = 15$ cm.

7.10 *N* long, thin, straight wires are placed closely and uniformly over the entire surface of a cylinder. Each wire is parallel to the axis of the cylinder and carries the current I_1 amp in the same direction (into the plane of the diagram). A single long wire carrying a current of I_0 amp (out of the plane) coincides with the axis of the cylinder.

Apply the circuital law

$$\oint B \cos \theta \, dl = \mu_0 i$$

and calculate the value of the magnetic induction at any point *P,* in the air, at a distance of *r* m from the axis. Consider two cases: (1) $r < a$ (in the space within the cylinder); (2) $r > a$ (in the space outside the cylinder).

Under what condition will the magnetic induction vanish at points outside the cylinder?

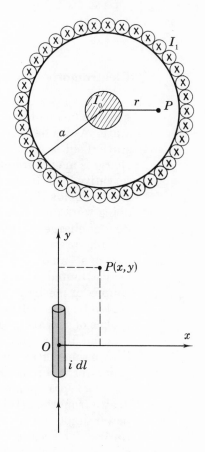

7.11 A current-element *i dl* is located at the origin, the current being directed along the positive *y*-axis. What is the magnitude of *d***B**, the contribution to the magnetic induction at any point *P* in the first quadrant of the *x,y* plane? Express your answer in terms of *x* and *y* (the coordinates of *P*), the current-element, and appropriate constants. Specify the direction and units of *d***B**.

Chapter 8.
Induced Electromotive Forces

8.1   Electromotive Force

Electric fields may be divided into two classes—static and non-static. As we have seen, the distinguishing characteristic of the static field is that no net work is done on a charge when the charge is moved around a closed path—i.e., the static field is a conservative field. In the present chapter we shall be concerned with electric fields that are nonconservative and that are capable of doing work on a charge in motion through a circuit. Indeed, if a flow of charge is to be set up and maintained, nonstatic forces *must* be present. Forces of this kind may be localized, as in the case of a Van de Graaff generator or a chemical cell, or they may be distributed over portions of a circuit, as in the case of thermo-couples or mechanical generators. In such devices, energy is converted from nonelectrical to electrical form, and the devices are spoken of as seats of electromotive force (abbreviated as emf).

As an illustration, let us consider the Van de Graaff generator shown schematically in Fig. 8.1. In our earlier discussion of this generator (Section 6.8), electrons were sprayed onto the belt at the lower spray points. In the present instance, electrons are withdrawn from the belt by reversing the polarity of the low-voltage power supply. This is equivalent to introducing positive charge on the belt. The positive charge sprayed on the belt is carried toward the spherical electrode, where it is removed. Owing to the accumulation of a charge on the sphere, a test charge q placed on the belt will be in a static field $\mathbf{E}_s$ and will experience an electrostatic force $q\mathbf{E}_s$. Moreover, the test charge will be transported to the

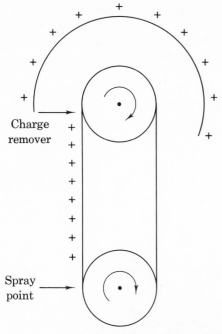

Charge
remover

Spray
point

Figure 8.1   A mechanical generator.

top, by virtue of the mechanical force exerted on it by the belt. We may measure the mechanical force in terms of an equivalent nonstatic field $\mathbf{E}_m$. This force $q\mathbf{E}_m$ is present on the belt and increases the potential energy of a positive test charge q by doing work on it against the static force $q\mathbf{E}_s$. The belt is a "seat of emf" within which the total field is $(\mathbf{E}_s + \mathbf{E}_m)$, only part of which is conservative. Furthermore, there is a conversion of mechanical energy into electrical energy, and the emf of the generator may be evaluated in terms of the net power delivered to the belt.

Next let us consider a simplified version of a chemical cell. Generally, when a metal electrode is immersed in an appropriate electrolyte, a potential difference is developed between the two, because of a tendency for charged atoms to enter the electrolyte. The forces responsible for this process are essentially nonelectrical, and we shall refer to them loosely as chemical forces. When the positive-ion concentration reaches a certain value, the rate at which ions enter the solution is equal to the rate at which they return to the electrode. In this state there is a layer of positive charge separated from the negatively charged electrode by a distance which is of the order of atomic dimensions. Between the charged layers there is an electrostatic field directed toward the electrode and an equivalent field or chemical force per unit charge

directed away from the electrode. If a second electrode of a dissimilar material is immersed in the electrolyte, a potential difference will also be set up between it and the electrolyte. The
magnitude of this voltage will be different from the magnitude
of the first.

As shown schematically in Fig. 8.2, charges will appear on the
electrodes, and, as a result, there will be a static field outside the
cell between the terminals of the cell. Within the cell we shall

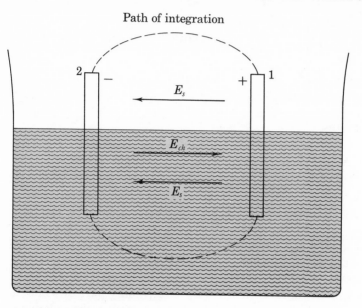

Figure 8.2   Chemical seat of emf.

represent the total field as the sum of $\mathbf{E}_s + \mathbf{E}_{ch}$, where $\mathbf{E}_s$ is the
electrostatic field and $\mathbf{E}_{ch}$ the equivalent chemical force per unit
charge. (Actually, the chemical forces are highly localized in the
vicinity of the electrode surfaces, and this representation is to
be regarded as a working model.) With zero current through the
cell, $\mathbf{E}_s + \mathbf{E}_{ch} = 0$. However, when the terminals are connected
through an external resistance, there will be a flow of charge from
terminal 1 to terminal 2, and the total field in the electrolyte will
no longer be zero. Instead, it will be such as to cause the migration
of positive ions from 2 to 1 and of negative ions from 1 to 2. This is
equivalent to an electric current within the cell from the electrode
at low potential to the electrode at higher potential—that is, work
is done on the charge by chemical forces against opposing electrostatic forces.

Analytically, electromotive force is defined as the work done per unit charge by the total electric field as one traces a closed path. In symbols, the emf $\mathcal{E}$ is given by the line integral

$$\mathcal{E} = \oint \mathbf{E} \cdot d\mathbf{l} \tag{8.1}$$

where $\mathbf{E}$ represents the total electric field at any point in the closed path of integration. The name for $\mathcal{E}$ (electromotive force) is an unfortunate misnomer, since $\mathcal{E}$ is not a force but energy per unit charge. It is measured in volts if the field is expressed in newton per coulomb and if distances are expressed in meters.

Returning to the example of the chemical cell, let the path of integration begin at a point on terminal 1, proceed to a point on terminal 2 outside the cell, then enter the electrolyte and return to the starting point. (Refer again to Fig. 8.2.) If we apply the defining relation (8.1) to this path, we obtain

$$\mathcal{E} = \underset{\substack{\text{outside} \\ 1 \to 2}}{\int} \mathbf{E}_s \cdot d\mathbf{l} + \underset{\substack{\text{inside} \\ 2 \to 1}}{\int} (\mathbf{E}_s + \mathbf{E}_{ch}) \cdot d\mathbf{l} \tag{8.2}$$

$$= \oint \mathbf{E}_s \cdot d\mathbf{l} + \underset{\substack{\text{inside} \\ 2 \to 1}}{\int} \mathbf{E}_{ch} \cdot d\mathbf{l}$$

But $\mathbf{E}_s$ is a conservative field, and its line integral over any closed path vanishes. Hence

$$\mathcal{E} = \underset{\substack{\text{inside} \\ 2 \to 1}}{\int} \mathbf{E}_{ch} \cdot d\mathbf{l} \tag{8.3}$$

The conclusion is that no static charge distribution can give rise to an emf; in this instance the emf arises from chemical forces.

We have seen that a charge may experience nonstatic forces of the chemical and mechanical variety. There are other nonstatic forces which may do work on charges. In thermocouples or in seats of thermal emf, such forces have their origin in quantum mechanical considerations of transport of charge. (The magnetic force may act as a constraint, but it does no work on a charge, since it acts at right angles to the velocity of the charge.) There are forces which arise from electric fields associated with changing magnetic fields—a topic that will be taken up in Section 8.3. We may lump all forces into a single quantity F_{ns} and state that emf represents work per unit charge supplied by F_{ns}.

If a charge q does not gain kinetic energy, the element of work done by F_{ns} in displacing q the distance dl must be equal to the increase in the potential energy of q and to the dissipative loss. As we discovered in our discussion of the flow of charge through conductors (see Section 5.3), dissipative forces arise in collision processes and produce heating of the conductor. For simplicity, we assume that all forces are parallel to the displacement. Then

$$F_{ns}\, dl = -F_{es}\, dl + F_{dis}\, dl \qquad (8.4)$$

where F_{es} and F_{dis} denote the electrostatic and dissipative forces respectively. After dividing through by q, we can write (8.4) as

$$d\mathcal{E} = dV + dH \qquad (8.5)$$

where $d\mathcal{E}$ represents the contribution to the emf, dV the increase in the potential, and dH the dissipative loss per unit charge. Let a charge be taken from point 2 to point 1 over a certain path—for example, through the cell in Fig. 8.2. This corresponds to the case where the cell furnishes current. Integrating (8.5) and rearranging, we have

$$(V_1 - V_2) = \mathcal{E} - \int_1^2 dH \qquad (8.6)$$

Now let the charge be transported in the opposite direction. We note that F_{ns} and F_{es} do not depend on the direction of motion of charge. However, F_{dis} is always opposite to the direction of displacement of charge. If we proceed from 1 to 2 the sign of the integral in (8.6), which represents the irreversible joulean heat loss, would not change, but the signs of the other two terms would be reversed—that is,

$$-(V_1 - V_2) = -\mathcal{E} - \int_1^2 dH \qquad (8.7)$$

or
$$(V_1 - V_2) = +\mathcal{E} + \int_1^2 dH \qquad (8.8)$$

This is the case where the cell is being charged by an external agent. This analysis illustrates the *reversible* nature of an emf. In the case described by (8.6), work is done by nonstatic forces at the expense of energy stored in the seat of emf. The source of energy may be chemical, as in the example of the cell, or it may be mechanical, as in the case of a generator. In the situation represented by (8.8), work is done against the nonstatic forces within the cell by external agents, and chemical energy is returned to the cell. Similarly, under appropriate circumstances an external potential difference applied to the terminals of a dynamo converts the dynamo into a motor which provides mechanical energy.

Equations (8.6) and (8.8) are recognizable as the circuit relations which represent, respectively, the terminal potential difference of a cell while the cell is being discharged, and the terminal potential difference while the cell is being charged. If the flow of charge ceases, the dissipation integral is zero, and from either relation

$$\mathcal{E} = V_1 - V_2 \tag{8.9}$$

In other words, the emf may be measured by the terminal potential difference under conditions of zero current through the cell.

8.2 Motional emf

The magnetic force $\mathbf{f} = q\mathbf{v} \times \mathbf{B}$ can give rise to an effective field $\mathbf{E} = \mathbf{f}/q = \mathbf{v} \times \mathbf{B}$ when a conductor is set into motion in a region where there exists a field of $\mathbf{B}$. Consider a conducting rod AC which moves with a constant velocity $\mathbf{v}$ at right angles to a uniform magnetic field $\mathbf{B}$, as shown in Fig. (8.3). It is seen that

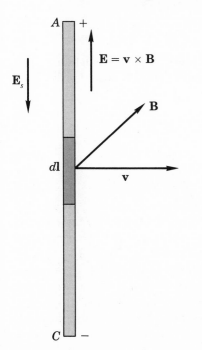

Figure 8.3 Motional emf. $\mathbf{v}$, $\mathbf{B}$, and $d\mathbf{l}$ mutually perpendicular.

a positive charge q in the conductor will experience a force $\mathbf{f} = q\mathbf{v} \times \mathbf{B}$ at right angles to the plane determined by $\mathbf{v}$ and $\mathbf{B}$. As long as the motion continues, the end A will be positively charged and the end C will be negatively charged. This separation of charge creates an electrostatic field $\mathbf{E}_s$ directed from A to C. In equilibrium, $\mathbf{E} + \mathbf{E}_s = 0$ and no charge flows.

An expression for the emf induced in the rod is formulated in the following way. For the special case where $\mathbf{v}$ is perpendicular to $\mathbf{B}$ and the induced field $\mathbf{E}$ is parallel to the displacement $d\mathbf{l}$, the emf induced in the element $d\mathbf{l}$ is

$$d\mathcal{E} = E\, dl = vB\, dl \tag{8.10}$$

The emf $\mathcal{E}$ in the rod of length L is obtained by integrating (8.10), with the result

$$\mathcal{E} = vB \int_0^L dl = vBL \tag{8.11}$$

where $\mathcal{E}$ is the emf induced in the length L when the conductor has a translational motion with constant speed $\mathbf{v}$ in a uniform $\mathbf{B}$-field which is fixed relative to the observer.

In the more general case, shown in Fig. 8.4, where the induced field $\mathbf{E}$ makes an angle θ with $d\mathbf{l}$, and where $\mathbf{B}$ is at angle ϕ with

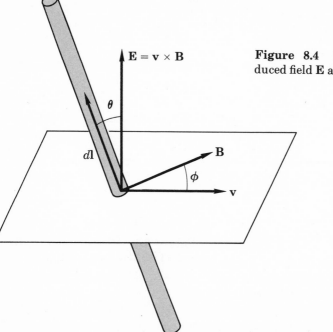

Figure 8.4   Motional emf. Induced field $\mathbf{E}$ at angle θ with $d\mathbf{l}$.

the velocity $\mathbf{v}$ of $d\mathbf{l}$, $d\mathcal{E}$ is equal to $\mathbf{E} \cdot d\mathbf{l}$, and $\mathbf{E}$ itself is $\mathbf{v} \times \mathbf{B}$. Thus

$$d\mathcal{E} = \mathbf{E} \cdot d\mathbf{l} = (\mathbf{v} \times \mathbf{B}) \cdot d\mathbf{l} \qquad (8.12)$$

The magnitude of the scalar quantity $d\mathcal{E}$, the emf induced in dl, becomes

$$d\mathcal{E} = E \cos\theta \, dl = (vB \sin\phi)\cos\theta \, dl \qquad (8.13)$$

There is no need to commit the content of (8.12) to memory. It is more important to follow the reasoning involved in setting up this relation; that is, for the work done per unit charge along dl we must use the component of $\mathbf{E}$ along $d\mathbf{l}$ and note that the magnitude of $\mathbf{E}$ depends on $\sin\phi$, the angle between $\mathbf{v}$ and $\mathbf{B}$. In formulas (8.10) and (8.12), the velocity of the conductor, or the velocity of the free charge in it, must be small relative to the speed of light. A complete description of forces induced by the relative motion of charges requires relativistic treatment. In practice, the speeds involved are low enough so that (8.12) gives correct results. When a conductor is moved in a magnetic field, the free electrons in the conductor acquire spiral motions under the action of the field. In the case of a filamentary conductor the free charges move mainly along its length, since they are constrained by the boundaries of the conductor.

Figure 8.5 represents a simple generator consisting of a conducting rod AC which slides without friction along parallel

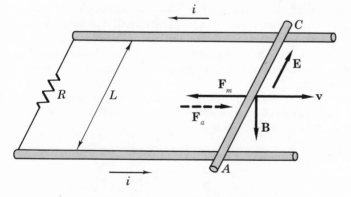

Figure 8.5   Emf produced by a sliding rod.

metal rails. There is a uniform magnetic induction $\mathbf{B}$ perpendicular to the plane of the rails. The circuit is completed by a resistance R. The induced field $\mathbf{E}$ is directed from A to C, so that positive charge flows out at end C. According to (8.11), the emf induced in AC is vBL, where L is the length of AC. Because of

THE GREAT EXPERIMENTER

While serving as a bookbinder's apprentice in a little village near London, Michael Faraday (1791–1867) became fascinated by books about science. At the age of fourteen he displayed the innate curiosity of a real experimenter and used his meager funds to buy materials with which to perform simple experiments. Today some people doubt the value to students of laboratory exercises and demonstration lectures. Faraday, the great experimenter, once commented in later life, "I was never able to make a fact my own without seeing it."

On one occasion, Faraday, who had no formal education, attended some lectures on chemistry given by Davy, the discoverer of laughing gas, sodium, and potassium. Afterward, Faraday submitted to Davy—then the director of the Royal Institute—a set of neatly written lecture notes and asked for a job as an assistant in the Institute. As a result he became a lecture attendant and his association with the Institute continued for many years. In 1825 he was appointed director of the Laboratory.

Faraday's many experimental researches led to such discoveries as the principle of the dynamo (see Problem 6.8), the laws of electrolysis, and the rotation of the plane of polarization (in optics) by a magnetic field. But it was his discovery of the law of induction (Section 8.3) which stands as a towering achievement in the annals of electromagnetism.

What were the circumstances that led to this discovery? Faraday knew that an electric current produced a magnetic field. He believed that—as a converse effect—magnetism could produce an electric current. For many years he searched for this effect with a variety of experimental arrangements. Since he was looking for a sustained effect, these efforts failed.

But Faraday was persistent. After a delay of six years he suddenly made the unexpected observation that currents were indeed induced in a circuit *but only when* the current in a neighboring circuit was interrupted. And the induced current was momentary rather than sustained. He also observed that transient currents were induced in a coil when the coil was set into motion relative to a permanent magnet, or when a magnet was inserted into a coil.

Faraday made all these observations in just a few days. In such a short time this self-taught, keen investigator succeeded in establishing one of the four fundamental laws of electrodynamics. [See (14.17) and (15.16).]

the induced current i, AC experiences a magnetic force $F_m = BiL$. This is a side thrust directed opposite to v. A force F_a equal and opposite to F_m must be applied to AC to keep it in motion. Assuming that R represents the resistance of the entire circuit, the induced current i has the magnitude

$$i = \frac{\mathcal{E}}{R} = \frac{vBL}{R}$$

(8.14)

The applied force is numerically equal to

$$F_a = BiL = \frac{vB^2L^2}{R}$$

(8.15)

The mechanical work done per unit time by this force is

$$F_a v = \frac{v^2 B^2 L^2}{R} = i^2 R$$

(8.16)

and we see that the power furnished by the seat of emf is just equal to the rate of heat production in the circuit. The retarding force F_m which results from the motion of the conductor in the field is an example of an electromagnetic reaction.

8.3   **The Faraday Law of Induction**

As we have seen, the motional emf has its origin in the Lorentz force. We shall now describe the circumstances under which a nonconservative electric field is created in a region of space because of changes in the flux of the magnetic induction **B**. The flux of **B** may be produced by conduction currents or by permanently magnetized matter. Faraday discovered emfs induced by varying magnetic fields in 1831, and Henry made the same discovery independently and almost concurrently. The law of induction was established experimentally and is formulated in terms of the flux crossing a surface.

We begin with the case of a rigid closed conducting loop which is at rest in the reference frame of the observer. If the field of **B** at points within the area bounded by the loop changes in time, then a current appears in the loop. The current is attributed to an induced emf and persists as long as **B** continues to change. Faraday's law states that the emf induced in a fixed circuit by changing the flux of induction **B** crossing the area bounded by the circuit is equal to the negative time rate of change of the flux.

Denoting the emf by $\mathcal{E}$, we can state the law of induction in symbols:

$$\mathcal{E} = -\frac{d\Phi}{dt} \tag{8.17}$$

From the definition of emf given in (8.1), $\mathcal{E} = \oint \mathbf{E} \cdot d\mathbf{l}$, where, as before, the symbol $\bigcirc$ indicates that the integration is to be performed over a closed path. Furthermore, the magnetic flux crossing a surface is $\Phi = \int \mathbf{B} \cdot d\mathbf{A}$. Then the law of induction appearing in (8.17) may be rewritten as

$$\oint \mathbf{E} \cdot d\mathbf{l} = -\frac{d}{dt}\int_S \mathbf{B} \cdot d\mathbf{A} \tag{8.18}$$

where now the flux is calculated through the surface whose boundary is the path of integration to be followed in evaluating the line integral. The flux crossing such a surface is said to "link" the circuit or the closed path of integration which forms the boundary of the area. (See Fig. 8.6 for a schematic representation.)

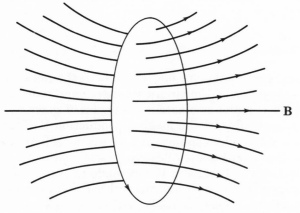

Figure 8.6 Flux of **B** linking with a closed path.

The negative sign in (8.17) indicates the sense of the induced electric field and hence the sense of circulation of positive charge or induced current. The sign of the emf is given by the line integral in (8.18). Hence we need to adopt a rule which relates the positive sense of tracing the periphery of the area with the positive normal to the open area. The convention is specified in terms of the right-hand screw rule—that is, the sense of the rotation which makes the screw advance along the outward normal is taken as the positive sense of describing the periphery. Thus in Fig. 8.6 the arrow on the closed path denotes the posi-

tive sense of circulation if the outward component of **B** is associated with the positive normal to the enclosed surface.

Consquently the induced emf is positive if the flux of **B** decreases—that is, if $d\Phi/dt$ is negative. The emf is negative if the
flux increases—that is, if $d\Phi/dt$ is positive. The two cases are illustrated in Fig. 8.7 for the same direction of **B**.

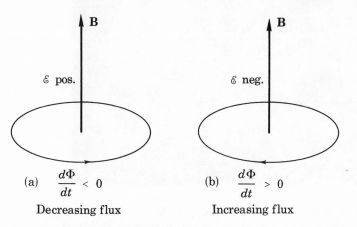

$$\text{(a)} \quad \frac{d\Phi}{dt} < 0 \qquad\qquad \text{(b)} \quad \frac{d\Phi}{dt} > 0$$

Decreasing flux   Increasing flux

Figure 8.7   The sign of induced emf.

The rule governing the sense of the induced emf (and also the
sense of the induced current) is a consequence of the law of conservation of energy. It is known as Lenz's law and can be stated
as follows: The sense of an induced emf (or current) is such as
to oppose the cause that gives rise to it. Thus in Fig. 8.7(a),
where the flux is decreasing, the induced current is so directed
that its own magnetic field opposes the change in the flux that
produces the current. Note that by Ampère's rule a current having the sense indicated by the arrow in the loop of Fig. 8.7(a) is
such as to increase the flux through the surface. In like manner,
the induced current in the loop shown in Fig. 8.7(b) is so directed that its own **B**-field opposes the change—in this instance,
the increase in flux. If the current is induced by the motion of a
conductor in a **B**-field, the direction of the current is such that
the magnetic force (side thrust) on the current opposes the motion of the conductor. If the magnetic field or the side thrust
due to the induced current did not oppose the cause that gives
rise to the current, then the current would increase indefinitely
without the expenditure of energy on the part of the external
agent.

The change in the flux linking a circuit or a closed path fixed

The 300 Mev Betatron at the University of Illinois. In front center is the original 2.3 Mev Betatron which is now located in the Smithsonian Institution. (See pages 191 and 197.) (Courtesy University of Illinois.)

in the laboratory may be brought about in a variety of ways. In Fig. 8.8, for example, the flux change arises from the time variation of the current in a neighboring circuit which is also fixed relative to the laboratory frame of reference. Or the flux-producing source (a current-bearing circuit or permanently magne-

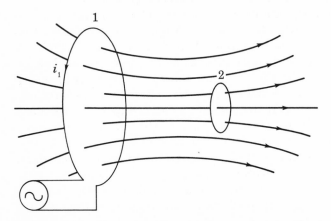

Figure 8.8 Circuits 1 and 2 are stationary. If i_1 varies with time, an emf is induced in circuit 2.

tized matter) may be moved relative to the fixed circuit. Experiments indicate that (8.17) is valid in all these cases.

We have made a distinction between motional emfs and emfs induced in a stationary circuit by a changing flux. If the relation in (8.12) is applied to a rigid circuit, or to part of a rigid circuit in motion in a **B**-field which is stationary (not dependent on the time), the result is equal to the emf calculated from Faraday's law as given in (8.17). However, if the circuit or a portion of it is in motion in a time-dependent field of **B**, we can calculate the emf by taking into account (1) the rate of change of flux due to the time variation of **B**, and (2) the rate of change of flux which arises from the motion of the circuit relative to the field. In the special case where **B** depends only on the time but not on position within the area, the flux at any instant is given by

$$\Phi(t) = A(t)B(t) \tag{8.19}$$

where $A(t)$ represents functionally how the area of the circuit is changing in time. In this example, the emf is obtained from the total derivative—that is,

$$\mathcal{E} = -\frac{d\Phi}{dt} = -\left(B\frac{\partial A}{\partial t} + A\frac{\partial B}{\partial t}\right) \tag{8.20}$$

Faraday's law represents a remarkable property of space—namely, that a nonconservative field of **E** accompanies a field of **B** which changes in time. The form of the law as given in (8.18) may be applied to a path in any region of space, whether or not the path coincides with a conducting circuit. Indeed, in one type of accelerator (the Betatron), electrons located in an evacuated region are accelerated by the electric field produced by a changing magnetic field. The magnetic field also constrains the electrons to move in a circular orbit which actually corresponds to the closed path that we have been referring to. We shall use this aspect of the law, which is one of the fundamental generalizations of electromagnetism, subsequently in our study of electromagnetic waves.

8.4 Illustrative Examples

Example 1. A rigid, slender rod OP of length R rotates in the x,y plane about the z-axis, which passes through one end of the rod. A uniform magnetic induction **B** is present over the area swept out by the rod. The induction is directed along the $+z$-axis. What is the induced emf in the rod if it rotates in the counterclockwise sense with an angular velocity ω? What is the sign of the charge appearing on the free end P?

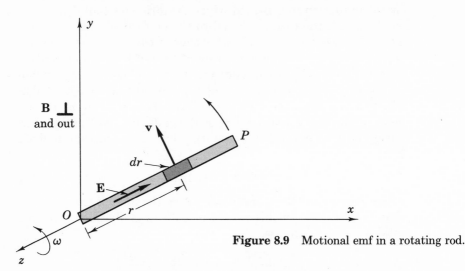

Figure 8.9   Motional emf in a rotating rod.

The emf induced in the element of length dr is given by (8.10), since for all angular positions of OP the induced electric field is directed radially. Consult Fig. 8.9. Upon substituting the tangential velocity $v = \omega r$ into (8.10), we obtain

$$d\mathcal{E} = \omega B r \, dr$$

Hence upon integration over the length of the rod

$$\mathcal{E} = \omega B \int_0^R r \, dr = \frac{\omega B R^2}{2} \tag{8.21}$$

To get a feeling for the magnitude of $\mathcal{E}$ we substitute the following reasonable values for the quantities involved: $B = 0.10$ weber/m², $R = 0.10$ m, $\omega = 377$ radian/sec (60 rps). Then $\mathcal{E} = 1.88 \times 10^{-3}$ v, or 188 mv.

The induced field $\mathbf{E}$ is given by $\mathbf{v} \times \mathbf{B}$. Hence $\mathbf{E}$ is directed from O to P and the end P is positively charged.

Example 2. Consider the fixed circular loop of Fig. 8.10. Calculate the induced emf in the loop if there is a uniform time-varying field of $\mathbf{B}$ directed at an angle θ with the normal to the plane of the loop. Assume that the time dependence of $\mathbf{B}$ is given by $B_0 \sin \omega t$, where B_0 and ω are constants.

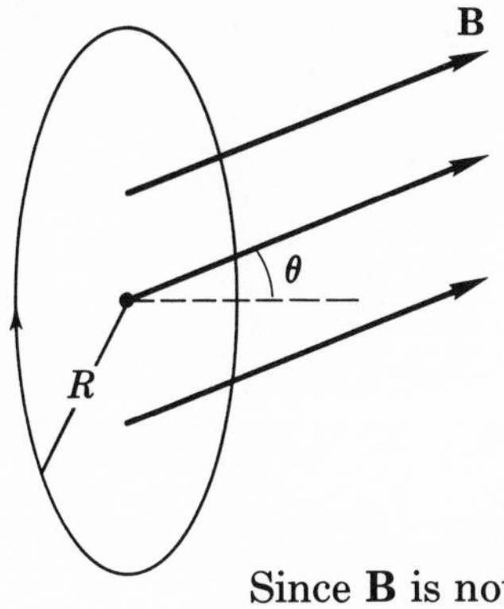

B

Figure 8.10   Emf induced in a fixed circular loop.

Since **B** is not a function of position within the area, the flux Φ which links the loop at any time t is the area of the loop times the normal component of B. This gives $\Phi = \pi R^2 B \cos \theta$. Then, from (8.17),

$$\mathcal{E} = -\frac{d}{dt}(\pi R^2 B_0 \cos \theta \sin \omega t) = -\mathcal{E}_0 \cos \omega t \qquad (8.22)$$

where $\qquad\qquad\qquad \mathcal{E}_0 \equiv \pi R^2 B_0 \omega \cos \theta$

represents the maximum value of $\mathcal{E}$. Plot the sinusoidal time dependence of the flux and observe that in the region $-\pi/2 \le \omega t \le \pi/2$, $d\Phi/dt > 0$. So $\mathcal{E}$ is negative. The sense of $\mathcal{E}$ shown in Fig. 8.10 applies to this case.

Example 3. Repeat the calculations in the preceding example but this time let **B** be nonuniform and time-dependent, as given by

$$B = \left(1 - \frac{r}{R}\right)B_0 \sin \omega t$$

The element of flux $d\Phi$ crossing a ring-shaped element of radius r and thickness dr is $B \cos \theta \, (2\pi r \, dr)$. To calculate Φ we need to integrate from $r = 0$ to $r = R$. The result is $\Phi = \Phi_0 \sin \omega t$, where $\Phi_0 = (\pi/3)R^2 B_0 \cos \theta$. The emf is then computed as before.

Example 4. In Fig. 8.11, assume that the magnetic induction **B** is uniform at all points within the circle of radius a and is directed normally inward to the plane of the circle. Assume also that the magnitude of **B** is described by $B = B_0 \sin \omega t$. Furthermore, let $B = 0$ at all points outside the circle. Determine the magnitude of the induced field **E** at any point whose distance from the center is r. Consider two cases: (1) $r < a$. (2) $r > a$.

Because of symmetry, lines of **E** are circular, with the center

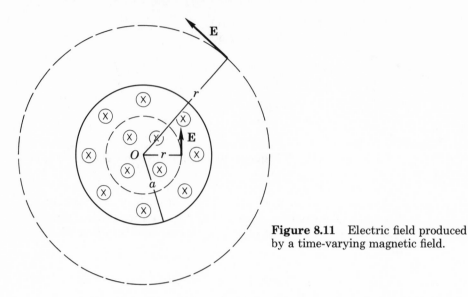

Figure 8.11 Electric field produced by a time-varying magnetic field.

at O. In terms of the tangential electric field $\mathbf{E}$, which has the same value at all points of a circle of radius r, the emf is given by $\mathcal{E} = \oint \mathbf{E} \cdot d\mathbf{l} = E \cdot 2\pi r$. If $r < a$, the flux linking the path of integration is $\Phi = \pi r^2 \cdot B_0 \sin \omega t$. If $r > a$, $\Phi = \pi a^2 B_0 \sin \omega t$. From (8.17)

$$2\pi r E = -\pi r^2 \omega B_0 \cos \omega t$$

For $r < a$,
$$E = -\frac{\omega B_0 r}{2} \cos \omega t \tag{8.23}$$

Similarly, for $r > a$,
$$E = -\frac{\omega B_0 a^2}{2r} \cos \omega t \tag{8.24}$$

Thus, the magnitude of the tangential field increases directly with the distance from the center for points inside. Outside the circle, E decays inversely as the distance. The functional dependence of E on position resembles that of B produced by a steady current in a long cylindrical conductor.

Example 5. Consider a rigid rectangular conducting loop $OPQR$ rotating with constant angular velocity ω about the side OP which lies along the y-axis. There is a uniform and stationary induction $\mathbf{B}$ which is parallel to the z-axis. (See Fig 8.12.) At any point such as Q, the vector linear velocity $\mathbf{v}$ is equal to $\omega \times \mathbf{r}$, where ω is the vector angular velocity and $\mathbf{r}$ is the distance from the axis to Q. The only contribution to the motional emf comes from the side QR, since $\mathbf{E} = \mathbf{v} \times \mathbf{B}$ has only a y component directed from Q to R. (On OP, $\mathbf{v} = 0$, and on PQ

and RO, $\mathbf{v} \times \mathbf{B} \cdot d\mathbf{l} = 0$, where $d\mathbf{l}$ is a displacement along PQ or OR.) From (8.12) the emf developed in $d\mathbf{l}$ is

$$d\mathcal{E} = \mathbf{v} \times \mathbf{B} \cdot d\mathbf{l} = vB \sin (\omega t)\, dl \qquad (8.25)$$

since the electric field $\mathbf{E}$ is along $d\mathbf{l}$. When we replace v by ωr and integrate over QR, whose length is denoted by L, we obtain

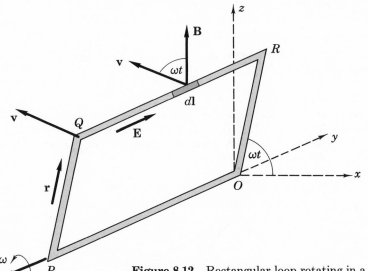

Figure 8.12 Rectangular loop rotating in a stationary field.

for the emf induced in the loop at the particular instant t, when the normal to the loop makes an angle ωt with $\mathbf{B}$,

$$\mathcal{E} = \omega r B \sin (\omega t) \int_0^L dl = \mathcal{E}_0 \, sin \, \omega t \qquad (8.26)$$

where $$\mathcal{E}_0 \equiv BLr\omega \qquad (8.27)$$

Thus the emf is maximum when $\mathbf{v} \perp \mathbf{B}$. The same result can be obtained by determining the flux through the loop. For the angular position shown, $\Phi = B_n A = (B \cos \omega t)Lr$, where A is the area of the loop. The magnitude of $\mathcal{E}$ is then computed from $d\Phi/dt$.

Example 6. In Fig. 8.13, $OPQR$ represents a rectangle three sides of which form a rigid metal frame. The fourth side is a metal rod which slides with constant velocity $\mathbf{v}$ in the $+x$ direction. Within all points of the frame there exists a uniform but time-dependent magnetic field $\mathbf{B}$ in the $+z$ direction. The magnitude of $\mathbf{B}$ is described by $B(t) = B_0 e^{-at}$, where B_0 and a

In the accompanying diagram, the slender conducting rod AC, pivoted at A, rotates in the counterclockwise sense with uniform angular velocity ω. DEF represents a copper plate whose edge DE is cut in the form of an arc of a circle whose center is at A and whose radius is AC. During rotation the rod AC makes contact at all points of the arc DE. The remaining sides of the rigid rectangle $FGHA$ complete the circuit. The entire arrangement is immersed in a **B**-field which is constant in magnitude. **B** is normal to the plane of the diagram and is directed toward the reader. What is the emf induced in the circuit as the contact point C moves from D to E?

"Solution" 1:

By Example 1, Section 8.4, we know that the motional emf induced in AC is $\omega BR^2/2$, where R is the length of AC.

"Solution" 2:

As the contact point C moves along DE, assume that positive charge flows along CF through the body of the conductor. If $AC = AD = DF = R$, the area of the triangle ACF is $R^2 \sin\theta$, and Φ, the flux linking with this area, is $BR^2 \sin\theta$. From Faraday's law, the magnitude of the emf should be given by

$$d\Phi/dt = BR^2 \cos\theta (d\theta/dt) \qquad \text{or} \qquad \omega BR^2 \cos\theta$$

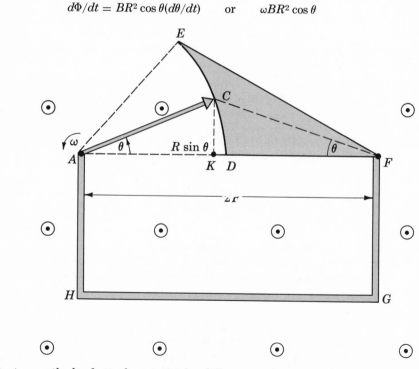

The two methods of attack seem to give different answers. And yet we have confidence in the physical laws underlying both suggested solutions. Where did we go wrong? How can we resolve the paradox?

are constants and t is the time. Calculate the emf induced in the rectangle as a function of the time.

Let the coordinate $x = vt$ determine the position of the rod at any time t. Since **B** is independent of position within the area

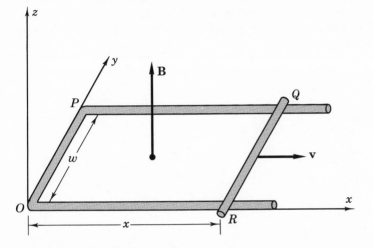

Figure 8.13 Emf induced in a rectangular loop when a portion of the circuit is in motion.

of the rectangle, the flux at any time is given by $A(t) B(t)$, where $A = wvt$ is the area of the rectangle. Applying (8.20), we obtain

$$\varepsilon = -\frac{d\Phi}{dt} = -\left[B(t)wv + wvt\frac{\partial B}{\partial t} \right] = -wvB(1 - at) \quad (8.28)$$

8.5   The Betatron

The Betatron, a device that accelerates electrons to high energies, is an elegant application of Faraday's law. In Fig. 8.14, which gives a schematic representation of the vacuum chamber of a Betatron, electrons are injected at A into the evacuated region within a toroid. They are constrained to move in a circular path by the application of a magnetic field normal to the plane of the diagram. The magnetic field is time-dependent and is produced by an alternating current in the windings of an electromagnet whose pole pieces lie above and below the evacuated toroidal chamber. (In the jargon of the laboratory, this chamber is called the "doughnut.") The electrons are essentially at rest when the magnetic field is zero. As the **B**-field increases in magnitude with the time, the changing magnetic flux linking with the path of the electron gives rise to an electric field **E** which is tangential to the electron orbit. Because of the symmetry, the lines of **E** are circular, with their common center on the axis of the electromagnet, which passes through O. (See Example 4, Section 8.4.)

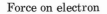
Force on electron

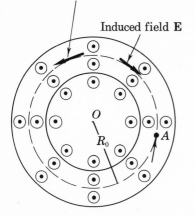
Induced field **E**

Figure 8.14 The vacuum chamber of a Betatron. The induction **B** is directed out of the plane and $\partial B/\partial t$ is positive.

At some instant of time let the induction **B** be directed out of the plane and let $\partial B/\partial t > 0$. Then, the sense of the induced field **E** will be clockwise. Since the electronic charge is negative, the tangential force which accelerates the electron will have the opposite sense. We shall study the motion of the electron to see if it is possible for it to move in an orbit of constant radius R_0.

Let B represent the magnitude of the induction at a distance r from O. Then the time-varying flux through the area bounded by a circular orbit of radius R_0 is

$$\Phi_0 = \int_0^{R_0} B \, dA = \int_0^{R_0} B \cdot 2\pi r \, dr \qquad (8.29)$$

By Faraday's law, the induced electric field E_0 tangential to the orbit of radius R_0 may be determined from

$$\mathcal{E} = \int_0^{2\pi R_0} \mathbf{E} \cdot d\mathbf{l} = 2\pi R_0 E_0 = -\frac{d\Phi_0}{dt} \qquad (8.30)$$

The tangential force exerted on a charged particle of mass m and positive charge q is $q\,\mathbf{E}_0$. By the use of (8.30) this force may be written as

$$qE_0 = -\frac{q}{2\pi R_0}\frac{d\Phi_0}{dt} \qquad (8.31)$$

Hence the equation for the tangential motion is

$$\frac{d}{dt}(mv) = -\frac{q}{2\pi R_0}\frac{d\Phi_0}{dt} \qquad (8.32)$$

where v is the speed and m the relativistic mass of the electron. If $d\Phi/dt > 0$, the minus sign indicates that the tangential force is clockwise on a positive charge. Since $q = -e$, the sense of the force on an electron is counterclockwise, as shown in Fig. 8.14.

The magnetic field provides the deflecting force. Hence the equation of motion which governs the transverse motion is

$$qvB_0 = \frac{mv^2}{R_0} \qquad (8.33)$$

If we integrate relation (8.32), subject to the initial condition that $v = 0$ when $\Phi_0 = 0$, we obtain

$$mv = -\frac{q\Phi_0}{2\pi R_0} \qquad (8.34)$$

But from (8.33) the expression for the momentum is found to be

$$mv = qB_0R_0 \qquad (8.35)$$

From the last two relations it follows that the electron can move in a stable circular orbit of radius R_0, provided B_0, the absolute value of B at the orbit, is given by

$$B_0 = \frac{1}{2}\left(\frac{\Phi_0}{\pi R_0^2}\right) = \frac{1}{2}\,B_{\text{avg}} \qquad (8.36)$$

But the quantity in parentheses is the average value of the field over the area bounded by the orbit. Hence the stability condition is that B_0, the magnetic field at the position of the orbit, must be equal to half B_{avg} and that this equality must hold throughout the acceleration interval.

The upper limit of this accelerator's performance is determined by the radiant energy emitted by the electron. If this loss per turn becomes comparable to the energy gained from the field per turn, the electron orbit will shrink. Assuming that E, the total energy of the electron, is much greater than its rest energy m_0c^2, then ΔE, the radiation loss per turn, has been shown to be

$$\Delta E = \frac{8.85 \times 10^{-8} \, E^4}{R_0} \quad \text{ev} \tag{8.37}$$

where E is expressed in Mev, and R_0 in meters. Then ΔE is in electron-volts.

Induced Electromotive
Forces: **Problems**

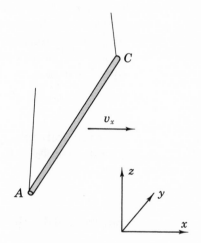

8.1 The slender rod AC (length 0.80 m) is set into oscillatory motion parallel to the horizontal plane $(x,y$ plane). Let the rod be located in a uniform magnetic induction $B_z = 0.15$ weber/m² directed along the vertical (z direction).

(a) All points of the rod have a velocity v_x parallel to the x-axis, and at a given instant the end A is negatively charged when v_x is directed toward the positive x-axis. Is the sense of B_z along the positive or negative z direction?

(b) The motion of the rod may be described by

$$v_x = 0.25 \sin\left(\frac{\pi}{2}t\right) \quad \text{m/sec}$$

where t is the time in seconds. For what values of t is the magnitude of the emf induced in the length AC a maximum? What is the maximum value?

(c) Set up an integral representing the average value of the emf over the time interval $t = 0$ to $t = 2$ sec. Evaluate the integral.

8.2 The rigid conductor $ACDE$ is rotated about the vertical (y-axis) at the rate of 2 rev/sec. The straight section CD is normal to this axis. The entire conductor is immersed in a uniform magnetic field of induction $B = 0.15$ weber/m² directed along the positive y-axis.

(a) The end E is found to be positively charged. Does the point D move toward or away from the observer?

(b) What is the magnitude of $d\mathscr{E}$, the emf induced in the radial element dr located at a distance r from the axis?

(c) If $AC = 0.10$ m, $CD = 0.02$ m, and $DE = 0.40$ m, what is the emf induced in (1) the length AC; (2) the length CD, (3) the length DE, and (4) the entire conductor $ACDE$?

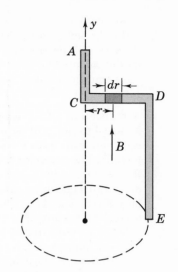

8.3 A square conducting loop, with a total resistance of R Ω and a weight of W new, is L m on a side. Suppose the loop is allowed to drop so that adjacent sides remain respectively horizontal and vertical. Suppose further that a horizontally directed and locally uniform magnetic induction **B** is normal to the top side and exists only over the top side, the magnetic field on the bottom side being zero. When the loop falls with constant speed v m/sec,

(a) What is the emf induced in the loop?

(b) What is the current in the loop?

(c) What is the magnetic force on the top side?

(d) Express the speed v in terms of W, B, L, and R.

8.4 A metal disk is rotated with constant angular velocity of ω radian/sec in the counterclockwise sense about an insulated axis perpendicular to the plane of the diagram. The disk is located in a region where there is a uniform magnetic field parallel to the axis of rotation and directed into the plane of the disk. The magnitude of the magnetic induction **B** is equal to 0.50 weber/m². The terminals A and C are connected to two sliding contacts, one at the rim and the other on the axle. The contacts are located at radial distances of 0.09 and 0.01 m respectively.

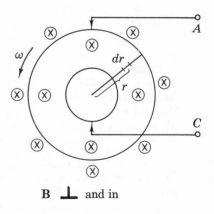

(a) Identify the terminal that is charged positively.

(b) The emf induced in the radial element dr at a distance r from the axis is $vB\,dr$. Starting with this relation, obtain an expression for the potential difference between the points A and C.

(c) Find the value of ω if the voltage across AC is to be equal to 1.0 v.

8.5 A copper rod AC of length L m is moved to the right with a velocity **v** under the force **F** applied externally. The rod slides on a pair of frictionless conducting rails which are parallel and are located in the horizontal plane. The rails are connected to a battery of emf 6 v with polarity as indicated. There is a uniform induction **B** everywhere parallel to the vertical and directed outward from the plane of the diagram.

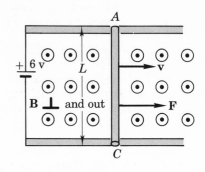

(a) What is the emf ε induced in AC? Give units.

(b) Which end of the rod, A or C, is at the higher potential?

(c) What is the net emf of the circuit?

(d) Complete the right-hand side of the equation $Fv = \cdots$.

The resistance of the closed circuit may be regarded as constant and equal to R Ω.

8.6 A slender metal bar AC of length l m is pivoted at A. It oscillates in a vertical plane with simple angular harmonic motion such that, at any instant of time t, the angle θ between the vertical and the axis of the bar is given by

$$\theta = \theta_0 \sin{(kt)}$$

where θ_0 and k are constants.

The bar oscillates in a uniform magnetic field, where the induction **B** expressed in weber/m² is everywhere perpendicular to the bar directed into the plane of the diagram.

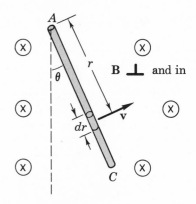

(a) Write the magnitude of $d\varepsilon$, the emf induced in an element of length dr, at an instant when v, the linear velocity of the element, is directed as shown. The element dr is located at a distance of r m from A. Make the necessary substitutions to express $d\varepsilon$ explicitly in terms of r and t.

(b) Evaluate the emf induced in the bar at the instant considered in part (a). State the units of the result and specify the sign of the charge appearing at end C.

(c) For what value of θ is the induced emf a maximum? What is the maximum value?

8.7 The square loop $ACDE$ is moved in the x,y plane with a constant speed of 0.010 m/sec so that the x-axis bisects the loop. As shown in the diagram, a uniform induction $\mathbf{B}$ of magnitude equal to 0.40 weber/m² is present over the shaded area $PQRS$, which also lies in the x,y plane and is bisected by the x-axis; outside this area $\mathbf{B} = 0$ everywhere.

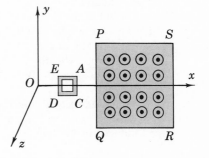

(a) Let AC, the leading edge of the loop, cross the boundary PQ at the time $t = 0$. Calculate the emf induced in the loop just after AC enters the magnetic field. Given: $AC = DC = 0.020$ m; $PQ = QR = 0.06$ m.

(b) What is the current in the loop at the instant specified in part (a)? The resistance of the loop is 0.016 Ω, and its self-inductance is negligible.

(c) What is the current in the loop just after ED enters the field?

(d) Let the sign of the induced emf be taken as negative if the current induced in the loop is in the clockwise sense. Plot a graph showing how the emf induced in $ACDE$ varies with the time over the interval $t = 0$ to $t = 10$ sec.

8.8 The magnetic induction $\mathbf{B}$ at all points within the circular area A is directed at an angle θ to the normal, and its magnitude is independent of position within the area. If the time variation of B is described by

$$B = B_0 \sin \omega t$$

determine the magnitude of the emf induced in the circular path comprising the boundary of the area.

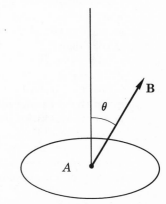

8.9 A rectangular coil $EFGH$ is near a long straight wire, with the long sides of the rectangle parallel to the wire. The instantaneous current in the long wire is i amp, and the magnetic induction $\mathbf{B}$ due to i is given by $\mu_0 i/2\pi r$, where r is the distance in meters from the wire to any point P.

(a) Refer to the diagram and write an expression for $d\Phi$, the element of flux linking with the elementary area of length l and width dr (shaded area).

(b) What is the flux which links with the rectangle $EFGH$? Give the units of the answer if all distances shown in the diagram are in meters. $\mu_0 = 4\pi \times 10^{-7}$ weber/amp-m.

(c) What additional information is needed in order to compute the emf induced in $EFGH$?

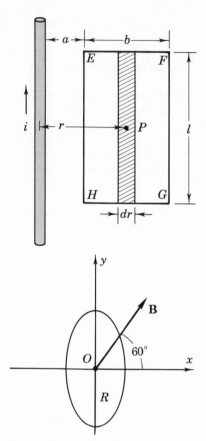

8.10 A time-varying current in a solenoidal winding is utilized to produce an induction field **B** whose dependence on the time t can be described by

$$B = B_0 \sin(\omega t) \text{ weber/m}^2$$

where $B_0 = 1.20$ weber/m^2 and $\omega = 60 \times 10^6$ radian/sec.

As shown in the diagram, a thin circular wire of radius R is situated in the field of **B**, which is assumed to have the same magnitude at all points within the area of the ring. Furthermore, **B** is everywhere parallel to the x,y plane and makes an angle of 60° with the x-axis, the axis of the ring whose center is at the origin O.

(a) What is the instantaneous emf (in volts) induced in the wire if the area of the turn is 2.25×10^{-4} m^2?

(b) At an instant when **B** is directed as shown and $\partial B/\partial t > 0$, would the force on a positive charge in the ring be in the clockwise or counterclockwise sense as seen by an observer situated on the positive x-axis? Explain.

(c) Assume that the radius of the circular turn is increased to $3R$ and the conditions described above are still valid. Is the maximum value of the induced emf increased, decreased, or unaltered? Explain.

8.11 The magnetic induction at O, the center of a large circular coil, is given by

$$B = I \times 10^{-6} \text{ weber/m}^2$$

where I is the current in the winding.

(a) For a given value of I, calculate the flux which links each turn of a small coil (100 turns, area 10^{-4} m^2) placed in the plane of the large coil concentrically about the center O. Assume that the value of **B** over the area of the small coil is independent of position.

(b) Let I vary in time in accordance with $I = 5 \sin(377t)$ amp. Express i as a function of time if $R = 15\ \Omega$.

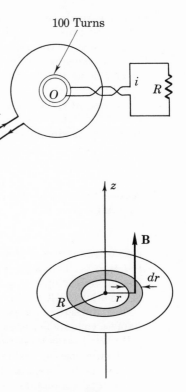

8.12   The axis of a circular loop of radius R m coincides with the z-axis. At all points within the area of the loop there is a nonuniform and time-varying magnetic induction **B** normal to the plane of the loop and directed along the $+z$-axis. The magnitude of **B** (in weber/m^2) at any point r m distant from the axis is given by

$$B = B_0 - Cr^2t^2$$

where t is the time, and where B_0 and C are positive constants.

(a) Write an expression for $d\Phi$, the instantaneous element of flux crossing the shaded annular (ring-like) area of radius r and thickness dr.

(b) Evaluate the instantaneous flux of **B** which links with the area of the loop of radius R.

(c) What is the emf induced in the loop? Does positive charge circulate in the clockwise or counterclockwise sense when the loop is observed from a point on the $+z$-axis?

Use proper units for the answers in all three parts.

8.13   The circuits 1 and 2 at the top of page 206 are isolated and insulated from each other. Circuit 1 contains a coil, a switch S, and a constant emf of the indicated polarity.

(a) The switch S is suddenly closed. Is the current in the resistance of circuit 2 directed from A to C or from C to A? Explain.

(b) Owing to the current in circuit 1, the normal component of the instantaneous magnetic induction at every point within the area of each of the three closely wound identical turns of circuit 2 is

$$B = 0.20(1 - e^{-5t})\ \text{weber/m}^2$$

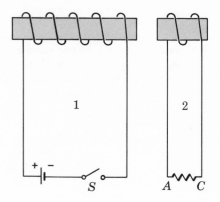

where e is the base of natural logs and t is the time in seconds. Write an expression for the magnitude of the instantaneous emf induced in circuit 2 if the area of each turn is 15×10^{-3} m².

(c) For what value of t is the emf induced in circuit 2 a maximum? What is the maximum value?

8.14   Assume that in a Betatron the time variation of the flux linking with the orbit is given by

$$\Phi = \Phi_0 \sin \omega t$$

An electron is accelerated during a quarter of a cycle, from $t = 0$ to $t = \pi/2\omega$. The radius of the stable orbit is 1.0 m, the operating angular frequency is $\omega = 120\pi$ sec^{-1}, and the maximum induction at the orbit is 0.40 weber/m².

(a) What is the average energy per turn imparted to the electron? Express your answer in electron-volts per turn.

(b) What is the total distance traveled by the electron during the acceleration period? Assume that the speed of the electron is essentially equal to the speed of light, $c = 3.00 \times 10^8$ m/sec, during the entire acceleration interval. Express your answer in miles.

(c) Calculate the number of revolutions made by the electron during the acceleration interval.

(d) Calculate the final energy of the electron from the product of the total number of turns and the mean average increment per turn.

(e) In relativistic mechanics the total energy E is given by $E^2 = (pc)^2 + E_0^2$, where p is the momentum, c the speed of light, and E_0 the rest-energy. If $E \gg E_0$, the kinetic energy is given by pc. Calculate the final energy from this relation and compare the result with that given in (d).

(f) How does the radiation loss per turn at the final energy compare with the average energy gain per turn?

8.15   Refer to Example 6, in Section 8.4. For what value of t is the emf equal to zero? Explain why the sense of the emf reverses at this value of the time.

Chapter 9.
Magnetic Properties of Matter

9.1   Introduction

In the preceding discussion of magnetic phenomena, we considered magnetic fields which were set up by moving charges or by conduction currents located in free space. Actually, all matter is composed of atomic systems which contain moving charges. The motion of an electron in an atom is of special importance. In a general way, this motion consists of a revolution in an orbit about the nucleus and a rotation or spin about an axis. (Nuclei also have a spin about an axis, but this motion is not significant for our present purpose.) The orbital motion of an electron is equivalent to a circulation of charge, or a current loop. We shall see that when an external field is applied to matter there is a change in the orbital frequency of revolution. This change weakens the applied field. In addition, as in the case of the current in a loop of wire, the applied field exerts a torque whose effect is to align the axis of the electronic orbit. The magnitude of the angular momentum associated with the spin is an intrinsic property of the electron and is not altered by the applied field. However, the orientation of the spin axis in the direction of the field appears to be the main reason for the unusual magnetic properties of special materials such as iron, cobalt, and nickel.

In interpreting the magnetic properties of matter in the bulk, we shall adopt the view that magnetic fields are produced by atomic currents. These currents, which are referred to as hidden or amperian currents, do not possess heating effects or give rise to transport of charge. Historically, magnetism was investigated

207

independently, rather than in connection with the study of electricity, until the discoveries of Faraday, Ampère, and others in the first quarter of the nineteenth century. Even without any detailed knowledge of atomic structure, Ampère suggested that currents inside matter could be regarded as the source of magnetic effects in the absence of conduction currents.

In our examination of the macroscopic properties, we shall make no detailed reference to the electronic motions themselves. Instead, we shall postulate the existence of amperian currents distributed throughout the volume of a given sample.

9.2   Magnetic Permeability

One way of classifying the magnetic properties of matter in the bulk is to compare the flux densities in various specimens when they are subjected to a known external field. The measurements are simplified if the magnetic field is produced by a conduction current in a closely wound toroidal coil, and if the specimen is made to occupy the closed ring-like region in the interior of the winding. The shape chosen for the specimen does away with the necessity for considering effects which arise when the boundaries of the specimen are at right angles to the field. This particular arrangement was used by Rowland in the study of magnetic effects and is often referred to as the Rowland ring.

The principle involved in the measurement of **B** may be understood by considering Fig. 9.1. The magnetic material constitutes

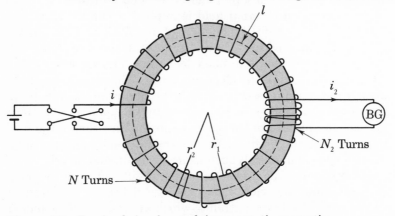

Figure 9.1 Rowland ring for studying magnetic properties of specimens.

the core of the toroid of N turns and cross-sectional area A. A secondary coil of N_2 turns is connected to BG, a galvanometer used ballistically. If the current in the toroid is reversed, an instantaneous emf e_2 induced in the secondary winding during the reversal displaces a charge Q_2 through the secondary circuit. This charge can be measured by the ballistic galvanometer. The flux density in the core can then be calculated from the following relations. The instantaneous secondary current i_2 is equal to e_2/R_2, where R_2 is the resistance of the secondary circuit. The element of charge dq_2 displaced in the secondary circuit in the time dt is $e_2\,dt/R_2$ or $N_2\,d\Phi/R_2$, since the absolute value of e_2 is $N_2(d\Phi/dt)$. Hence the charge passing through the galvanometer as the current in the toroid is changed from $-i_1$ to $+i_1$ is given by

$$Q_2 = \frac{N_2}{R_2} \int_{-\Phi_1}^{+\Phi_1} d\Phi = \frac{2\Phi_1 N_2}{R_2} \qquad (9.1)$$

where Φ_1 is the magnitude of the flux in the core at the beginning or at the end of the reversal. As proved in (7.24), the flux density within the toroid is not constant over its cross section. However, if the ring thickness is small relative to the mean radius of the toroid, the flux Φ_1 may be represented by BA with sufficient accuracy, provided B stands for the flux density at any point on the mean circumference (the dotted circle in Fig. 9.1). The mean circumference has a length l defined by $2\pi(r_1 + r_2)/2$, where r_1 and r_2 are the inner and outer radii of the toroid. Replacing Φ_1 by BA in (9.1), we find

$$B = \frac{R_2 Q_2}{2N_2 A} \qquad (9.2)$$

As a reference value of B, we take the flux density when the region of the core is evacuated. Let this value be denoted by B_0. By the circuital law [again see (7.24)]

$$B_0 = \mu_0 Ni/l \qquad (9.3)$$

where $\mu_0 = 4\pi \times 10^{-7}$ weber/amp-m, l is the mean circumferential length, i is the current in the winding, and N is the number of turns of the toroidal winding.

If the space enclosed by the winding is filled by any other specimen, we can measure B in each case by using the same coil and same current i. (In this connection, i is called the magnetizing current.) To illustrate the properties of various magnetic types, we propose to determine the flux density when the core is filled in succession with graphite, liquid oxygen, and iron. Although our suggested scheme for obtaining B is sound in principle, a particular investigation may involve technical difficulties which we shall ignore in our discussion of this conceptual experiment.

Measurements reveal that when the core material is graphite, the flux density B_C is very slightly less than B_0; for a liquid oxygen core, B_{O_2} is slightly more than B_0; and for an iron core B_{Fe} is enormously greater than B_0. In comparing flux densities for the various core materials, we make use of the ratio B/B_0, which is called the *relative permeability* of the substance. It is here represented by K_m and is defined by

$$K_m = \frac{B}{B_0} \qquad (9.4)$$

The comparison between various materials is summarized in the table below:

Material	B	$B/B_0 = K_m$	Magnetic type
Free space	B_0	1.00	...
Graphite	B_C	<1.00	Diamagnetic
Liquid oxygen	B_{O_2}	>1.00	Paramagnetic
Iron	B_{Fe}	$\gg 1.00$	Ferromagnetic

If K_m is less than unity, the material is said to be *diamagnetic*. If K_m is greater than unity, the material is said to be *paramagnetic*. In the extreme case, where K_m is very much larger than unity, the material is said to be *ferromagnetic*. Actually, for graphite, K_m is less than unity by 5 parts in 100,000, while for liquid oxygen, $K_m = 1.004$. Thus, except for ferromagnetic substances where K_m ranges from 10 to 10,000, most materials are essentially nonmagnetic and exhibit feeble magnetic effects only in the presence of an external field. On the other hand, ferromagnetic materials can be permanently magnetized and can display strong effects in the absence of an external field.

In our study of dielectric properties of matter, we defined the dielectric constant K by C/C_0, where C_0 was the capacitance of a capacitor whose plates were located in a vacuum, and C was the capacitance when the space between the plates was filled with a dielectric. We observed that K was always greater than unity. We have seen that in the magnetic case, the relative permeability K_m may be less than unity. In the electrostatic case, the increase in the capacitance was brought about by the weakening of the field in the dielectric as compared to the field in free space. The

magnetic analog is the diamagnetic behavior of matter, where
the influence of the medium is to reduce the field of **B** relative
to its value in a vacuum. The paramagnetic and ferromagnetic
behavior of matter involves orientation effects similar to those
found in dielectrics with permanent dipole moments.

9.3   Magnetic Moment

We have introduced the term *magnetic moment* in connection
with the magnetic induction produced by a steady current in a
circular loop. In (7.12) the magnetic moment **m** was defined by

$$\mathbf{m} = \mu_0 i \mathbf{A} \qquad (9.5)$$

where the area of the loop bounded by i is represented as **A**, a
vector normal to the plane of the loop. The right-handed screw
rule gives the sense of **A** as related to the sense of circulation of
positive charge around the loop, as shown in Fig. 9.2. [Some-

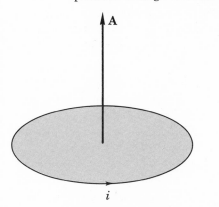

Figure 9.2   The magnetic moment
m of a current loop is $\mu_0 i \mathbf{A}$.

times the moment is defined as $i\mathbf{A}$. When defined as in (9.5) the
relation between the field vectors **D**, **E**, and **P** in electrostatics
has the same form as the relation between the magnetic field
vector **B** and other auxiliary vectors to be introduced later.] As
we have seen, the components of **B** produced by the current in a
loop can be conveniently expressed in terms of **m**. In particular,
from (7.9), the field on the axis at the center of a circular turn
of radius a is $\mu_0 i \mathbf{A}/2\pi a^3$ or $\mathbf{m}/2\pi a^3$. Atomic current loops or amperian currents form the basis of a model used to predict the
magnetic properties of matter. The moment as defined in (9.5) is
expressed in weber-meter.

For the special case of a charge q moving with speed v in a circular orbit of radius r, the equivalent current i is q/T, where T is the period. But $T = 2\pi r/v$. Hence the magnetic moment may be calculated by the use of (9.5). This gives

$$m = \mu_0\left(\frac{qv}{2\pi r}\right)\pi r^2 = \mu_0 qvr/2 = \mu_0 qr^2\omega/2 \qquad (9.6)$$

In the hydrogen atom the velocity of the electron in the orbit of lowest energy is found to be $h/2\pi m_e r$, where m_e is the electronic mass and h is a universal constant known as *Planck's constant*. By substitution in (9.6), the magnetic moment of the electron in the first circular orbit of hydrogen is found to be

$$m_H = \mu_0\left(\frac{he}{4\pi m_e}\right) \qquad (9.7)$$

where e denotes the magnitude of the electronic charge. The quantity in parenthesis is known as the *Bohr magneton*, whose numerical value is 9.273×10^{-24} amp-m².

Atomic magnetic moments have been measured by sending a well-defined beam of atoms through an inhomogeneous magnetic field, which deflects the beam. A sketch of the apparatus is shown in Fig. 9.3. The magnitude of the deflection is a measure of the

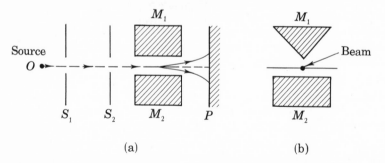

(a)   (b)

Figure 9.3   Atomic beam apparatus for measuring atomic magnetic moments. In (a), O is the source of atoms; S_1 and S_2 are defining slits; M_1 and M_2 are the deflecting magnets; and P is the detecting plate. In (b), M_1 and M_2 are the pole pieces of the magnet as seen end-on. The particular shape produces a nonuniform field, so that an atom with a moment is subjected to a vertical translatory force.

magnetic moment. Experiments of this sort have indicated that **m** is not oriented at an arbitrary angle with the field; rather, its projection in the direction of the applied field is confined to values which are integral multiples of the Bohr magneton. Observations show that certain atoms, such as He, Ne, Zn, and Cd, with closed electronic shells have no magnetic moments, and that others, such as H, Li, Cu, and Ag, have unit magnetic moment.

9.4   **The Origin of Diamagnetism**

In this section we shall present a calculation to show how the application of a magnetic field modifies the electronic orbital currents. A rigorous solution of this problem belongs to the domain of quantum mechanics. However, a simplified treatment based on principles developed thus far will give an explanation of diamagnetism that is correct in general outline though not in details.

Consider the motion of an electron in a circular orbit and assume that the applied field **B** is normal to the orbit. Before the magnetic field is applied, the electron (charge $q = -e$, mass m_e) is revolving in an orbit of radius r with angular velocity ω_0. The equation of motion is

$$m_e \omega_0^2 r = F_c \tag{9.8}$$

where F_c is the attractive coulomb force due to the positive nuclear charge. When an induction **B** is applied, there are two effects: (1) The orbit links with a changing flux, and an induced electric field **E** acts tangentially on the electron. (2) The electron is subject to the magnetic force $-e(\mathbf{v} \times \mathbf{B})$, which acts radially.

Figure 9.4 shows the various quantities of importance to the motion. For the situation shown in Fig. 9.4(a), where **B** is directed away from the reader and is increasing, the application of Lenz's law indicates that the tangential force on the electron reduces the tangential velocity **v**—that is, its effect is to slow the electron down. On the other hand, the magnetic force is directed away from the center and is opposed to the coulomb attraction. We shall show that under these influences the radius of the orbit remains essentially unchanged but that the electron is either slowed down or speeded up depending on the sense of the vector $(\mathbf{v} \times \mathbf{B})$. In Fig. 9.4(b) the electron velocity has been reversed. Lenz's law still predicts the same sense for the induced field **E**, since **B** is still directed away from the reader and is increasing. However, now the electron is speeded up, and the magnetic force is toward the center.

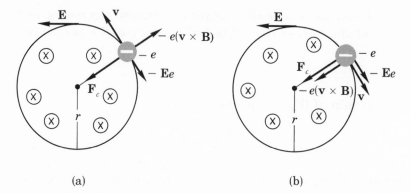

(a)   (b)

Figure 9.4 Diamagnetism. $B \perp$ and into plane, increasing in time; hence, by Lenz's law, E is counterclockwise for both (a) and (b). In (a), electron velocity v is counterclockwise, and the tangential force slows the electron down. Magnetic force away from center. In (b), v is clockwise, and the tangential force speeds the electron up. Magnetic force toward center.

By Faraday's law, the magnitude of the tangential electric field is given by (see also example 4, Section 8.4)

$$2\pi r E = -\frac{d}{dt}(\pi r^2 B)$$

or

$$|E| = \frac{1}{2} r \frac{dB}{dt} \tag{9.9}$$

In deducing (9.9), it has been assumed that the electron orbit is unaltered. When the magnetic field is switched on—that is, while the applied field is changing from 0 to its final value B_f—there is a change in the momentum of the electron, which can be described by

$$\frac{d}{dt}(m_e \omega r) = Eq$$

Whence, by the use of (9.9),

$$\frac{d\omega}{dt} = \frac{q}{2m_e} \frac{dB}{dt} \tag{9.10}$$

Consequently, the change in the angular velocity from ω_0 to ω_f may be obtained from

$$\Delta \omega = (\omega_f - \omega_0) = \int_{\omega_0}^{\omega_f} d\omega = \frac{q}{2m_e} \int_0^{B_f} dB = \frac{q}{2m_e} B_f \tag{9.11}$$

The magnetic force either decreases or increases the force toward the center, as is indicated in Fig. 9.4(a) and (b). The electron can remain in the same orbit if the modification of the central force is just enough to compensate for $\Delta\omega$, the corresponding change in the angular velocity. With the aid of (9.8), we can also evaluate $\Delta\omega$ from

$$m_e(\omega_0 + \Delta\omega)^2 r - F_c = \pm qvB_f = \pm q\omega_f rB_f \qquad (9.12)$$

for the situations pictured in Fig. 9.4. Even for the highest values of B (~ 5 weber/m^2) obtainable, $\Delta\omega \ll \omega_0$. In solving for $\Delta\omega$ from (9.12), $(\Delta\omega)^2$ may be neglected relative to other terms in the expansion on the left. Also, ω_0 may be considered nearly equal to ω_f. With these approximations, for the numerical value of $\Delta\omega$ we obtain

$$\Delta\omega = \frac{q}{2m_e} B_f \qquad (9.13)$$

Consequently the value of $\Delta\omega$ deduced from the change in the central force does not contradict the result for $\Delta\omega$ as calculated from the change in the orbital momentum on the assumption that the orbital radius remains unaltered. In other words, the magnetic force compensates very nearly for the change in the centripetal force arising from an increase or decrease in the angular velocity. We can conclude that the application of the field either speeds up or slows down the electron in its orbit, depending on the sense of the magnetic force.

In passing we note that the quantity on the right-hand side of (9.13) is known as the *Larmor frequency*. It is the angular frequency with which **m** precesses about the field when the field is not normal to the plane of the orbit.

We can calculate the change in the magnetic moment resulting from the change in the angular frequency by the following steps. From (9.6) we obtain

$$\Delta m = \mu_0 qr^2 \, \Delta\omega/2 \qquad (9.14)$$

Substituting the result found in (9.13) in (9.14), we see that

$$\Delta\mathbf{m} = -\mu_0 q^2 r^2 \mathbf{B}/4m_e \qquad (9.15)$$

where the subscript of **B** has been dropped and where the minus sign has been included to indicate that $\Delta\mathbf{m}$ is antiparallel to **B** as we shall see from the discussion which follows.

Figure 9.5 shows the change in the magnetic moment arising from the application of the field. The figures are drawn for a circulating charge which is negative. In Fig. 9.5(a) the electron is slowed down, the equivalent loop current is reduced, and the initial magnetic moment which is parallel to **B** is reduced. In Fig. 9.5(b) the electron circulation is reversed, the electron is speeded up, and the magnetic moment is increased in magnitude. But in this case the moment is directed opposite to **B**. In each case Δ**m** is such as to give rise to a diminution in the externally applied field. This effect accounts in a general way for the diamagnetic behavior of matter.

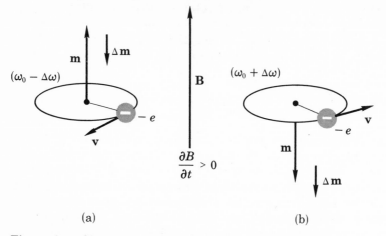

(a)   (b)

Figure 9.5   Changes in the magnetic moment arising from changes in the angular velocity. In (a), the electron is slowed down, while in (b), the electron is speeded up. In either case, the sense of Δ**m** is opposed to that of **B**.

We apply the reasoning to an atom of helium, which has two electrons circulating in opposite senses. In the absence of an external field, the net magnetic moment of the atom is zero. If a magnetic field is applied, the individual moments are altered, as shown in Fig. 9.5(a) and (b). By referring to Fig. 9.6(b) we see that the atom acquires a net magnetic moment of 2 Δ**m** in such a direction as to weaken the field of **B**. In this simplified treatment we have ignored the spin magnetic moment of the two electrons. In general, orbital and spin moments must be combined to obtain the resultant magnetic moment of the atom.

In order to account for the diamagnetic behavior of matter in the bulk, we must sum up over all the orbits in an atom and also over all the atoms present per unit volume of the sample. Actually, the electron orbits are inclined to the field, and the magnetic force which acts at right angles to the angular momentum of the electron gives rise to a precession about the direction of **B**. In any case, our model is only approximately correct, since

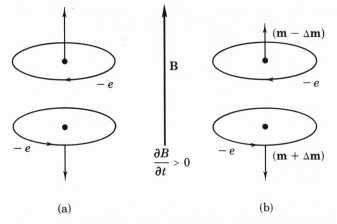

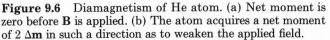

Figure 9.6   Diamagnetism of He atom. (a) Net moment is
zero before **B** is applied. (b) The atom acquires a net moment
of 2 Δ**m** in such a direction as to weaken the applied field.

electronic motions in atoms are not confined to well-defined orbits. However, the approach presented above implies correctly
that all matter is *diamagnetic*. This aspect is often obscured by
more prominent magnetic effects, such as paramagnetism and
ferromagnetism.

9.5   Origin of Paramagnetism

The diamagnetic effect is present whether or not the atom possesses a magnetic moment initially. If the atom has, or acquires,
a magnetic moment composed of the vector sum of the orbital
and spin moments of all its electrons, the applied field will exert
a torque on the resultant atomic moment. Consequently there
will be a tendency to align the moment with the field. This behavior is similar to the rotation experienced by a rigid current
loop placed in a field of **B**. As shown in Section 6.5, the torque
on the loop is such as to rotate the loop and bring the normal
to the loop into alignment with **B**. As a result of the orientation
effect, the field of the current whirl will add to the external
field. Briefly, this is the origin of paramagnetism.

There are other considerations. The circulating electron has
angular momentum about the nucleus, and the magnetic torque
gives rise to a precessional motion about the field rather than to
complete alignment along the field. In addition, according to the

laws of atomic physics, the magnetic moment vector, which is proportional to the angular momentum, may assume only a discrete set of orientations relative to the field. Moreover, in an assemblage, the individual atoms possess thermal motions which tend to destroy the alignment effects. As we mentioned in Section 6.5, however, a magnetic dipole aligned with the field is in stable equilibrium, and the potential energy of the dipole is at a minimum. At room temperature and in a weak field, a relatively small number of atomic moments are aligned. From statistical analysis, it may be shown that the probability of finding any one atom having an energy U due to orientation in the field is proportional to $e^{-U/kT}$, where k is the Boltzman constant and T is the absolute temperature. The torque exerted by the field on an atom of permanent magnetic moment $\mathbf{m}$ is $\mathbf{m} \times \mathbf{B}/\mu_0$, and within an additive constant the potential energy $U = -\mathbf{m} \cdot \mathbf{B}/\mu_0$ or $-(1/\mu_0)mB \cos \theta$, where θ is the angle between $\mathbf{m}$ and $\mathbf{B}$. Hence the probability of finding a given moment at an angle θ in a fixed field $\mathbf{B}$ and at a constant temperature T is given by

$$e^{(mB/\mu_0 kT) \cos \theta} \qquad (9.16)$$

From this we can calculate the average value of $(m \cos \theta)$, the component of the moment along $\mathbf{B}$. If the constant $(mB/\mu_0 kT) \ll 1$, we find that

$$(m \cos \theta)_{\text{avg}} \cong \frac{m^2 B}{3\mu_0^2 kT} \qquad (9.17)$$

The inequality used in obtaining the result in (9.17) is valid for paramagnetic materials in weak fields and at sufficiently high temperatures. It is seen that paramagnetic behavior is temperature-sensitive and that it increases with decreasing temperature. On the other hand, the diamagnetic effect discussed in Section 9.4 is independent of temperature.

9.6   Magnetization Vector M

In our study of the electromagnetic field, we have specified the force on charges in terms of the electric vector $\mathbf{E}$ and the induction vector $\mathbf{B}$. In principle, these two vectors can be determined at a given field point if the positions and velocities of all the source charges are known. Because such information is not generally available, auxiliary field vectors are introduced to describe the role played by polarized and magnetized matter. Thus, to describe the electrostatic field, two other vectors, **D** and **P**, were introduced in addition to the force field vector **E**. A similar procedure will be followed in treating the situation where magnetized matter is present. In this section we introduce one of these auxiliary quantities to describe the field produced by atomic currents.

We have already stated that, at distant field points, the induction due to a current loop can be specified in terms of the magnetic dipole moment **m**. In a working model of the magnetized state, the magnetic effects of orbital and spin motions in a volume of molecular dimensions are combined and represented by a fictitious or amperian current loop. A sample of magnetized matter is then pictured, as in Fig. 9.7(a), as an assemblage of

(a)   (b)

Figure 9.7   (a) Model of the magnetized state. (b) Definition of **M**.

elementary loops distributed throughout the volume of the specimen. A vector **M**, called the *magnetization* at a point inside matter, is defined as the magnetic moment per unit volume. (This is the analog of the polarization **P**, which was introduced in our study of dielectrics in Section 4.4.) The field of **M** is obtained by adding vectorially the individual moments in a small volume v and by dividing the resultant moment by v. In symbols,

$$\mathbf{M} \equiv \frac{\sum\limits_{j=1}^{N} \mathbf{m}_k}{v} \tag{9.18}$$

where $\mathbf{m}_k$ is the magnetic moment of the kth loop. See Fig. 9.7(b). The volume v must be large enough to contain a large number of current whirls, yet it must be small enough to guarantee that **M** varies smoothly within the medium as we pass from point to point. In the unmagnetized state, the individual current loops will be oriented randomly, and the sum in (9.18) will equal zero. In this instance **M** is also zero. On the other hand, if the individual moments are essentially parallel, the substance is intensely magnetized and **M** will be close to its saturation (maximum) value.

We proceed to describe how **M** may be associated with the amperian currents within matter. Consider first the case where the magnetization vector **M** throughout the sample has the same magnitude and direction—that is, **M** is uniform. Referring to Fig. 9.8, we observe that at points within the magnetized cy-

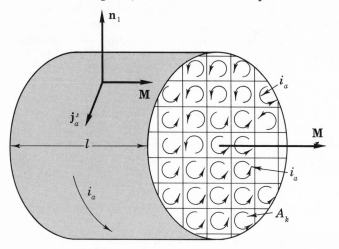

Figure 9.8   Cylindrical specimen magnetized uniformly along axis.

lindrical specimen the circulating currents virtually cancel one another but leave a surface amperian current i_a. To obtain the relation between M and this surface current we apply the defining relation (9.18) and obtain

$$M = \frac{\sum\limits_{}^{N} m_k}{Al} = \frac{\mu_0 i_a \sum\limits_{}^{N} A_k}{Al} = \frac{\mu_0 i_a}{l} \tag{9.19}$$

where i_a is the circulating amperian current in any one of the N loops, and where $\overset{N}{\sum} A_k = A$, is the cross section of the cylinder. But the ratio i_a/l is the current per unit length measured along the surface of the cylinder at right angles to the circulating current i_a. The ratio may be called the surface density of current to be denoted by $\mathbf{j}_a^s$. Hence, for the relation between the magnitudes of the magnetization and the surface density of amperian current, we have.

$$\mu_0 j_a^{\,s} = M \tag{9.20}$$

If $\mathbf{n}_1$ is a unit vector drawn normally to the surface of the cylinder, the three vectors may be related by the cross product

$$\mu_0 \mathbf{j}_a^s = \mathbf{M} \times \mathbf{n}_1 \tag{9.21}$$

where the direction of $\mathbf{j}_a^s$ is given by the right-hand screw rule. The result in (9.21) was deduced for the special case of uniform magnetization. It can be proved that it holds true in general.

We might examine the case where the magnetization is not uniform. Consider the change in the distribution of atomic loops in the right-hand portion of Fig. 9.7(a). In that region there is a net amperian current i_a directed upward, and the magnetization $\mathbf{M}$ will be a function of the coordinates. To find the relation between $\mathbf{M}$ and the amperian current density $\mathbf{j}_a$, let us consider several cells located within a sample of nonuniformly magnetized matter. For simplicity, we shall assume that $\mathbf{M}$ has only one component, M_y, and that this component is dependent only on x. Consult Fig. 9.9, which shows the circulating currents i_z', i_z'',

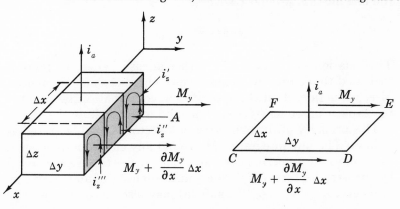

Figure 9.9 Specimen magnetized along y-axis. Nonuniform **M**.

and i_z''' in the three-volume elements and the associated y components of the magnetization. By definition, (see 9.18) we may write

$$M_y A \, \Delta y = \mu_0 i_z' A \tag{9.22}$$

$$\left(M_y + \frac{\partial M_y}{\partial x} \Delta x \right) A \, \Delta y = \mu_0 i_z''' A \tag{9.23}$$

for the first and last volume element respectively. In the above relations A is the area of rectangular element normal to M_y. In (9.23) the quantity in parentheses is the value of M_y associated with i_z'''. It is computed by adding $(\partial M_y/\partial x)\,\Delta x$, the change in M_y, to its value in the first cell.

Next we proceed to evaluate the line integral of M_y around the path $CDEF$, a rectangle in the x,y plane with sides parallel to the coordinate axes. Since M_y is normal to CF and DE, and since $M_x = 0$, the line integral may be expressed as

$$\oint \mathbf{M} \cdot d\mathbf{l} = \int_C^D \left(M_y + \frac{\partial M_y}{\partial x} \Delta x \right) dy - \int_E^F M_y \, dy$$

$$= \frac{\partial M_y}{\partial x} \Delta x \, \Delta y \qquad (9.24)$$

But, from (9.22) and (9.23), the result of the integration is equal to $\mu_0(i_z''' - i_z')$. Moreover, the addition of circulating currents at the boundaries of the cell in the middle gives $(i_z''' - i_z'') + (i_z'' - i_z')$, or $(i_z''' - i_z')$. But this is the net amperian current in the z direction crossing the area $\Delta x \, \Delta y$. Denoting this current by i_a, we reduce the right-hand member in (9.24) to $\mu_0 i_a$, and we can write the line integral around $CDEF$ as

$$\oint \mathbf{M} \cdot d\mathbf{l} = \mu_0 i_a \qquad (9.25)$$

This relation was deduced for a special case. When the proof is extended to include the general case where each component of $\mathbf{M}$ is a function of all three positional coordinates, the result is the same. Consequently, (9.25) is valid in general.

This property of the magnetization vector $\mathbf{M}$ may be stated as follows: The line integral of $\mathbf{M}$ around any closed path is equal to μ_0 times the amperian current which crosses the area encircled by the path. In terms of $\mathbf{j}_a^v$, the volume density of amperian currents is $i_a = \int \mathbf{j}_a^v \cdot d\mathbf{A}$. Thus (9.25) may also be written as

$$\oint \mathbf{M} \cdot d\mathbf{l} = \mu_0 \int \mathbf{j}_a^v \cdot d\mathbf{A} \qquad (9.26)$$

where the surface integration at the right is carried out over the area bounded by the path around which the line integral is evaluated.

Now let us summarize this section on magnetization. The vector $\mathbf{M}$ at any point within magnetized matter is the resultant magnetic moment per unit volume, where the magnetic moments arise from hidden circulating currents which do not transport charge or produce heating. The most important property of **M** is given by the line integral in (9.25).

The magnetization vector **M** is sometimes referred to as the magnetic polarization vector. Electrically polarized matter is described in terms of the polarization vector **P** (electric dipole moment per unit volume). The properties of the vectors **P** and **M** are quite different. The latter represents a nonconservative field and satisfies relations (9.21) and (9.25). The former is a conservative field whose properties are given by (4.12) and (4.15).

The magnetization as defined in this treatment is expressed in the same units as those of **B**—namely, weber per square meter. The units of **m** are μ_0-amp-m². Now **M** has the dimensions of **m** divided by cubic meters; hence it is expressed in μ_0-amp-meter^{-1}, which are also the dimensions of **B** as seen from

$$dB = \frac{\mu_0 i \, dl \sin \theta}{4\pi r^2}$$

9.7   The Magnetic Intensity Vector H and Related Topics

The amperian surface and volume current densities may be used to calculate the induction vector **B** at points inside or outside magnetized matter. The formulation is similar to that used in calculating **B** from conduction currents *in vacuo* by the application of

$$d\mathbf{B} = \frac{\mu_0}{4\pi} \frac{i \, d\mathbf{l} \times \mathbf{r}_1}{r^2}$$

except that amperian currents are to be treated as the equivalent sources. Formally, $\mathbf{B}_a$, the field due to magnetized matter or amperian currents, is given by

$$\mathbf{B}_a = \frac{\mu_0}{4\pi} \left[\int_{\text{volume}} \frac{\mathbf{j}_a^v \times \mathbf{r}_1}{r^2} \, dv + \int_{\text{surface}} \frac{\mathbf{j}_a^s \times \mathbf{r}_1}{r^2} \, dA \right] \qquad (9.27)$$

where the first integral is to be evaluated over the whole volume of the material, and the second is to be evaluated over the boundaries of the specimen. To make the actual evaluation we must know how the volume and surface current densities ($\mathbf{j}_a^v$ and $\mathbf{j}_a^s$) vary with position within or on the boundaries of the magnetic specimen. In practice such an approach is not feasible, so that it is customary to attack the problem in a different way.

We have emphasized that conduction currents and amperian currents may serve as the sources of the vector $\mathbf{B}$ for all field points whether such points are located in free space or in the interior of magnetic materials. For free space or nonmagnetic materials the circuital law was given in (7.21). Now we are in a position to generalize the circuital law for $\mathbf{B}$ to include the effect of amperian currents. The circuital law will now be written as

$$\oint \mathbf{B} \cdot d\mathbf{l} = \mu_0(i + i_a) = \mu_0 i_T \qquad (9.28)$$

where i_T represents the total current crossing the area bounded by the path of integration. The total current is the sum of the conduction current i, as specified in (7.21), and the amperian current i_a. But the vector $\mathbf{M}$ satisfies the relation

$$\oint \mathbf{M} \cdot d\mathbf{l} = \mu_0 i_a \qquad (9.29)$$

If we subtract (9.29) from (9.28), we obtain

$$\oint (\mathbf{B} - \mathbf{M}) \cdot d\mathbf{l} = \mu_0 i \qquad (9.30)$$

At this point we introduce the auxiliary vector $\mathbf{H}$, which is called the *magnetic intensity*. We define it by

$$\mathbf{H} \equiv \frac{1}{\mu_0}(\mathbf{B} - \mathbf{M}) \qquad (9.31)$$

In terms of $\mathbf{H}$, (9.30) becomes

$$\oint \mathbf{H} \cdot d\mathbf{l} = i \qquad (9.32)$$

This definition imparts to $\mathbf{H}$ the property that the line integral of $\mathbf{H}$ around any closed path is equal to the conduction current crossing the area whose periphery is the path around which the line integral is evaluated. In (9.32) we note that the constant μ_0 is no longer present. It is seen that $\mathbf{H}$ has the units of amp-m^{-1}.

Considerable maturity is required to understand the subtle points involved in the definition of the vector $\mathbf{H}$. Illustrative examples of its use will be given subsequently. The following comments are intended to clarify the meaning of the triad of vectors $\mathbf{B}$, $\mathbf{M}$, and $\mathbf{H}$. We are concerned here with steady electric currents and not with rapidly varying currents or with circuits containing gaps. In such cases the circuital law for $\mathbf{H}$ is modified to include an additional term (displacement current) on the right-hand side of (9.32).

1. *Comments on* **B**. The vector **B** is the fundamental field vector for evaluating the force on a moving charge. $\mathbf{B} = \mathbf{B}_i + \mathbf{B}_a$, where $\mathbf{B}_i$ arises from conduction currents and $\mathbf{B}_a$ from equivalent atomic currents. No auxiliary field vectors would be needed for the calculation of **B** if such currents could be specified completely. In general, this is not feasible.

2. *Relation between* **B** *and* **H** *in free space.* If no magnetized matter is present in the field, then amperian currents are absent and $\mathbf{M} = 0$. So (9.31) reduces to

$$\mu_0 \mathbf{H} = \mathbf{B} \tag{9.33}$$

where **H** is determined completely from conduction currents by the use of

$$d\mathbf{H} = \frac{1}{4\pi} \frac{i \, d\mathbf{l} \times \mathbf{r}_1}{r^2} \tag{9.34}$$

or, if the current distribution is sufficiently symmetric, from (9.32).

3. *The* **H** *Field*. If permanently magnetized matter is present in the field but there are no conduction currents, the line integral in (9.32) vanishes—that is, **H** satisfies the relation

$$\oint \mathbf{H} \cdot d\mathbf{l} = 0 \tag{9.35}$$

This implies that the **H**-field *in this case is a conservative field* which may be derived from a scalar potential and may formally be thought to arise from a distribution of "magnetic charges" or "poles." Such entities do not exist in nature, and so far we have not introduced them into our description of magnetization effects. Indeed, from a consideration of the definition in (9.31), we see that **H** depends on conduction and amperian currents. It is, however, possible to adopt an equivalent description in which **H** depends on conduction currents and "magnetic charges" or "poles." In this connection the determination of the auxiliary vector **H** produced by magnetized matter located in the neighborhood of the external field point is mathematically equivalent to the determination of **E** in the vicinity of polarized matter.

The magnetized state can alternately be described by assuming volume and surface distribution of "poles" in exactly the same way that dielectric polarization was described in terms of charge densities. In fact, by analogy it is possible to write a "law of force" between poles of strength p_1 and p_2—namely,

$$F = \frac{1}{4\pi\mu_0} \frac{p_1 p_2}{r^2}$$

where p is expressed in webers. Returning to (9.32), we may separate $\mathbf{H}$ into two parts, $\mathbf{H}_i$ and $\mathbf{H}_c$, where $\mathbf{H}_i$ is the nonconservative field that satisfies (9.32) and $\mathbf{H}_c$ is the conservative field that satisfies (9.35). The line integral in (9.32) is still satisfied because of the nature of $\mathbf{H}_c$. Thus

$$\oint (\mathbf{H}_i + \mathbf{H}_c) \cdot d\mathbf{l} = \oint \mathbf{H}_i \cdot d\mathbf{l} + 0 = i \qquad (9.36)$$

If we imitate the situation in electrostatics where point charges serve as the source of the conservative field, the vector $\mathbf{H}$ becomes

$$\mathbf{H} = \frac{1}{4\pi} \int \frac{i\, d\mathbf{l} \times \mathbf{r}_1}{r^2} + \frac{1}{4\pi\mu_0} \int \frac{dp}{r^2}\, \mathbf{r}_1 \qquad (9.37)$$

where dp is an element of pole strength on the surface or in the interior of the medium.

The auxiliary vector $\mathbf{H}$ is useful in problems where there are boundaries of magnetic materials. Its most important property is described by the circuital law $\oint \mathbf{H} \cdot d\mathbf{l} = i$, where i is the conduction current which links the path of integration. This property is independent of the presence or absence of magnetized matter. The line integral is referred to as the *magnetomotive force* (mmf).

4. $\mathbf{B}$ *and* $\mathbf{H}$ *when magnetized matter is present in the field.* For points outside matter, $\mathbf{M} = 0$ and $\mu_0\mathbf{H} = \mathbf{B}$. However, here $\mathbf{B}$ contains contributions from conduction and amperian currents (or, alternately, from the equivalent pole representation). For points inside matter, $\mathbf{M}$ is no longer zero and (9.31) is valid.

5. *Comparison of magnetic and electric fields.* The field of $\mathbf{E}$ determines the force on a charge, and in this sense it is the homolog of $\mathbf{B}$. The auxiliary vectors $\mathbf{P}$ and $\mathbf{M}$ play similar roles in describing the macroscopic field arising from polarized dielectrics and magnetized matter. Dielectrics which contain permanent dipoles are oriented under the external field in much the same way that magnetic dipoles become preferentially oriented and thus add to the externally applied field. In purely diamagnetic behavior, the effect of the medium is to weaken $\mathbf{B}$ relative to its value in free space. This is to be compared with the weakening of the $\mathbf{E}$-field within a dielectric. The surface integral of the auxiliary vector $\mathbf{D}$ gives the free charge within the surface regardless of the presence of polarized materials. The line integral of $\mathbf{H}$ around a circuit gives the conduction current crossing the circuit regardless of the presence of magnetized matter.

It is instructive to compare the fields in a uniformly and permanently polarized dielectric slab with the fields in a similarly magnetized sample of matter. In this case $\mathbf{D} = 0$, and the $\mathbf{E}$-field in the interior is due only to surface charges and is directed from the positive to the negative. The polarization $\mathbf{P}$ is oppositely directed. In the magnetic specimen, the $\mathbf{H}$-field which originates from poles is antiparallel to $\mathbf{M}$, but $\mathbf{M}$ is parallel to $\mathbf{B}$.

The electrostatic fields are conservative, while the magnetic fields are in general nonconservative, although, as (9.37) indicates, the part of the field of $\mathbf{H}$ associated with pole distributions is conservative.

In formal mathematical terms, the relation $\mathbf{B} = \mu_0\mathbf{H} + \mathbf{M}$ is to be compared with $\mathbf{D} = \varepsilon_0\mathbf{E} + \mathbf{P}$. But from the physical viewpoint the analog of $\mathbf{B}$ is $\mathbf{E}$, and the analog of $\mathbf{H}$ is $\mathbf{D}$.

9.8   Linear Magnetic Materials

If the magnetic moment induced in an atom or if the contribution by a permanent moment to the magnetization is proportional to the field, the magnetization $\mathbf{M}$ is proportional to $\mathbf{H}$ and to $\mathbf{B}$. Most magnetic materials obey such a linear relationship; the outstanding exception is the case of ferromagnetic materials, which will be discussed separately in Chapter 10. In addition, if the medium is homogeneous and isotropic, the field vectors are collinear, and the general relation $\mathbf{B} = \mu_0\mathbf{H} + \mathbf{M}$ can be simplified. Setting

$$\mathbf{M} = \chi\mathbf{H} \tag{9.38}$$

we obtain at once

$$\mathbf{B} = (\mu_0 + \chi)\mathbf{H} = \mu\mathbf{H} \tag{9.39}$$

where χ is called the *magnetic susceptibility* and μ is called the *magnetic permeability*. Both χ and μ are expressed in the same units as those of μ_0 (weber per ampere-meter or henry per meter), as is seen from

$$\mu = \mu_0 + \chi \tag{9.40}$$

In a vacuum, $\mathbf{M} = 0$. Hence $\chi = 0$ and $\mu = \mu_0$, the permeability of free space. The relative permeability K_m, which was introduced earlier, is given by the ratio

$$K_m = \frac{\mu}{\mu_0} = 1 + \frac{\chi}{\mu_0} \tag{9.41}$$

For a diamagnetic substance, $\chi < 0$, $\mu < \mu_0$, and $K_m < 1$. Similarly, for paramagnetic materials, $\chi > 0$, $\mu > \mu_0$, and $K_m > 1$. The following relationships follow at once from the general definition of **B**.

$$\mathbf{M} = (\mu - \mu_0)\mathbf{H} = \left(\frac{\mu - \mu_0}{\mu}\right)\mathbf{B} \qquad (9.42)$$

9.9   Boundary Conditions

We can relate the values of **B** and **H** in one medium to the corresponding values in a second medium by applying the fundamental laws which **B** and **H** must satisfy. The details of the procedure are quite similar to those followed in obtaining the boundary conditions on **D** and **E** in our study of dielectrics. We apply the flux theorem to the pillbox-shaped closed surface—see Fig. 9.10(a)—whose cylindrical surface area is negligible relative

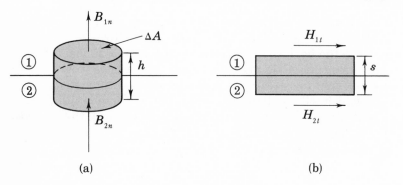

(a)   (b)

Figure 9.10   Boundary conditions on **B** and **H**.

to ΔA, the area of the top and bottom. This geometry may be achieved by making the cylindrical height h as small as desired. Let B_{2n} and B_{1n} denote the components of **B** normal to the boundary separating the two simple media of permeability μ_2 and μ_1. Since the net outward flux of **B** over the surface of the pillbox is zero, we may write $-B_{2n}\,\Delta A + B_{1n}\,\Delta A = 0$, since the flux of **B** over the cylindrical surface is negligible. It follows that

$$B_{2n} = B_{1n} \qquad (9.43)$$

—that is, the normal component of **B** is continuous across the boundary.

Next we apply the circuital law for **H** to the rectangle in Fig. 9.10(b), where s, the dimension of the rectangle transverse to the boundary, is much smaller than the length l of the sides parallel to the boundary. Neglecting the contributions to the line integral of **H** coming from the transverse dimensions, we apply the circuital relation and get

$$H_{2t}l - H_{1t}l = i_s l \qquad (9.44)$$

where H_{2t} and H_{1t} are the tangential components of **H** in media 2 and 1 respectively. In the right-hand member of (9.44), i_s represents the conduction current per unit length along the boundary. If $i_s = 0$, then (9.44) reduces to

$$H_{2t} = H_{1t} \qquad (9.45)$$

which states that the tangential component of **H** is continuous across the boundary.

Figure 9.11 shows how **B** and **H** are refracted at the boundary for the simple case where **B** and **H** are collinear in each me-

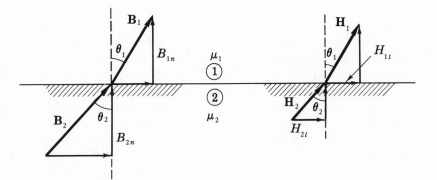

Figure 9.11   Refraction of the lines of **B** and **H** where $\mu_1 < \mu_2$.

dium. The diagram is drawn on the assumption that $\mu_2 > \mu_1$. Applying (9.43) and (9.45) to the vector diagrams for **B** and **H** in Fig. 9.11, we obtain

$$B_1 \cos \theta_1 = B_2 \cos \theta_2 \qquad (9.46)$$

and

$$H_1 \sin \theta_1 = H_2 \sin \theta_2 \qquad (9.47)$$

These relations yield the law of refraction—namely,

$$\frac{\tan \theta_1}{\tan \theta_2} = \frac{\mu_1}{\mu_2} \qquad (9.48)$$

Chapter 10.
Ferromagnetism

10.1   Ferromagnetic Media

A special class of materials, including the metals of the iron group (Fe, Co, Ni) and certain alloys (Si-Fe, Permalloy, Mumetal, Alnico), have unusual magnetic properties. These so-called *ferromagnetic* materials are nonlinear and may be magnetized permanently. They exhibit abnormally high values of the magnetization and are extremely useful in practical applications. In the preceding chapter we dealt with linear media, where the susceptibility χ and the permeability μ as defined by (9.38) and (9.39) are constants. These relations do not apply to ferromagnetic media. However, it is customary to retain the forms of the definitions, since χ and μ are, in general, functions of $\mathbf{H}$. Because of the complex dependence of $\mathbf{B}$ on $\mathbf{H}$, the definition of μ given in (9.39) may lead to predictions whose physical validity must be examined by appeal to experiment.

Assume that a completely unmagnetized ferromagnetic sample forms the core of a toroidal winding. Starting from zero, let the current in the winding be increased steadily. In this case the values of $\mathbf{H}$ can be calculated from the circuital law expressed by (9.32). The induction $\mathbf{B}$ can be measured by a ballistic galvanometer, as described previously. Then a graph of B vs H—the so-called magnetization curve—resembles the plot in Fig. 10.1. Using the expression B/H, we can also obtain μ, which, when divided by μ_0, yields values of K_m. These are also plotted in Fig. 10.1 as a function of H. If, instead of B, the magnetization M is plotted as a function of H, the resulting curve shows saturation.

The gradual increase in B with H appearing in Fig. 10.1 is brought about by the $\mu_0 H$ term in $B = \mu_0 H + M$. Beyond the saturation value of M, B increases only because of the increase in H caused by the increase in the conduction current in the winding.

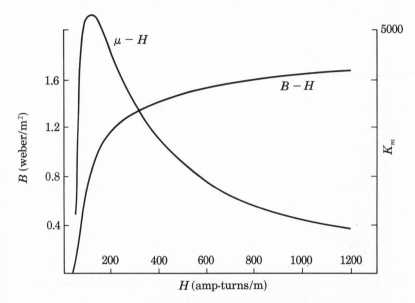

Figure 10.1 B vs H and μ vs H curves for a sample of iron.

In addition to the saturation effect just referred to, ferromagnetic materials display hysteresis effects. If, upon reaching a particular value of B on the B-H curve, H is decreased, B does not follow the B-H curve in Fig. 10.1. Instead, B diminishes more slowly and reaches the value B_R when $H = 0$. (B_R is called the *retentivity*.) The remarkable feature is that B does not vanish as H vanishes. If H is increased in magnitude in the reverse direction, B is reduced to zero at $H = -H_c$. (H_c is termed the *coercive force*.) Further variations in H lead to the values of B shown in the hysteresis loop of Fig. 10.2. The term hysteresis is derived from a Greek verb which means "to lag." In this connection it describes the lagging of B behind H for decreasing and increasing values of H. The loop is symmetric with respect to the origin O.

The hysteresis loop furnishes information about the properties of ferromagnetic materials. For instance, in making a permanent magnet, one would select a material with a large retentivity and a large coercive force. After the exciting field has been removed,

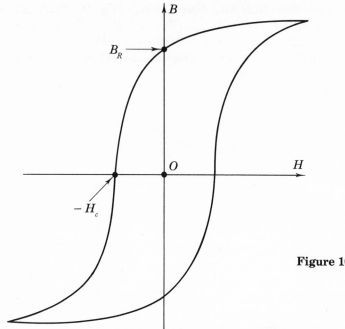

Figure 10.2 Hysteresis loop.

the residual magnetization will be high, and large external fields will be required to demagnetize the specimen.

In electromagnets, transformers, and other applications, ferromagnetic materials are used to enhance the magnetic flux, and the behavior of the material again can be predicted by a study of the loop. In transformer cores, where H varies periodically, heat is generated in the ferromagnetic material as a consequence of the hysteresis effect. (This is to be distinguished from the heat produced by eddy currents.) The area enclosed by the hysteresis loop is a measure of the heat loss per cycle. To minimize such losses, the material must possess a narrow loop.

10.2   Origin of Ferromagnetism

Ferromagnetism is a property of the crystalline state. For example, isolated atoms of iron are only paramagnetic. On the other hand, solids formed from mixtures of aluminum, copper, and manganese exhibit ferromagnetism. There are two main considerations which account for the large magnetization produced by the application of rather small external fields. The first is that large magnetization results not from the orbital, but from the magnetic moment associated with the unpaired electron spin. Iron, cobalt, and nickel are among the important elements which form ferromagnetic crystals. These elements belong to the $3d$ transition group, in which the M shell is incomplete. Their remarkable magnetic properties originate in part from the parallel alignment of spins.

To illustrate, consider the six $3d$ electrons of iron. Stability conditions based on quantum mechanics predict that the spin configuration $\uparrow\downarrow\uparrow\uparrow\uparrow\uparrow$, in which there are four uncompensated electrons, will have lowest energy. The forces which bring about such an alignment of the electron spins of neighboring atoms are referred to as "exchange" interactions.

According to the qualitative picture of intrinsic magnetization presented above, a ferromagnetic material should be in a nearly saturated state of magnetization below a certain critical temperature. Experience indicates that a piece of iron shows little or no magnetization unless it has been exposed to an external field. This observation leads to the second aspect of the phenomenon—namely, the presence of a domain structure in the specimen. According to this view, a given sample is subdivided into domains whose volumes range from 10^{-12} m³ to 10^{-16} m³. Since there are 8.5×10^{28} atoms of iron per cubic meter, on the average a domain contains 10^{15} atoms. Within each domain there is almost complete alignment of spins. But, since the domains are randomly oriented, the specimen as a whole appears unmagnetized.

When subjected to an applied field, the large-scale magnetization process involves changes in the configuration of domains. Such changes consist of the growth and rotation of domains. The schematic diagrams in Fig. 10.3 show (a) the unmagnetized state,

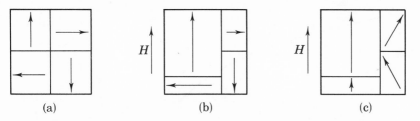

(a)   (b)   (c)

Figure 10.3 Schematic representation of domains: (a) unmagnetized sample, (b) growth in domain volume upon the application of a field, (c) rotation of domains.

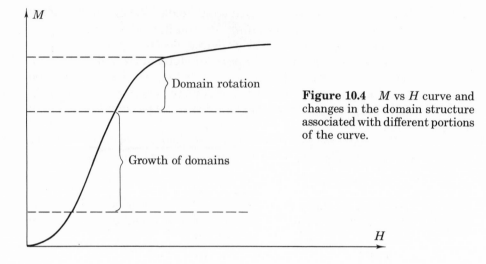

Figure 10.4   *M* vs *H* curve and changes in the domain structure associated with different portions of the curve.

(b) the magnetization by an increase in the volume of a domain upon the application of a field, and (c) the rotation of domains. Figure 10.4 shows a typical magnetization curve (*M* vs *H* plot) and the processes which predominate over different regions of the curve.

Ferromagnetism is a strongly temperature-dependent property. As the temperature is increased, the magnetization decreases gradually, and the material becomes demagnetized at the Curie temperature. Above this temperature the material becomes paramagnetic. The behavior is shown schematically in Fig. 10.5.

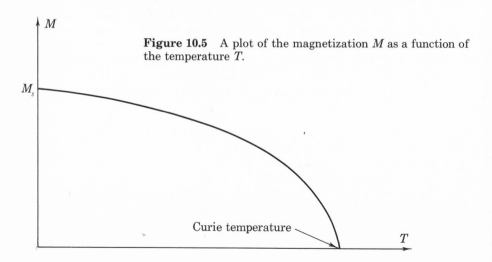

Figure 10.5   A plot of the magnetization *M* as a function of the temperature *T*.

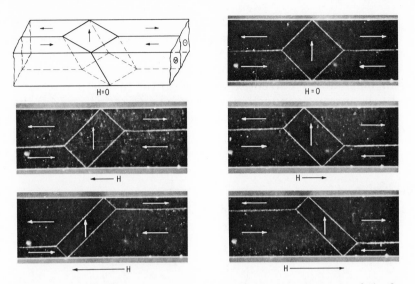

Changes in the configuration of magnetic domains in an iron crystal. As the applied magnetic field **H** grows or changes in direction, the domain walls in the crystal move in a smooth, reversible pattern. The iron "whisker" shown in this figure measures 100μ on each side. (Courtesy R. W. DeBlois and C. D. Graham, Jr., General Electric Research Laboratory.)

The Curie temperatures for Fe, Co, and Ni fall at $770°C$, $1127°C$, and $358°C$ respectively.

A group of substances known as *ferrites* (mixtures of the oxides of Fe, Co, Ni, Mn, etc.) are of practical importance because they exhibit a large magnetization and at the same time are poor conductors. The ferrites are useful in high-frequency applications where low-resistance magnetic materials cannot be employed because of large eddy current losses. In the ferrites the unequal electronic spins of neighboring atoms are antiparallel: $\downarrow\uparrow\downarrow\uparrow\uparrow\downarrow\downarrow\uparrow$.

A domain with a spin structure of this sort has a net magnetic moment. Materials possessing domains of this variety are said to be ferrimagnetic.

10.3   Illustrative Examples

Example 1. *Rowland ring.* Measurements were made on the hysteresis loop of an iron specimen forming the core of a Rowland ring. The mean radius of the ring was 0.039 m and the cross-sectional area of the core was 1.20×10^{-4} m². The magnetizing coil consisted of 1000 turns of wire wound uniformly. For a particular loop, a maximum change in flux of 2.88×10^{-4} weber/m² was attained in the core corresponding to a change of 0.100 amp in the magnetizing current. Compute (a) the magnetic intensity, (b) the magnetic induction, (c) the magnetization, and (d) the surface density of the amperian current. Refer to the discussion of the Rowland ring in Section 9.1, and to Fig. 10.6. Consider the winding as equivalent to N circular turns, each carrying a conduction current i.

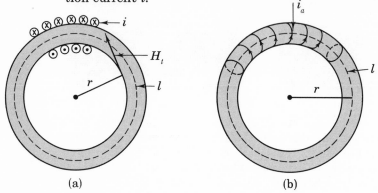

(a)   (b)

Figure 10.6 Toroidal winding showing (a) conduction, (b) amperian currents.

(a) According to the discussion in Section 9.7, there are two kinds of source for H: conduction currents, and volume and surface distribution of poles. H due to the current in the winding can be determined from the circuital law in (9.32). From Fig. 10.6(a) the total conduction current encircled by the path of integration is (Ni). Hence

$$\oint \mathbf{H} \cdot d\mathbf{l} = 2\pi r H_t = Ni \qquad (10.1)$$

where H_t is the component of H tangential to a circular path of radius r coaxial with the toroidal axis. With the aid of (10.1) and the numerical data given above, we find:

$$H_t = \frac{1000 \times 0.050}{2\pi \times 0.039} = 204 \text{ amp-turns/m}$$

Note that the change in the magnetizing current is twice the value of i to be substituted in (10.1). Because of symmetry considerations, H_t is the only component of $\mathbf{H}$ originating from conduction currents.

Next we shall investigate to see if surface and volume pole

densities, defined respectively as σ_M and ρ_M, may contribute to
H. The connection between the magnetization $\mathbf{M}$ and the pole
densities may be written by simulating the relation between the
polarization vector $\mathbf{P}$ and induced charge densities as given by
(4.12) and (4.16). Thus

$$\sigma_M = \mathbf{M} \cdot \mathbf{n}_1 \qquad (10.2)$$

and

$$\rho_M = -\left(\frac{\partial M_x}{\partial x} + \frac{\partial M_y}{\partial y} + \frac{\partial M_z}{\partial z} \right) \qquad (10.3)$$

Now, for simple materials $\mathbf{M}$ is parallel to $\mathbf{H}$; therefore $\mathbf{M}$ can
have only a tangential component M_t. Moreover, for the partic-
ular sample there are no boundaries normal to $\mathbf{M}$; so, by (10.2),
the surface density of poles is zero. If M_t is resolved into x and y
components, the evaluation of the derivatives in (10.3) shows that
ρ_M is also zero. Therefore a magnetized core in the form of a toroid
does not contribute to the magnetic intensity, and $\mathbf{H}$ calculated
from conduction currents by (10.1) gives the total field of $\mathbf{H}$. This
discussion should clarify why the geometry of the Rowland ring
facilitates the determination of $\mathbf{H}$.

(b) The change in the flux is twice the maximum flux. Assuming $\mathbf{B}$ to be uniform across the cross-sectional area,

$$B = \frac{1.44 \times 10^{-4}}{1.20 \times 10^{-4}} = 1.20 \text{ weber/m}^2$$

If the ring thickness is small relative to the inner and outer radii,
the above value of $\mathbf{B}$ is approximately the tangential (and only)
component of $\mathbf{B}$ along the mean circumference.

(c) From (9.31), $\mathbf{B} = \mu_0 \mathbf{H} + \mathbf{M}$. Hence

$$\mathbf{M} = \mathbf{B} - \mu_0 \mathbf{H} = 1.20 - 4\pi \times 10^{-7} \times 204 \cong 1.20 \text{ weber/m}^2$$

which shows that the magnetizing field contributes an insignifi-
cant amount to the flux density, practically all of which is due
to the magnetization of the core.

(d) From (9.25), $\oint \mathbf{M} \cdot d\mathbf{l} = \mu_0 i_a$. With the aid of Fig. 10.6(b),
i_a, the total amperian current encircled by the path of integra-
tion is $j_a^s \times 2\pi r$. Consequently

$$2\pi r \times M_t = \mu_0 (j_a^s) \times 2\pi r$$

or

$$j_a^s = \frac{M_t}{\mu_0} = \frac{1.20}{4\pi \times 10^{-7}} = 9.55 \times 10^5 \text{ amp/m}$$

which is nearly a million amperes per meter of length along the
circumference! The calculation assumes that j_a^v, the volume den-

sity of amperian currents, is zero. This is equivalent to the exist-ence of uniform magnetization within the volume.

Example 2. *Toroidal core with gap.* As a second example, let us assume that a small air gap of width d has been cut in a per-manently magnetized ring of iron [Fig. 10.7(a)]. It is required

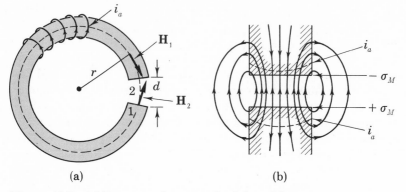

(a)   (b)

Figure 10.7   (a) Permanently magnetized ring with gap. (b) Schematic diagram of the **H**-field arising from pole densities $+\sigma_M$ and $-\sigma_M$ on the faces of the gap.

to calculate (a) H_2, the magnetic intensity in the gap, and (b) H_1, the intensity in the material. It is also required to express H_1 and H_2 in terms of M_1, the permanent magnetization in the iron.

The permeability of air is very nearly μ_0. So we shall consider the gap to be in free space. In this example there are no conduc-tion currents; therefore the field of **H** arises only from the mag-netization **M**. For the sake of simplicity, we shall assume that **M** is constant within the material and is directed tangentially to a concentric circular path of length l. Consequently, the volume density of poles ρ_M will be zero. But in this instance there will be a surface distribution of poles, σ_M on the faces of the gap normal to **M**. In accordance with (10.2) $\sigma_M = M$, since the normal com-ponent is the only component of **M**. Since the conduction current i is zero, (9.32) yields

$$H_1(l - d) + H_2 d = 0 \tag{10.4}$$

where the subscripts refer to the media involved, and where it is understood that H refers to the tangential field. Next we apply (9.43), the boundary condition on the component of **B** normal to the faces of the gap. The continuity of the normal component is described by

$$B_1 = B_2 \tag{10.5}$$

which in conjunction with the defining relation (9.31) gives

$$\mu_0 H_1 + M_1 = \mu_0 H_2 + 0 \qquad (10.6)$$

since M_2, the magnetization in the gap, is zero. Solving (10.4) and (10.6) for H_1 and H_2, we find

$$H_1 = -\frac{M_1}{\mu_0}\frac{d}{l} \qquad \text{(in the core)} \qquad (10.7)$$

$$H_2 = \frac{M_1}{\mu_0}\left(1 - \frac{d}{l}\right) \qquad \text{(in the gap)} \qquad (10.8)$$

Subtracting H_1 from H_2, the change in H at the face of the gap is

$$H_2 - H_1 = \frac{M_1}{\mu_0} = \frac{\sigma_M}{\mu_0} \qquad (10.9)$$

As d is made smaller, H_1, the field in the core, approaches zero. Similarly, the field in the gap becomes

$$H_2 \cong \frac{\sigma_M}{\mu_0} \qquad (10.10)$$

which reminds one of the **E**-field in the region between closely spaced charged parallel plates. The example illustrates again that **H** is discontinuous at the boundaries and has sources at the interface.

These calculations imply that **M** is constant and independent of the surroundings in which the core is located. Only in this case it is meaningful to consider the concept of magnetic charge as a property of the material independent of outside influences. In electrostatics, a charge on an isolated system is an intrinsic property of the system unaltered by external influences. On the other hand, pole densities used to describe the magnetic state do not possess a unique value. Rather, they are subject to change as the magnetization is modified by the action of external fields.

The **B**-field in the core is found from

$$B_1 = \mu_0 H_1 + M_1 = M_1\left(1 - \frac{d}{l}\right) \qquad (10.11)$$

Similarly, B_2, the induction in the gap, is

$$B_2 = \mu_0 H_2 + 0 = M_1\left(1 - \frac{d}{l}\right) \qquad (10.12)$$

Accordingly, **B** is continuous across the boundary, which is as it should be.

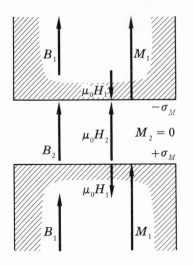

Figure 10.8 The **B**, **H**, and **M** vectors in the gap and just inside the medium.

Unlike the field of **H**, the field of **B** has no sources. Figure 10.7(b) shows a sketch of the field of **H**. The **B**, **M**, and **H** vectors in the gap and just inside the medium are indicated in Fig. 10.8. Inside the material, **H** is antiparallel to **M**. The lines of **H** start from + "poles" and end on − "poles." This is the same convention that is used in drawing the electrostatic field. The introduction of a gap in the ring gives rise to a "demagnetizing" field intensity within the core, so that the induction **B** is reduced depending on the width of the gap.

Example 3. *Cylindrical bar magnet.* As another example, we shall determine the magnetic intensity within a bar magnet. As an idealization, we shall suppose that **M** is uniform within the bar and is directed along the axis of the cylinder. To illustrate the use of amperian currents, we shall express **H** and **B** in terms of j_a^s, the amperian surface current density. Figure 10.9 gives a cross-sectional and an axial view of the cylinder. The only current that we have to deal with is the amperian current along the surface of the bar. If j_a^s is the surface density, then $i_a = j_a^s l$ represents the current on the surface of the cylinder of length l. We have already seen that the induction on the axis of a solenoid of length l and n turns per unit length [see (7.14)] is

$$B = \frac{\mu_0 n i}{2}(\cos \beta_2 - \cos \beta_1) \tag{10.13}$$

where i is the conduction current in the winding. The angles in (10.13) are indicated in Fig. 10.9. In the present situation ni,

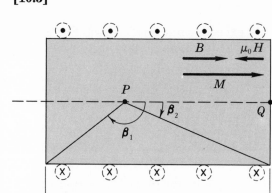
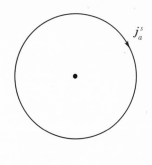

Figure 10.9   Cylindrical bar magnet.

the current per unit length of the solenoid, may be replaced by j_a^s, which may be envisaged as the amperian current in a flat turn of unit width. From (9.20), $M = \mu_0 j_a^s$. Utilizing the defining relation $H = 1/\mu_0 \, (B - M)$, the magnitude of H at a point P on the axis may be expressed as

$$H_P = \frac{j_a^s}{2}(\cos \beta_2 - \cos \beta_1 - 2) \qquad (10.14)$$

If P is inside the cylinder, $\beta_1 > \pi/2$ and $\beta_2 < \pi/2$. This makes $\cos \beta_1$ negative. Hence the contents of the parentheses, and also H, are negative. However, from (10.13) B is positive for the same angles subtended at P by the ends of the bar. The conclusion is that **H** within the bar magnet is directed oppositely to **B**.

At the point Q on the axis at one end, $\beta_2 = \pi/2$, while $\beta_1 > \pi/2$. Hence, H inside the magnet at Q is

$$H_Q = -\frac{j_a^s}{2}(\cos \beta_1 + 2) \qquad (10.15)$$

With the aid of the result given by (10.13) the induction at Q is

$$B_Q = -\frac{\mu_0 j_a^s}{2} \cos \beta_1 \qquad (10.16)$$

which, by the continuity of the normal component of **B**, is the value of **B** on either side of the boundary at Q. Hence the normal component of H outside becomes

$$H_Q = -\frac{j_a^s}{2} \cos \beta_1 \qquad (10.17)$$

If (10.15) and (10.17) are combined, it follows that the normal component of **H** outside exceeds that inside by j_a^s. For a long magnet, $\cos \beta_1 \rightarrow -1$, so that (9.20) and (10.17) give

$$H_Q = \frac{j_a^s}{2} = \frac{M}{2\mu_0} = \frac{\sigma_M}{2\mu_0} \qquad (10.18)$$

Similarly, just inside the bar

$$H_Q = -\frac{j_a^s}{2} = -\frac{M}{2\mu_0} = -\frac{\sigma_M}{2\mu_0} \qquad (10.19)$$

so that once again **H** may be thought of as originating from a source of magnetic charges. The axial fields at one end for the case of a long bar magnet ($\cos \beta_1 = -1$) are indicated in Fig. 10.10. Equations (10.18) and (10.19) are reminiscent of the electrostatic field on either side of a layer of charge with surface density σ.

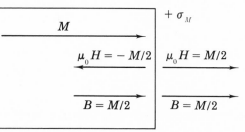

Figure 10.10   Idealized long bar magnet. **B**, **M**, and **H** fields at end face.

The calculation of the magnetic intensity for off-axis points can also be carried out. The **B** and **H** fields are shown schematically in Fig. 10.11.

Example 4. *Torque on bar magnet.* According to (6.17), the torque T on a current loop of area A immersed in an externally applied magnetic induction B is equal to

$$T = iAB \sin \alpha \qquad (10.20)$$

where α is the angle between the direction of the field and the normal to the area of the loop. The magnitude of the torque can be expressed in terms m, the magnetic moment of the loop as defined by $m = \mu_0 iA$. Hence

$$T = \frac{1}{\mu_0} mB \sin \alpha \qquad (10.21)$$

We shall assume that the bar magnet is magnetized uniformly

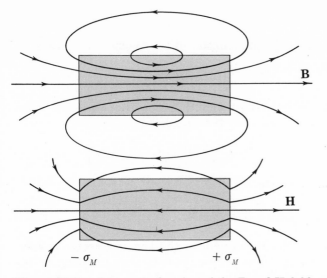

Figure 10.11 Schematic drawing of the **B** and **H** fields of a bar magnet.

and permanently, so that its magnetization **M** does not change when placed in a field **B**. Consider an element of the bar magnet of length dx. As shown in Fig. 10.12, this element constitutes an amperian current loop of moment $dm = \mu_0(j_a^s \, dx)A$. By (9.20) the amperian surface current density j_a^s can be replaced by $1/\mu_0 M$, which leads to the expression

$$dm = MA \, dx \qquad (10.22)$$

(This result could have been written down directly, since M is defined as the magnetic moment per unit volume.) Hence the torque dT on an element of length dx is

$$dT = \frac{1}{\mu_0}(MA \, dx)B \sin \alpha \qquad (10.23)$$

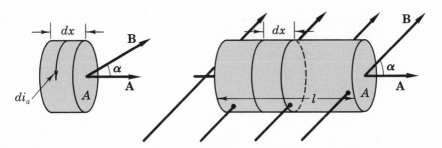

Figure 10.12 Calculation of the torque on a bar magnet placed in an external field **B**.

243

Upon integrating over the length l of the magnet, we obtain

$$T = \frac{1}{\mu_0} (MAl)B \sin \alpha \qquad (10.24)$$

where MAl represents the magnetic moment of the entire magnet. Setting $\mathfrak{M} = MAl$, (10.24) becomes

$$T = \frac{1}{\mu_0} \mathfrak{M}B \sin \alpha \qquad (10.25)$$

or, in vectorial notation,

$$\mathbf{T} = \frac{1}{\mu_0} \mathfrak{M} \times \mathbf{B} \qquad (10.26)$$

where $\mathfrak{M}$, the magnetic moment of the bar, is a vector parallel to the axis of the bar. The torque tends to align the magnet into parallelism with $\mathbf{B}$. Since the units of $\mathbf{M}$ are weber per square meter, $\mathfrak{M}$ is expressed in weber-meter, which is also the unit of the magnetic dipole moment ($\mu_0 iA$). The torque has the dimensions of force times distance (newton-meter).

In the terminology of poles, $\mathfrak{M}$ can be replaced by $\sigma_M Al$ or pl, where $p = \sigma_M A$ is the pole strength in weber on each end face of the bar. The quantity pl is called the *dipole moment* of the magnet. In electrostatics its analog is the electric dipole moment ql associated with two point charges of equal magnitude q but of opposite sign, with the charges separated by a distance l. In terms of this model the torque on the magnet can be interpreted in terms of oppositely directed forces, each of magnitude $p\mathbf{B}/\mu_0$, acting on the end faces of the magnet. (See Fig. 10.13.) The above description involves certain idealizations. The surface

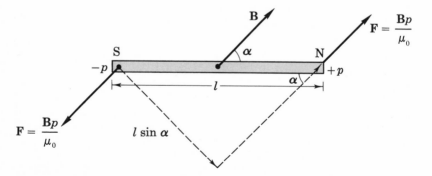

Figure 10.13 Torque on magnet in terms of north and south poles located at ends of bar. Torque of couple $T = Fl \sin \alpha = (Bpl/\mu_0) \sin \alpha$ or $\mathbf{T} = \mathfrak{M} \times \mathbf{H}$, where $\mathbf{B}/\mu_0 = \mathbf{H}$ and $\mathfrak{M} = pl$.

density of poles has been assumed to be uniform over the end face, and, in Fig. 10.13, the north and south poles are to be regarded as concentrated "magnetic charges."

If the angle α between $\mathfrak{M}$ and B is small, $\sin \alpha$ may be replaced by α, and the magnitude of the restoring torque on the magnet becomes

$$T = \mathfrak{M}B\alpha/\mu_0$$

Under this condition the torque is proportional to the angular displacement, and the magnet may be set into angular simple harmonic oscillation about its equilibrium position. From mechanics, the expression for the period is

$$P = 2\pi\sqrt{\frac{\mu_0 I}{B\mathfrak{M}}} \tag{10.27}$$

where I is the moment of inertia of the magnet about its center.

Ferromagnetism: **Problems**

10.1 Within an extensive uniformly magnetized medium, consider a cylinder whose diameter is 2.00×10^{-5} m and whose length is 5×10^{-5} m. The cylinder is of the same material as that of its surroundings and is located so that the resultant of the individual dipole moments is directed along the axis of the cylinder and has the magnitude 6.30×10^{-15} weber-m. Calculate the magnitude and specify the direction of the magnetization vector **M** at any point within the cylinder. Specify the units of your result.

10.2 What is the magnitude of the line integral $\oint \mathbf{H} \cdot d\mathbf{l}$ for each of the two contours A and C? The slender rods in the diagram represent parallel copper conductors in air. In each conductor there is a steady current i equal to 2.0 amp.

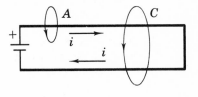

10.3 The diagram represents the central section of a long, uniformly magnetized right circular cylinder. The magnetization **M** is uniform and has the direction of the cylinder axis. Consider the rectangular path *ACDE*. Side *AC* (length *l*) lies within the cylinder and is parallel to its axis, while side *ED* lies outside. Apply the circuital law for **M** to path *ACDE* and evaluate the amperian current per meter of length along the surface. Recall that **M** = 0 along *ED*.

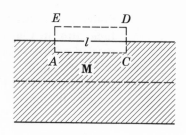

10.4   There is a closely wound coil on the outside of the cylindrical specimen referred to in Problem 10.3. The coil has 1500 turns/m and the current in each turn is 1.20 amp. Evaluate the line integral $\oint \mathbf{H} \cdot d\mathbf{l}$ over the closed path *ACDE* shown above. Specify the units of your answer.

10.5   The material within the core of a Rowland ring is initially in the unmagnetized state. Starting with this state, the magnetizing field *H* is increased from zero to the value of 100 amp-turns/m. At this value of *H*, the relative permeability has the unusual value of 0.90.

(a) Calculate the flux density *B* within the material of the core. The permeability of free space is $4\pi \times 10^{-7}$ mks units.

(b) Is the material of the core dia-, para-, or ferro-magnetic? Give the basis for your answer.

(c) If all matter is removed from the core, what would be the flux density within the ring when $H = 100$ amp-turns/m?

10.6   For a certain sample of steel, the permeability μ varies with the flux density *B* (in weber per square meter) according to

$$\mu = [70 \times 10^{-4} - 1.2(B - 0.07)^2] \text{ weber/amp-m}$$

provided $0.02 < B < 0.12$.

(a) What is the value of the magnetic intensity *H* when $B = 0.09$ weber/m²? Repeat for $B = 0.05$ weber/m².

(b) Sketch the μ vs *H* curve for the range of validity of the given formula.

(c) Sketch the *B* vs *H* curve with the aid of results from (a) and (b).

10.7   In the interior of a permanent magnet, the **H**-field is opposite to the **B**-field. What portion of the hysteresis loop corresponds to such a magnetic state?

10.8   Consider a toroidal coil of *N* turns wound closely around a ferromagnetic core of cross-sectional area *A* and a mean circumferential length *l*. When the magnetizing current in the coil is increased, the power furnished to the coil, exclusive of i^2R losses, is $\mathcal{E}i$, where $\mathcal{E} = NA(dB/dt)$.

(a) Show that $\mathcal{E}i = VH\,(dB/dt)$, where H is the magnetizing field and V is the volume of the specimen.

(b) Express the work done during a hysteresis cycle by an integral and explain how the energy furnished per cycle is related to the hysteresis loop.

10.9 For a sample of transformer iron, K_m, the relative permeability varies with the flux density B (in weber per square meter) according to the relation $K_m = 5500 - 10^6\,(B - 0.07)^2$ provided $0.02 < B < 0.12$.

(a) For what value of B is the permeability μ a maximum?

(b) What is the maximum value of μ? Take $\mu_0 = 4\pi \times 10^{-7}$ weber/amp-m.

10.10 Starting with the unmagnetized state, the magnetizing field H produced by the current in the winding of a toroidal coil is increased in time at the constant rate of 20,000 amp-turns/m-sec. The accompanying table gives a few values of H and μ, the permeability of the material of the coil while H is increasing.

(a) Assuming that $H = 0$, at the time $t = 0$, calculate the flux density B in the core at the instants $t = 0.005$ sec and $t = 0.060$ sec.

(b) Is the material of the core dia-, para-, or ferro-magnetic? Base your answer on the behavior of relative permeability of the core. Take $\mu_0 = 4\pi \times 10^{-7}$ mks units.

H amp-turns/m	μ in mks units
0	0.3×10^{-3}
100	1.2×10^{-3}
200	6.0×10^{-3}
400	3.4×10^{-3}
600	2.4×10^{-3}
800	1.9×10^{-3}
1000	1.6×10^{-3}
1200	1.2×10^{-3}

10.11 For sufficiently large values of the magnetizing field $\mathbf{H}$, K_m, the relative permeability, depends on H in accordance with the relation

$$K_m = 1 + \frac{C}{\mu_0 H}$$

where C is a constant and $\mu_0 = 4\pi \times 10^{-7}$ weber/amp-m.

(a) Obtain an expression which shows how B, the flux density, varies with H.

(b) As H is increased indefinitely, does the permeability approach a limiting value? If so, what is the limiting value?

(c) For the special case of a toroidal winding of n turns per unit length along the mean circumference, write an expression for the contribution to the total flux density coming only from the current in the winding.

10.12   A sample of iron, in the shape of a ring, forms the core of a closely wound toroid. The magnitude of the magnetic intensity **H** at any point on the mean circumference is given by

$$H = 1500 \, i \text{ amp-turns/m}$$

where i is the magnetizing current.

   Starting with the unmagnetized state, H is steadily increased until B, the total flux density in the iron, is in excess of 1.20 weber/m². For these higher values of B, the relation between B and H may be described by

$$B = 1.32 + 0.00028 \, H \text{ weber/m}^2$$

where H is expressed in ampere turns per meter.

   When the current in the winding reaches the value of 2.00 amp, find the values of:

   (a) The flux density due only to the current in the winding. Take $\mu_0 = 12.5 \times 10^{-7}$ weber/amp-m.

   (b) The permeability of the iron.

   (c) The flux density due only to amperian currents in the core.

10.13   A specimen of iron in the form of a ring is provided with a closely spaced toroidal winding. The magnitude of the magnetic intensity **H** at any point on the mean circumference within the winding is given by

$$H = 400 \, i \text{ amp-turns/m}$$

where the magnetizing current i is expressed in amperes.

   Beginning with an unmagnetized sample, the value of i is increased from 0.10 amp to 0.250 amp. Consult data in the accompanying table and calculate:

   (a) The change in the flux density due only to the current in the winding. Take $\mu_0 = 12.5 \times 10^{-7}$ weber/amp-m.

   (b) The corresponding change in B, the total flux density within the iron.

H amp-turns/m	μ weber/amp-m
20	5000×10^{-7}
40	7000×10^{-7}
60	16000×10^{-7}
80	60000×10^{-7}
100	70000×10^{-7}

10.14 A sample of iron forms the core of a closely wound toroid whose winding has 1500 turns and a mean circumference of 1.00 m. Starting with the unmagnetized state, the magnetizing current in the winding is increased until the magnetic intensity **H** is in excess of 1800 amp-turns/m. Over the range $H = 1800$ to $H = 3200$ amp-turns/m, μ, the permeability of the iron core, may be described by $\mu = 1.32/H + 0.00060$ weber/amp-m. When the current in the winding reaches the value of 2.00 amp, find:

(a) The value of B, the flux density in the iron.

(b) The relative permeability. Take $\mu_0 = 12.5 \times 10^{-7}$ weber/amp-m.

10.15 A sample of iron, in the shape of a ring, forms the core of a closely wound toroid of 750 turns and a mean circumferential length of 0.30 m.

Starting with the unmagnetized state, the magnetic intensity is steadily increased until a flux density of 1.00 weber/m² (near the saturation region) is established in the iron. Over a narrow range, in the neighborhood of saturation, the relation between the permeability μ and the magnetic intensity H is given by

$$\mu = \left(\frac{0.4}{H} + 12 \times 10^{-4}\right) \text{henry/m}$$

where H is expressed in amp-turns/m.

(a) Determine the value of H required to set up the specified flux density of 1.00 weber/m².

(b) By integrating the magnetic intensity **H** over the mean circumference, find the value of the magnetizing current corresponding to $H = 1000$ amp-turns/m.

10.16 A long solenoidal coil of n turns per meter is wound on a long hollow iron cylinder of inner radius a and outer radius b. The permeability of the iron corresponding to a current i in the winding is μ. Obtain the magnitudes of **B**, **H**, and **M** within the hollow space and also within the body of the iron pipe.

10.17 A long copper rod 1.0 cm in diameter is surrounded by a long iron cylinder whose inner and outer diameters are 3.0 cm and 5.0 cm respectively. The axis of the copper rod coincides with that of the iron pipe. When the current in the copper rod is 10 amp, the relative permeability of the iron is 400.

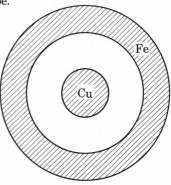

(a) Compute the magnetization **M** at a point 2.0 cm from the common axis of the system.

(b) Assume that the amperian currents are uniformly distributed over the surfaces of the iron cylinder. Determine the magnitudes of these currents and specify the directions of the induced current densities relative to the direction of the current density in the copper.

(c) Prove that the amperian current density within the body of the iron cylinder is zero.

(d) Does the presence of the iron cylinder affect the magnitude of **H** at points outside the cylinder?

10.18   In the discussion of the fields associated with an idealized bar magnet, the permanent magnetization **M** was assumed to be uniform and directed along the axis of the cylinder. 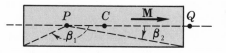 Consequently, the expression for the magnitude of **B** at any axial point P within the bar was found to be

$$B = \tfrac{1}{2} M (\cos \beta_2 - \cos \beta_1)$$

in terms of the angles specified in the diagram. Consider the limiting case of a very long, thin magnet. At the field points specified below, express the magnitude of **B** and **H** in terms of **M**, the uniform magnetization within the magnet.

(a) Axial point Q located *just outside* the magnet at one end.

(b) Axial point C located at the center of the magnet.

10.19   A long bar magnet is suspended so that it is free to rotate about a vertical axis. When set into simple harmonic oscillation at a location where the horizontal component of the earth's magnetic induction is 2.0×10^{-5} weber/m², its period is observed to be 24 sec. The magnet is moved to a second location where its period is observed to be 20 sec. Calculate the magnitude of the horizontal component of the earth's magnetic field at the second location.

10.20   (a) Obtain an expression for the magnitude of **H** at the interior point P on the axis of an idealized bar magnet by referring to the formula in Problem 10.18 and the accompanying diagram.

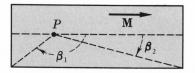

(b) At the inner point P describe the sense of **B** and **H** relative to that of **M**. Furnish the reason for your specification.

Chapter 11.
Energy of Charge
and Current Distributions—
Capacitance and Inductance

11.1   Energy of the Electrostatic Field

We shall calculate the mutual potential energy between a set of
n point charges q_1, q_2, . . ., q_n. We begin with the state where all
the charges are separated from each other by great distances and
then calculate the energy required to assemble the charges. In
Fig. 11.1, assume that q_1 is fixed. No work is done in placing q_1

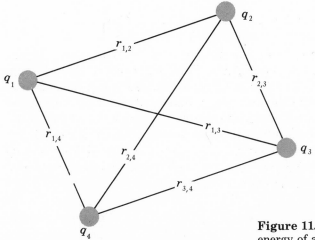

Figure 11.1   The mutual potential
energy of a set of point charges.

in position. Then, if q_2 is brought up to within a distance of $r_{1,2}$ from q_1, the work done is

$$u_2 = q_2 V_1 = \frac{1}{4\pi\varepsilon_0} \frac{q_1 q_2}{r_{1,2}} \tag{11.1}$$

where V_1 is the potential due to the charge q_1 at a distance $r_{1,2}$ from q_1. For a third charge q_3, positioned at distances $r_{1,3}$ and $r_{2,3}$ respectively from q_1 and q_2, which have been previously located, the work done is

$$u_3 = \frac{1}{4\pi\varepsilon_0} \left(\frac{q_1 q_3}{r_{1,3}} + \frac{q_2 q_3}{r_{2,3}} \right) \tag{11.2}$$

In like manner, when q_1, q_2, and q_3 are fixed and q_4 is moved into position, the energy expenditure is

$$u_4 = \frac{1}{4\pi\varepsilon_0} \left(\frac{q_1 q_4}{r_{1,4}} + \frac{q_2 q_4}{r_{2,4}} + \frac{q_3 q_4}{r_{3,4}} \right) \tag{11.3}$$

The work required to bring into the field the remaining charges can be written in the same way. Upon adding (11.1), (11.2), (11.3), and other terms up to U_n corresponding to the introduction of the nth charge, the expression for the total energy can be expressed as

$$U = \frac{1}{2} q_1 \left[\frac{1}{4\pi\varepsilon_0} \left(\frac{q_2}{r_{1,2}} + \frac{q_3}{r_{1,3}} + \frac{q_4}{r_{1,4}} + \cdots + \frac{q_n}{r_{1,n}} \right) \right] +$$

$$\frac{1}{2} q_2 \left[\frac{1}{4\pi\varepsilon_0} \left(\frac{q_1}{r_{2,1}} + \frac{q_3}{r_{2,3}} + \frac{q_4}{r_{2,4}} + \cdots + \frac{q_n}{r_{2,n}} \right) \right] +$$

$$\frac{1}{2} q_3 \left[\frac{1}{4\pi\varepsilon_0} \left(\frac{q_1}{r_{3,1}} + \frac{q_2}{r_{3,2}} + \frac{q_4}{r_{3,4}} + \cdots + \frac{q_n}{r_{3,n}} \right) \right] + \cdots \tag{11.4}$$

In (11.4) each term appearing in (11.1), (11.2), etc. has been rearranged into two equal parts. This form leads to the following interpretation: The first quantity in brackets is just the potential at the location of the first charge due to all the other charges except q_1. Similarly, the second quantity in brackets represents the potential at the position of q_2 due to all the other charges q_1, q_3, $q_4, \ldots, q_n$. Denoting by q_i the charge at the ith location and by V_i the potential at this point due to all charges except the ith, the sum in (11.4) may be abbreviated as

$$U = \frac{1}{2} q_1 V_1 + \frac{1}{2} q_2 V_2 + \frac{1}{2} q_3 V_3 + \cdots = \frac{1}{2} \sum_{i=1}^{n} q_i V_i \tag{11.5}$$

where U, the energy expended in assembling the n point charges, is expressed in terms of the potential V_i, which is a function of the positions of all the charges except q_i.

An alternative proof of the result in (11.5) supposes that, at each location, the charges are built up slowly in small steps until the final values $q_1, q_2, q_3, \ldots, q_n$ are reached. At a given instant, the charges at points 1, 2, 3, $\ldots$, n are given by $\alpha q_1, \alpha q_2, \alpha q_3,$ $\ldots, \alpha q_n$, where α is a fraction less than unity. At this stage of the charging process the potentials are $\alpha V_1, \alpha V_2, \alpha V_3, \ldots, \alpha V_n$. During the process of building up the charges, α varies continuously from 0 to 1. As a step in this process, let an incremental charge $dq_1 = q_1 \, d\alpha$ be brought from a large distance to point 1. Similarly, let $dq_2 = q_2 \, d\alpha$ be brought to point 2. The work done in this step is

$$dU = (\alpha V_1)q_1 \, d\alpha + (\alpha V_2)q_2 \, d\alpha + \cdots + (\alpha V_n)q_n \, d\alpha$$

$$= (V_1 q_1 + V_2 q_2 + \cdots + V_n q_n)\alpha \, d\alpha \qquad (11.6)$$

Hence

$$U = (V_1 q_1 + V_2 q_2 + \cdots + V_n q_n) \int_0^1 \alpha \, d\alpha = \frac{1}{2} \sum_{i=1}^{n} q_i V_i \quad (11.7)$$

which agrees with the result obtained in (11.5).

If the charges are distributed continuously with a volume density ρ and surface density σ, the corresponding formula becomes

$$U = \frac{1}{2} \int_{\text{volume}} \rho V \, dv + \frac{1}{2} \int_{\text{surface}} \sigma V \, dA \qquad (11.8)$$

where $\rho \, dv$ and $\sigma \, dA$ are the charges in a volume or a surface element at a point where V is the potential arising from the assembled charge.

By methods which lie outside the scope of the present treatment, one can relate the potential energy U of the charge distribution to the electric field produced by the distribution. The calculation shows that U can also be expressed as

$$U = \frac{\varepsilon_0}{2} \int_{\substack{\text{all} \\ \text{space}}} E^2 \, dv \qquad (11.9)$$

where dv is a volume element at the point where the field strength is E. According to (11.9), the energy required to establish the charge configuration and the field resulting from it may also be calculated by associating with each field point an energy density u given by

$$u = \frac{\varepsilon_0 E^2}{2} \qquad (11.10)$$

An inquisitive mind might raise a question about the location of the electrostatic energy. Strictly, the calculations carried out above represent the energy necessary to assemble a system of interacting charges. On the basis of the fields associated with static charges, there is no way of describing the location of the energy. Is it meaningful to ask where this energy resides? One cannot appeal to the law of conservation of energy for an answer. This law simply states that the increase in the energy acquired by the system of charges is furnished by an external source that has, as a consequence, suffered an equal decrease in energy.

The concept that the work done in assembling the charges is stored in the field with a density $\varepsilon_0 E^2/2$ is a convenient one. In the case of dynamic fields we shall see that energy is transmitted from one place to another by electromagnetic disturbances, such as radio and light waves. Often we have very little information concerning the distribution and motion of the charges in the source which give rise to the propagation of energy. Confronted by such a situation, we shall find it desirable to localize the energy in the field and to assume further that the energy conservation law applies to a given volume of space. Such an assumption implies that a change in the energy of a given volume is accompanied by the flow of energy into or out of that volume. Experiments do not contradict predictions based on the idea of energy density in the field.

Although the result in (11.10) is true strictly for empty space, a similar expression can be written for the energy density in linear, homogeneous, isotropic dielectrics. In this case energy is distributed with a density

$$u = \frac{1}{2}DE = \frac{1}{2}\varepsilon E^2 \qquad (11.11)$$

where ε is the permittivity of the isotropic dielectric.

11.2   Energy of Charged Systems: Capacitance

As a specific example of the concept of field energy, let us consider a parallel-plate capacitor (Fig. 11.2) with a surface charge density $+\sigma$ on one plate and $-\sigma$ on the other. If the separation

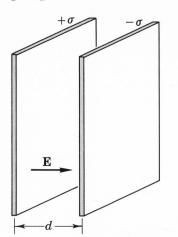

Figure 11.2   Parallel-plate capacitor.

d between the plates is small relative to the linear dimensions of the plates, there will be negligible fringing of the field at the edges, and we may assume that the electrostatic field is confined to the region between the plates. Let V_2 and V_1 denote the potentials of the positive and negative plates respectively. Since the charges reside only on the surfaces of the plates, the first integral in (11.8) is zero, and the energy of the system is obtained from the second integral—namely,

$$U = \frac{1}{2}\int \sigma V_2 \, dA - \frac{1}{2}\int \sigma V_1 \, dA = \frac{1}{2}(V_2 - V_1)\sigma \int dA$$

or
$$U = \frac{1}{2}VQ \qquad (11.12)$$

where $V \equiv (V_2 - V_1)$, the potential difference between the plates, and $Q = \sigma A$, the magnitude of the charge on one of the plates of surface area A. This result may also be obtained by calculating the work done in transferring charge from one plate to the other. If v is the potential difference between the plates at some stage of the charging process, then the work done in transporting a charge dq from the negative to the positive plate is

$$dU = v \, dq \qquad (11.13)$$

In an arrangement consisting of a pair of conductors, one of which carries a charge $+q$ and the other an equal and opposite charge $-q$, the magnitude of the charge is related to the potential difference v by the relation

$$q = Cv \qquad \text{or} \qquad C \equiv q/v \qquad (11.14)$$

where C is a constant called the capacitance of the pair of conductors. Relation (11.14) is a statement of the proportionality between q and v. The numerical value of the proportionality constant C depends on the shape and position of the conductors and on the dielectric constant of the intervening medium. The unit of capacitance is the farad. A capacitor is said to have a capacitance of one farad when a charge of one coulomb placed on one of the plates gives rise to a potential difference of one volt between the plates.

Returning to (11.13), we see that, with the aid of the defining relation (11.14), dU becomes $q\,dq/C$. Whence

$$U = \frac{1}{C}\int_0^Q q\,dq = \frac{Q^2}{2C} = \frac{CV^2}{2} = \frac{QV}{2} \qquad (11.15)$$

where Q and V stand for the final value of the charge and the potential difference.

The electric field $\mathbf{E}$ is constant in the space between the plates, and its magnitude can be expressed in terms of σ or in terms of V. By Gauss's law, $E = \sigma/\varepsilon_0$, and from the definition of potential difference $E = V/d$. Since the volume of the space between the plates is Ad, the energy per unit volume is computed from

$$u = \frac{1}{2}\frac{QV}{Ad} = \frac{1}{2}\frac{(\sigma A)Ed}{(Ad)} = \frac{1}{2}\varepsilon_0 E^2 \qquad (11.16)$$

This outcome verifies the general expression for the field energy density of the parallel-plate arrangement, which is a special case. Finally, by making appropriate substitutions for Q and V, we find for a parallel-plate arrangement in vacuum

$$C = \frac{Q}{V} = \frac{\sigma A}{Ed} = \frac{\varepsilon_0 A}{d} \qquad (11.17)$$

which shows that C varies directly with the area of the plates and inversely with their separation d. From this relation, it is seen that ε_0, the permittivity of free space, may be expressed conveniently in farad per meter. From Coulomb's law, ε_0 has the dimensions of coulomb^2 per newton-meter.

As a second example of the method which may be used for calculating the energy of a charged system, we consider the case of a spherical capacitor. (See Fig. 11.3.) Again, the electric field is confined to the free space between two concentric spherical conductors of radii a and b. The charge on the inner sphere is $+Q$. An equal and opposite charge lies on the inner surface of the outer sphere. If the potentials of the inner and outer conducting

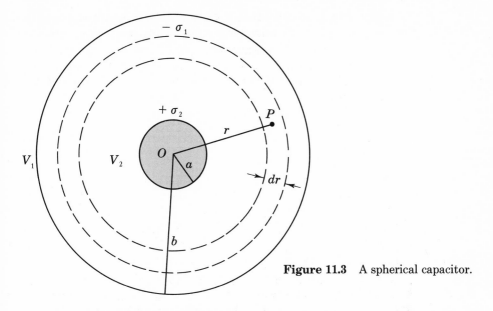

Figure 11.3　A spherical capacitor.

shells are V_2 and V_1 respectively, by (11.8) the work done in assembling the charges is

$$U = \frac{1}{2}\underbrace{\int \sigma_2 V_2 \, dA_2}_{\text{inner sphere}} - \frac{1}{2}\underbrace{\int \sigma_1 V_1 \, dA_1}_{\text{outer sphere}}$$

$$= \frac{1}{2}V_2 \int \sigma_2 \, dA_2 - \frac{1}{2}V_1 \int \sigma_1 \, dA_1$$

$$U = \frac{1}{2}(V_2 - V_1)Q = \frac{1}{2}VQ \tag{11.18}$$

since the integration of the charge density over the surface of inner shell gives Q, while the corresponding integral over the outer shell gives $-Q$. As before, $(V_2 - V_1)$ is set equal to V, the potential difference between the conductors.

The electric field at P at a distance r from the center at O $(a \leq r \leq b)$ is equal to $Q/4\pi\varepsilon_0 r^2$. Hence

$$V = V_2 - V_1 = -\frac{Q}{4\pi\varepsilon_0} \int_b^a \frac{dr}{r^2} = \frac{Q}{4\pi\varepsilon_0}\left(\frac{b-a}{ab}\right) \tag{11.19}$$

Upon substitution in (11.18) the energy of the capacitor becomes

$$U = \frac{Q^2}{8\pi\varepsilon_0}\left(\frac{b-a}{ab}\right) \tag{11.20}$$

As before, U may also be calculated by transferring an element of charge dq from the outer to the inner surface when the potential difference between them is v at some stage of the charging process. At the same instant the magnitude of the charge on each conductor is q. Applying the result already found in (11.19), we may write

$$v = \frac{q}{4\pi\varepsilon_0}\left(\frac{b-a}{ab}\right)$$

and

$$dU = v\,dq = \frac{1}{4\pi\varepsilon_0}\left(\frac{b-a}{ab}\right)q\,dq$$

Hence

$$U = \int_0^Q dU = \frac{Q^2}{8\pi\varepsilon_0}\left(\frac{b-a}{ab}\right) \tag{11.21}$$

which agrees with the result given in (11.20).

Finally, we may start with the field energy density u given in (11.10) and integrate u over the volume between the conductors. This is the region which includes all points where $\mathbf{E}$ is different from zero. For the volume element we take $4\pi r^2\,dr$. (See Fig. 11.3.) Also, $E = Q/4\pi\varepsilon_0 r^2$.

Hence

$$U = \int_a^b u\cdot 4\pi r^2\,dr = \frac{Q^2}{8\pi\varepsilon_0}\int_a^b \frac{dr}{r^2}$$

$$= \frac{Q^2}{8\pi\varepsilon_0}\frac{(b-a)}{ab} \tag{11.22}$$

In passing, we evaluate the capacitance of the spherical capacitor using the expression for V from (11.19). This yields

$$C = \frac{Q}{V} = \frac{4\pi\varepsilon_0 ab}{(b-a)} \tag{11.23}$$

If the radius b of the outer shell is allowed to increase indefinitely, then

$$C = \lim_{b\to\infty}\frac{4\pi\varepsilon_0 ab}{(b-a)} = 4\pi\varepsilon_0\lim_{b\to\infty}\frac{a}{(1-a/b)} = 4\pi\varepsilon_0 a \tag{11.24}$$

This result is sometimes spoken of as the capacitance of a sphere of radius a.

11.3   Force on a Charged Surface

The magnitude of the force of attraction **F** between the plates
of a parallel-plate capacitor may be calculated from the expression for the energy stored in the capacitor. In terms of a variable separation x (see Fig. 11.4) and in view of (11.15) and (11.17),
the expression for the energy becomes

$$U = \frac{Q^2}{2C} = \frac{\sigma^2 A^2}{2\varepsilon_0 A} x = \frac{\sigma^2 A}{2\varepsilon_0} x \qquad (11.25)$$

Let an external force F, which is equal in magnitude to the attractive force between the plates, produce a displacement dx.

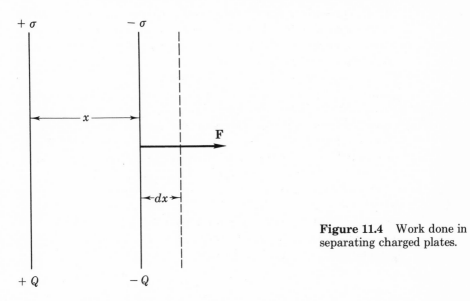

Figure 11.4   Work done in
separating charged plates.

From (11.25), the increase in U associated with an increase in
x is

$$dU = \frac{\sigma^2 A}{2\varepsilon_0} dx \qquad (11.26)$$

provided that the charge on the plates is held constant. Equating dU to $F\,dx$, the work done by the external force, we find

$$F = \frac{\sigma^2 A}{2\varepsilon_0} \qquad (11.27)$$

Substituting the value of the electric field $E = \sigma/\varepsilon_0$, it follows that the force per unit area acting normally to the charged surface is

$$\frac{F}{A} = \frac{\sigma E}{2} = \frac{\varepsilon_0 E^2}{2} \tag{11.28}$$

Although this result was derived for a special geometry, the expression for the normal stress appearing in (11.28) is valid for any conductor charged to a surface density σ. If a medium of dielectric constant k fills the space above the charged surface, then F in (11.27) is reduced by k, and the stress is given by

$$\frac{F}{A} = \frac{k\varepsilon_0 E^2}{2} = \frac{\varepsilon E^2}{2} \tag{11.29}$$

In the preceding calculation the position of one of the plates was changed without altering its charge—that is, the plates were insulated. However, the potential difference between the plates was increased as a result of an increase in x. This follows from $V = Ex$, since E is constant for constant Q.

One of the plates may be displaced without altering the potential difference between the plates, provided the capacitor is connected to an external source of charge and energy. This may be accomplished by connecting the plates to a battery of constant emf V. If the distance x between the plates is increased by dx, then C, which is equal to $\varepsilon_0 A/x$, is changed by $dC = -\varepsilon_0 A\, dx/x^2$, and the capacitance is decreased by this amount. Consequently, at constant V, the charge on the capacitor is reduced and an amount of charge dq is transferred to the battery. Now the potential energy stored in the capacitor is $\frac{1}{2}V^2 C$. Hence upon decrease of C, the loss of potential energy at constant V is

$$dU_V = \frac{1}{2}V^2\, dC \tag{11.30}$$

The charge q on the plates depends on x, according to $V(\varepsilon_0 A/x)$, and the force of attraction at any x is $\sigma^2 A/2\varepsilon_0$ or $\varepsilon_0 V^2 A/2x^2$. Hence the work done by the applied force equals

$$dW = F\, dx = \frac{1}{2}V^2 \frac{\varepsilon_0 A}{x^2}\, dx = \frac{1}{2}V^2\, dC \tag{11.31}$$

Finally, from $q = VC$, $dq = V\, dC$, so that the work done on the battery at constant V is given by

$$V\, dq = V^2\, dC \tag{11.32}$$

This interesting outcome shows that, when x is increased while

V is held constant, charge is transferred from the capacitor to the battery. Comparison of the outcome in (11.32) with those found in (11.30) and (11.31) indicates that half the energy gained by the battery comes from the potential energy lost by the capacitor, while the other half is contributed by the mechanical work done by the external force. Conversely, if x is allowed to decrease, charge will be transferred to the capacitor. In this case, the source of constant potential will supply the increase in potential energy of the capacitor and also an equal amount to provide for the mechanical work done by the force of attraction.

11.4 Mutual Inductance

In the following sections we shall examine the problem of the energy expenditure involved in establishing magnetic fields. In this connection we shall first introduce the definitions of mutual inductance and of self-inductance.

Let us examine the case of two filamentary circuits, 1 and 2. (See Fig. 11.5.) Corresponding to the current i_1 in circuit 1, there is a magnetic flux which links with one turn of circuit 2. This flux shall be denoted by $\Phi_{2,1}$. According to the definition of flux given in (7.18), $\Phi_{2,1}$ is calculated from the value of B produced by i_1 at points in the area of circuit 2. The flux $\Phi_{2,1}$ will thus depend on the dimensions, shapes, and relative positions of the circuits and on μ, the permeability of the medium, which is assumed to be

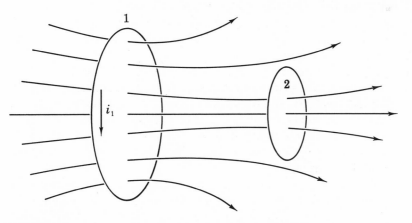

Figure 11.5 Mutual inductance between two fixed filamentary circuits.

nonmagnetic. If these geometrical factors are fixed, then the flux is directly proportional to i_1, or

$$\Phi_{2,1} = Ki_1 \tag{11.33}$$

where the constant of proportionality contains geometrical quantities. If the two circuits are separated further or are oriented differently, (11.33) is still valid, but the constant will have a different value. If i_1 is a function of the time, then an emf given by

$$e_2 = -N_2 \frac{d\Phi_{2,1}}{dt} = -N_2 K \frac{di_1}{dt} \tag{11.34}$$

will appear in circuit 2. It is assumed that the circuits are fixed relative to each other and that the same flux links with all N_2 turns of circuit 2. The induced emf can also be written as

$$e_2 = -M_{2,1} \frac{di_1}{dt} \tag{11.35}$$

where $$M_{2,1} \equiv N_2 K = N_2 \Phi_{2,1}/i_1 \tag{11.36}$$

In the equalities above, the factor $M_{2,1}$ is called the coefficient of mutual induction, or simply the *mutual inductance* of circuit 2 relative to circuit 1. If we had considered $\Phi_{1,2}$, the flux linking circuit 1 due to a current i_2 in circuit 2, then for the emf e_1 induced in circuit 1 we could have written

$$e_1 = -M_{1,2} \frac{di_2}{dt} \tag{11.37}$$

In a subsequent discussion it will be shown that $M_{2,1} = M_{1,2}$, so that in the case of two circuits we need not distinguish between them. We shall therefore use M to denote the mutual inductance between two circuits.

Mutual inductance of two circuits may be defined from (11.35) or from (11.37) as the ratio between the emf induced in one circuit and the time rate of change of current in the other circuit. The unit of inductance is called the henry. The mutual inductance of two circuits is one henry if an emf of one volt is induced in one circuit while the current in the other circuit is changing at the rate of one ampere per second.

The defining relation (11.36) may be used to determine the dependence of M on geometrical quantities. This definition is valid when the area of the circuit over which B is integrated can be specified. This is very nearly the situation if the transverse dimension of the wire forming the circuit is thin. As an example, let us calculate the mutual inductance of two flat, compactly wound coils of N_1 and N_2 turns respectively. As indicated in Fig. 11.6, the axis of coil 1 (radius a) passes through the center of coil 2 (radius b). The normal to the plane of coil 2 (the second-

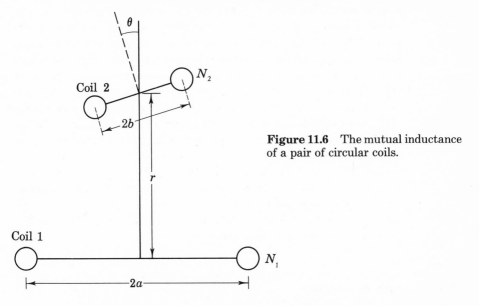

Figure 11.6   The mutual inductance of a pair of circular coils.

ary) makes an angle θ with the axis of coil 1 (the primary). We shall assume that r, the center-to-center distance between the primary and the secondary, is large relative to the radius b of the secondary. This results in the simplification that the induction B has the same value at all points of the area enclosed by the secondary.

As given by (7.7), the induction B at an axial point at a distance r from the center of the primary is

$$B_1 = \frac{\mu N_1 i_1 a^2}{2(a^2 + r^2)^{3/2}} \tag{11.38}$$

where μ is the constant permeability of the medium, and N_1 stands for the number of primary turns. The flux linking one turn of the secondary is obtained from

$$\Phi_{2,1} = (B_1 \cos \theta)\pi b^2 \tag{11.39}$$

Whence, by (11.36),

$$M_{2,1} = \frac{N_2 \Phi_{2,1}}{i_1} = \frac{\mu N_1 N_2 \pi a^2 b^2 \cos \theta}{2(a^2 + r^2)^{3/2}} \tag{11.40}$$

The unit of the result is the henry (weber/amp), if lengths are in meters and if the mks value of μ (in weber/amp-m) is used. It is sometimes convenient to specify the unit of μ from a relation of this sort. From (11.40) one finds that μ can be expressed in henry per meter. At a fixed r, $M_{2,1}$ is a maximum where $\theta = 0$. When θ increases toward $\pi/2$, then $M_{2,1}$ approaches zero in the limit. The two circuits are said to be magnetically coupled as long as an appreciable flux due to one circuit links with the other. In this example the coupling increases as θ is decreased toward 0. As indicated by (11.35), for a given rate of change of primary current, the induced voltage increases with an increase in coupling.

To compute $\Phi_{1,2}$, the flux linking each turn of circuit 1 due to a current in circuit 2, the steps in the calculation leading to the value of $M_{2,1}$ may, in principle, be reversed. In this case, B_2 varies considerably over the area of circuit 1, and the calculation of $\Phi_{1,2}$ is complex. In another example, that of the mutual inductance of two coaxial solenoidal coils whose lengths are long relative to their common diameter, it is not difficult to calculate both $\Phi_{2,1}$ and $\Phi_{1,2}$ by making reasonable assumptions.

11.5   Self-inductance

The change in the current in a single rigid and isolated circuit gives rise to a change in flux, which in turn produces an induced emf. In this situation the circuit links with its own flux. In the circuit shown in Fig. 11.7, there is a definite flux Φ which links with a given turn. If this flux is time-dependent, there will be an induced emf in this turn. Let the circuit consist of a closely wound coil of N turns. Assuming that the same emf is induced in each turn, e, the emf induced in the coil, is

$$e = -N\frac{d\Phi}{dt} \tag{11.41}$$

As before, the flux linking a given turn may be taken to be proportional to the current i, so that

$$\Phi = Gi \tag{11.42}$$

where the proportionality factor G depends on the permeability of the medium and on the shape and dimensions of the turn. In

N Turns

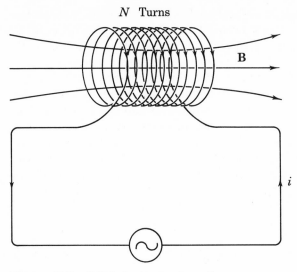

Figure 11.7   Self-inductance of a coil.

terms of (11.42), the emf induced in the coil due to changes in its own current is rewritten as

$$e = -NG\frac{di}{dt} = -L\frac{di}{dt} \tag{11.43}$$

where L is called the *self-inductance* of the coil as defined by

$$L \equiv NG = \frac{N\Phi}{i} \tag{11.44}$$

In empty space or in a medium of constant permeability, L is independent of i but depends on geometrical factors, as in the case of mutual inductance. The unit of self-inductance is also called the henry. The unit may again be defined by referring to (11.43). Thus, the self-inductance of a circuit is one henry when the emf of self-induction is one volt while the circuit current is changing at the rate of one ampere per second. Or, alternately, from (11.44), the self-inductance is one henry if a circuit current of one ampere gives rise to a total flux linkage ($N\Phi$) of one weber-turn.

The determination of L presents mathematical difficulties in all but a few circuits whose geometry makes it possible to evaluate Φ. As before, if the thickness of the conductor is small, the area involved in the calculation of Φ may be taken as that which lies outside the conductor. This limitation can be removed by dividing the flux into two parts—the first comes from the magnetic field within the conductor, while the second comes from the field external to the conductor. The inductance arising from the internal flux may be calculated from considerations of magnetic field energy.

As an example of the method, let us calculate the self-inductance of a compactly wound toroidal coil of N turns and circular cross section. (See Fig. 11.8.) The coil is wound on a nonferromagnetic core, so that μ is a constant independent of the current i. We shall calculate the flux by taking the value of B at a distance equal to the central radius r. From (7.24), $B = \mu Ni/2\pi r$, so that, if A is the cross-sectional area,

$$\Phi = BA = \frac{\mu Ni}{2\pi r} \times \pi \frac{(b - a)^2}{4}$$

which reduces to $\Phi = \dfrac{\mu Ni(b - a)^2}{4(a + b)}$ (11.45)

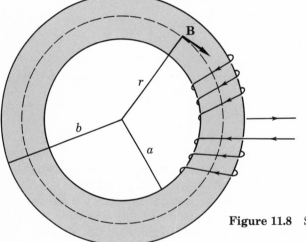

Figure 11.8   Self-inductance of a toroid.

if r is replaced by $(a + b)/2$. The constancy of B over A is an approximation which is good if $r \gg (b - a)$. The defining relation (11.44) yields for L

$$L = \frac{N\Phi}{i} = \frac{\mu N^2(b - a)^2}{4(a + b)}$$ (11.46)

The result shows that L is proportional to the square of the number of turns. In general, the inductance of the remainder of the circuit, including the seat of emf and the lead wires, is negligible compared to that associated with the coil of N turns. Hence the inductive effect is concentrated in the region of solenoidal or toroidal coils of a large number of turns.

11.6 Energy of Current Distributions

The establishment of currents requires the expenditure of energy. The energy is furnished by seats of emf (batteries, generators, and so forth) and appears as heat, magnetic field energy, mechanical work, or radiant energy. The latter is energy which leaves the circuit and is propagated as waves. In the present discussion, radiative losses will be neglected, since we shall deal only with currents varying slowly in time.

Consider first an isolated circuit containing a constant emf $\mathcal{E}$, and an inductance L, which is represented diagrammatically by the symbol $\overset{\frown}{\text{000}}$. Let R be the total circuit resistance. The circuit elements are shown in Fig. 11.9. When S is closed, the cir-

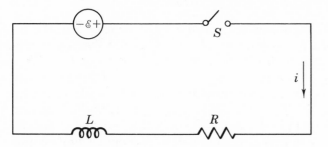

Figure 11.9 Energy relations in an inductive circuit.

cuit current rises from zero to an equilibrium value. At any instant t, the instantaneous current i obeys the relation

$$\mathcal{E} - L\frac{di}{dt} = iR \qquad (11.47)$$

in which the left-hand member is the net emf in the circuit. Also it is assumed that L is independent of the current in the circuit and that the circuit obeys Ohm's law. If both sides of (11.47) are multiplied through by i and transposed, we find

$$\mathcal{E}i = Li\frac{di}{dt} + i^2R \qquad (11.48)$$

where εi is the time rate at which work is done by the applied emf, and $i^2 R$ is the power dissipated as heat. The quantity Li (di/dt) represents power delivered to the self-inductance present in the circuit. It follows from (11.44) that the inductive effect is associated with the magnetic flux of the current distribution, and the term Li (di/dt) can be interpreted as the time rate at which energy is supplied in the magnetic field of the inductance. This viewpoint will be discussed subsequently.

The work U done by the constant emf from $t = 0$ to $t = T$ is found by integrating (11.48) with respect to time. This yields

$$U = \varepsilon \int_0^Q dq = L \int_0^I i\, di + R \int_0^T i^2\, dt \qquad (11.49)$$

In the limits appearing in the integrals, Q is the charge that passes through the seat of emf ε in the time T, and I is the value of the current at $t = T$. The last integral on the right-hand side of (11.49) is the irreversible joulean heat developed in the time T. The value of the first integral on the right-hand side will be denoted by U_m. The integration gives

$$U_m = \frac{1}{2}LI^2 \qquad (11.50)$$

The quantity U_m is a measure of the magnetic energy or the energy possessed by the current distribution when the instantaneous current starting from zero has reached the value I.

In the case of charge assemblies, the electrostatic energy was assumed to be distributed throughout the field with an energy density equal to $\varepsilon_0 E^2/2$. Similarly, one may regard the magnetic energy as residing in the magnetic field. The expression for the energy density in this case can be derived from general considerations. The result is $\mu_0 H^2/2$. We shall verify this expression by considering the field associated with a very long solenoidal coil. According to (7.15), the flux density B inside the solenoid is $\mu_0 ni$, where n is the number of turns per unit length. With the aid of (11.44), the inductance of a central portion of length l and cross-sectional area A is given by

$$L = \frac{N\Phi}{i} = \frac{nlBA}{i} = \mu_0 n^2 A l \qquad (11.51)$$

If the solenoid is located in vacuum, the current I established in the winding may be expressed as

$$I = \frac{B}{\mu_0 n} = \frac{H}{n} \qquad (11.52)$$

Substituting the above relations in (11.50), the magnetic energy assumes the form

$$U_m = \frac{\mu_0 H^2 Al}{2} \tag{11.53}$$

Now, Al is the volume of the space within that portion of the solenoid whose length is l. Hence (11.53) indicates that magnetic energy is distributed within this volume with a density

$$u_m = \frac{U_m}{Al} = \frac{\mu_0 H^2}{2} = \frac{B^2}{2\mu_0} \tag{11.54}$$

In the mks system of units, u_m is expressed in joule per cubic meter.

In this simple example, B was uniform. However, the result holds even if B varies with position. The magnetic energy appearing in (11.50) was calculated from the work done against the induced emf. An alternate procedure for computing this energy is to integrate the energy density over all space. The element of energy dU_m in the volume element dv is $u_m \, dv$. Hence, using the expression given in (11.54), we can represent the magnetic energy by

$$U_m = \int_{\substack{\text{all} \\ \text{space}}} u_m \, dv = \frac{1}{2\mu_0} \int_{\substack{\text{all} \\ \text{space}}} B^2 \, dv \tag{11.55}$$

A similar expression holds if the circuit is located in a magnetic medium of constant permeability μ. In such a case it is only necessary to replace μ_0 by μ.

Next we consider two rigid circuits, each consisting of a single turn. We shall be concerned only with the magnetic energy which is derived from the work done against the induced emfs. The circuits will be referred to by the numerals 1 and 2. (See Fig. 11.10.) The flux of induction which links with circuit 1 is composed of two parts. Part of the flux is due to the current i_1 in circuit 1 itself, and the remainder arises from the current i_2 in the neighboring circuit 2. In accordance with the defining relations for mutual inductance and self-inductance as given by (11.36) and (11.44), these fluxes are given by $L_1 i_1$ and $M_{1,2} i_2$ respectively. Hence Φ_1, the flux through circuit 1, is

$$\Phi_1 = L_1 i_1 + M_{1,2} i_2 \tag{11.56}$$

Furthermore, it shall be assumed that the circuits are fixed in

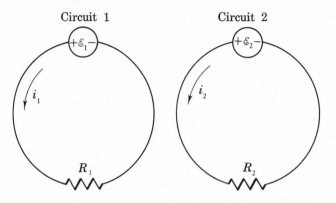

Figure 11.10   Magnetic energy of two rigid circuits.

position and that the self-inductance L_1 and the mutual inductance $M_{1,2}$ are independent of the currents involved. The emf induced in circuit 1 is

$$-\frac{d\Phi_1}{dt} = -L_1 \frac{di_1}{dt} - M_{1,2} \frac{di_2}{dt} \qquad (11.57)$$

In like manner, the emf induced in circuit 2 is

$$-\frac{d\Phi_2}{dt} = -L_2 \frac{di_2}{dt} - M_{2,1} \frac{di_1}{dt} \qquad (11.58)$$

In order to calculate the magnetic energy of the two currents, it is sufficient to compute the work done against the induced emfs. The element of work done in a time dt is

$$dU_m = \left(i_1 \frac{d\Phi_1}{dt} + i_2 \frac{d\Phi_2}{dt} \right) dt \qquad (11.59)$$

In the process of establishing the currents, we shall assume that initially i_1 and i_2 are zero and that these currents grow so that at any instant $i_1 = \alpha I_1$ and $i_2 = \alpha I_2$, where α is a fraction which increases from 0 to 1 and where I_1 and I_2 represent the final values of i_1 and i_2. Substituting the right-hand members of (11.57) and (11.58) into (11.59), we obtain the total magnetic energy by integrating with respect to α over the range $\alpha = 0$ to $\alpha = 1$. The result is

$$U_m = \frac{1}{2} (L_1 I_1^2 + M_{1,2}I_1I_2 + M_{2,1}I_2I_1 + L_2 I_2^2) \quad (11.60)$$

Another way of establishing the final currents I_1 and I_2 is as follows: With circuit 2 open ($i_2 = 0$), allow i_1 to increase and assume the final value I_1. The magnetic energy is $\frac{1}{2}L_1I_1^2$. Next allow i_2 to increase to the value I_2, holding I_1 constant. This results in two contributions to the field energy: one that is equal to $\frac{1}{2}L_2I_2^2$, which arises from the building up of the current I_2, and a second that is given by

$$\int_0^{I_2} M_{1,2} \frac{di_2}{dt} I_1 \, dt$$

or $I_1 I_2 M_{1,2}$. This contribution to the magnetic energy is the amount of work done against the emf induced in circuit 1 due to a changing current in circuit 2. Accordingly, the total magnetic energy in this process is

$$U_m = \frac{1}{2}L_1I_1^2 + I_1I_2M_{1,2} + \frac{1}{2}L_2I_2^2 \qquad (11.61)$$

Now the magnetic energy must be independent of the manner in which the currents are established. Since the final currents are the same, the magnetic energy represented by the right-hand sides of (11.60) and (11.61) must be the same. Comparison of the two results indicates that $M_{1,2}$ equals $M_{2,1}$. It has already been pointed out that the mutual inductance of circuit 2 relative to circuit 1 equals that of circuit 1 relative to circuit 2, and the above argument based on the equality of magnetic energies constitutes a proof of the statement. Denoting the mutual inductance between a pair of coupled circuits by M, we can write the magnetic energy of the system as

$$U_m = \frac{1}{2}L_1I_1^2 + I_1I_2M + \frac{1}{2}L_2I_2^2 \qquad (11.62)$$

The first and the last terms on the right side of (11.62) represent self-energies associated only with the currents in the individual circuits. The middle term denotes a mutual interaction energy which arises from the magnetic coupling of the two circuits.

11.7   Forces on Rigid Circuits

In the preceding section, we calculated the magnetic energy of two rigid circuits which were not free to move. Now we consider a pair of rigid circuits (see Fig. 11.11) one of which is free

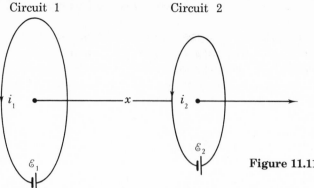

Circuit 1   Circuit 2

i_1 x i_2

$\mathcal{E}_1$ $\mathcal{E}_2$

Figure 11.11   Force on rigid circuits.

to undergo a displacement relative to the other under the action of magnetic forces. Let circuit 1 be fixed while circuit 2 is displaced a distance dx, along the x direction. This movement changes the mutual inductance M but not the self-inductances L_1 and L_2, since the circuits are rigid. A change in M implies a change in the flux through each circuit. A change in flux results in induced emfs with the attendant alteration of circuit currents.

The force acting on the movable circuit can be expressed in terms of the circuit currents and the space rate of change of M. We shall outline the steps in obtaining the actual expression but will not include all the algebraic details. The flux linking with circuit 2 is $\Phi_2 = L_2 i_2 + M i_1$, and the emf induced in circuit 2 owing to its motion is

$$-\frac{d\Phi_2}{dt} = -L_2\frac{di_2}{dt} - M\frac{di_1}{dt} - i_1\frac{dM}{dt} \qquad (11.63)$$

since both M and i_1 vary with the time. If $\mathcal{E}_2$ is the constant applied emf in circuit 2 and R_2 is its resistance, the equation for circuit 2 is represented by $\mathcal{E}_2 = (d\Phi_2/dt) + i_2 R_2$, and the power delivered to circuit 2 by the external emf is given by

$$\mathcal{E}_2 i_2 = i_2\frac{d\Phi_2}{dt} + i_2^2 R_2 \qquad (11.64)$$

Similarly,
$$\mathcal{E}_1 i_1 = i_1\frac{d\Phi_1}{dt} + i_1^2 R_1 \qquad (11.65)$$

is the rate at which the constant emf $\mathcal{E}_1$ furnishes energy to circuit 1.

On the other hand, the magnetic energy at any instant t may be expressed as

$$U_m(t) = \frac{1}{2}L_1 i_1^2 + i_1 i_2 M + \frac{1}{2}L_2 i_2^2 \qquad (11.66)$$

and the rate of increase of magnetic energy may be obtained by differentiating U_m. In evaluating dU_m/dt, we must bear in mind that L_1 and L_2 are constants but that i_1, i_2, and M depend on the time.

The power delivered to both circuits is $(\mathcal{E}_1 i_1 + \mathcal{E}_2 i_2)$. This input must be equal to the sum of the following three terms: (a) the power dissipated as heat, (b) dU_m/dt, the rate of increase of magnetic energy, and (c) the rate at which mechanical work is done by the magnetic interaction between the circuits. The last term is denoted by $F_x(dx/dt)$, where F_x is the component of the force in the direction of the displacement dx. Stated analytically,

$$\mathcal{E}_1 i_1 + \mathcal{E}_2 i_2 = (i_1^2 R_1 + i_2^2 R_2) + \frac{dU_m}{dt} + F_x \frac{dx}{dt} \qquad (11.67)$$

The left-hand side of (11.67) can be expressed in terms of the inductances, the currents, and their time derivatives by the use of (11.64) and (11.65). On the right-hand side, dU_m/dt can be expanded by using (11.66). After making the indicated substitutions and performing the differentiations involved, it follows that

$$F_x \frac{dx}{dt} = i_1 i_2 \frac{dM}{dt} \qquad (11.68)$$

Consequently, since $(dM/dt) = (\partial M/\partial x)(dx/dt)$, the mechanical force is expressed by

$$F_x = i_1 i_2 \frac{\partial M}{\partial x} \qquad (11.69)$$

In Fig. 11.11 the currents are in the same sense. By the right-handed screw rule, i_1 and i_2 are both positive. The direction of F_x is determined by the sign of $\partial M/\partial x$. The latter is negative, since M decreases with increasing separation. Therefore, in this instance F_x is negative, and circuit 2 is attracted toward circuit 1. The attractive nature of the force is also predicted by elementary considerations.

A similar analysis indicates that the torque T_θ exerted on circuit 2 is given by

$$T_\theta = i_1 i_2 \frac{\partial M}{\partial \theta} \qquad (11.70)$$

where T_θ is the torque about the axis of rotation and where θ is the angle through which circuit 2 is rotated.

In Section 11.3, it was shown that the source of potential had to furnish mechanical energy and electrostatic energy at equal rates when the distance between the plates was allowed to decrease while the potential of each plate was held fixed. There is an analogous situation in the interaction of two circuits. Consider the case where the currents i_1 and i_2 are kept constant while circuit 2 is displaced. This can be accomplished by adjusting the external emfs. From (11.66) it is seen that, during a movement dx, the time rate of change of the magnetic energy is

$$\frac{dU_m}{dt} = i_1 i_2 \frac{dM}{dt} \tag{11.71}$$

since in this displacement the currents are kept constant. But from (11.68) this is exactly equal to the rate at which mechanical work is done. From a consideration of (11.67), it follows that the external sources of emf must supply magnetic as well as mechanical energy at equal rates. In other words, half the energy furnished by the sources appears as mechanical energy, while the other half is stored in the field.

11.8   Internal Self-inductance

So far, the definition of self-inductance has been limited to filamentary circuits or thin conductors. By applying the concept of magnetic energy it is possible to extend the definition and determine the contribution coming from the field within the wire. We have seen that U_m, the work done in establishing a current I, is $\frac{1}{2}LI^2$, and that an alternate way of evaluating U_m is given by

$$\frac{1}{2\mu_0} \int_{\substack{\text{all} \\ \text{space}}} B^2 \, dv$$

The definition of L was first introduced in connection with time-varying currents. As an alternate approach we may define L by using the field energy relations. Thus, combining (11.50) and (11.55), we obtain

$$L = \frac{1}{I^2} \int \frac{B^2 \, dv}{\mu} \tag{11.72}$$

By means of this formulation we shall compute the self-inductance due to the B field within a long, straight cylindrical conductor of radius R and constant permeability μ. The current I is assumed to be uniformly distributed over the section with constant density j. Refer to the diagrams in Fig. 11.12. From the

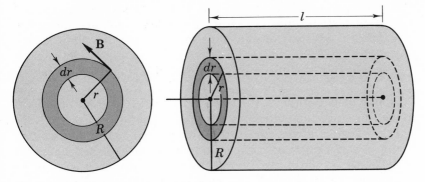

Figure 11.12   Internal self-inductance.

circuital law we find at once that B at any point inside at a distance r from the axis is given by $B = Cr$, where $C \equiv \mu j/2$. For the volume element dv, we take a cylindrical shell of length l and radius r. Thus, $dv = 2\pi r l \, dr$. Upon substitution of these quantities in (11.72) and integrating over r from 0 to R, we find upon simplification

$$L = \frac{\mu l}{8\pi} \tag{11.73}$$

This result gives the internal self-inductance for a length l of the long cylinder. The internal inductance per unit length, expressed in henry per meter, is $\mu/8\pi$.

11.9   Comments Concerning the Energy Density Formulas

In a preceding section we calculated the energy required to establish the electrostatic field by evaluating the work done in transferring charge against electrostatic forces. The result led to the alternative interpretation that the work done in assembling charges could be considered as stored in the field and distributed over all space with an energy density $\frac{1}{2}\epsilon_0 E^2$. Similarly, the energy expenditure required to establish a steady current was achieved by computing the work done against induced emfs. The outcome of this procedure again indicated that the work done in building up the currents could be associated with an energy density $\frac{1}{2}(B^2/\mu_0)$ distributed throughout the magnetic field.

The discussion did not specify the manner in which the charges or currents were established. It is necessary to realize that the formulation is a correct measure of the work done only if the fields are established slowly. When the charge assemblages and current distributions are built up rapidly, there are additional significant effects. Consider for example a parallel-plate capacitor which is connected suddenly to a seat of emf of low internal resistance. In the initial stages of the charging process, there is an acceleration of charge and a rapidly varying current. The charge distribution on the capacitor is not in equilibrium. During this stage there are time-varying magnetic and electric fields in the region of the capacitor plates as well as in the surrounding space. A pulse of radiation involving electric and magnetic fields will leave the circuit and travel outward into space. When equilibrium is reached, the customary static field will be established in the region of the plates. In addition, at distant points one will find an electric and a magnetic field associated with a wave which represents an outward flow of radiant energy.

Under these conditions the formula $\frac{1}{2}(Q^2/C)$ is a measure of the electrostatic field energy stored in the capacitor. The actual work done in charging the capacitor at a rapid rate exceeds this amount by the energy carried away by the electromagnetic wave. Although the expressions for the energy densities given by $\frac{1}{2}\varepsilon_0 E^2$ and $\frac{1}{2}(B^2/\mu_0)$ were deduced for the case where only the stationary state was involved, it may be proved that the energy density in dynamic fields (when $\mathbf{E}$ and $\mathbf{B}$ are changing in time) is also given by expressions which have the same form. Thus, $\frac{1}{2}(\varepsilon_0 E^2 + B^2/\mu_0)$ represents the total energy density in the field. Indeed, if at a given instant the values of $\mathbf{B}$ and $\mathbf{E}$ are measured at all points of the field, then the integration of the total energy density over all space will represent the correct measure of the work done in charging the condenser from the initial state to the particular time in question.

Energy of Charges and Currents: Problems

11.1   Three point charges q_1, q_2, and q_3 are located at the corners of an equilateral triangle whose side is l.

(a) Calculate the potential energy of the system by computing the work done in assembling the charges one at a time. Let $q_1 = q_2 = q_3 = 2 \times 10^{-6}$ coul and $l = 0.02$ m.

(b) Assume one of the charges is released from its location at one of the corners with zero velocity. What is its initial acceleration?

(c) Calculate the final kinetic energy of the released charge. Take $c = 1/4\pi\varepsilon_0 = 9 \times 10^9$ mks units.

11.2   A parallel-plate capacitor is charged to a potential difference of 1000 v. The region between the plates has a dielectric constant of unity, and the separation between the plates is 1 mm. With what force per unit area do the plates attract each other?

11.3   A metal plate of area A is suspended in air from a balance arm so that it is horizontal and parallel to a second metallic plate. The plates are separated by a distance d. What force must be applied to the other arm of the balance if the plates are to remain at the separation d when a potential difference V is applied to the plates? Answer the same question for the case where the region between the plates is filled with a nonconducting liquid of dielectric constant k. The plates remain connected to the source of potential difference V while the dielectric is added.

11.4   Suppose that in the preceding problem the source of potential was disconnected prior to the addition of the dielectric. What force must be applied to the arm of the balance?

11.5   When an uncharged capacitor is charged by a seat of constant emf, the heat dissipated in the charging process is equal to the final electrostatic energy of the capacitor. Prove this assertion.

11.6   Positive charge is distributed within a sphere of radius 3 m, so that the volume density of charge ρ depends only on the distance r from the center and varies in accordance with the relation $\rho = 10^{-7}r$ coul/m³. Calculate the potential energy of this charge distribution.

11.7   A filamentary rigid current circuit is located in a uniform magnetic field of induction **B**. The force on each element $d\mathbf{l}$ is given by $i\,d\mathbf{l} \times \mathbf{B}$. The circuit is allowed to move under the action of this force, such that an element of the circuit is displaced by an amount $d\mathbf{s}$ while the current i is kept constant. By direct calculation show that the mechanical work done by the circuit is $i\,d\Phi$, where $d\Phi$ is the increase in flux through the circuit.

11.8   Apply the method used in Section 11.4 and calculate the self-inductance in henries of a long, single-layer solenoid wound closely with a total of 1000 turns. The solenoid is 1 m long and the diameter of the winding is 0.04 m.

11.9   A circular turn of radius b is placed coaxially on the axis of a circular turn of radius a ($a \gg b$). The axial distance between the turns is x. Calculate the force of interaction between the two rigid turns if the constant currents in the loops are i_a and i_b respectively. See (11.40) and (11.69).

11.10   There is a steady current I in a long cylindrical conductor of radius a. Calculate the magnetic energy density at a point within a thin cylindrical shell of length l, radius r ($r < a$), and thickness dr. What is the total magnetic energy inside the conductor per unit length of the conductor? Assume the current is distributed uniformly over the cross section of the conductor.

11.11   The core of a long solenoid is cut transversely, and the two halves are pulled apart by a distance dx. If the cross-sectional area is A, the volume of the gap is $A\,dx$. From (11.54) the magnetic energy associated with this volume is ($B^2 A\,dx/2\mu_0$). If the force required to separate the two halves is F, we can equate the work done by F to the increase in magnetic energy. This yields $F = B^2 A/2\mu_0$.

    Find the numerical value of this force if the magnetizing field is 2000 amp-turns/m and if the relative permeability of the core is 4000 and its cross section is 0.01 m². $\mu_0 = 4\pi \times 10^{-7}$ mks units.

11.12   A 1 μf capacitor, initially charged to a potential difference of 100 v, is suddenly connected to the terminals of a 4 μf capacitor which is initially uncharged. When the steady state is again established, calculate the charge on each capacitor and the final energy of the combination. How does the final energy compare with the energy stored initially in the 1 μf capacitor? Account for the difference. The symbol μf stands for microfarad or 10^{-6} farad.

11.13   Consider a more general case of the situation described in the preceding problem. Initially, let the charges on the individual capacitances C_1 and C_2 be Q_1 and Q_2 respectively. Let the charged capacitors be combined so that similarly charged terminals are connected together. Show that there is a loss of energy equal to $(C_2Q_1 - C_1Q_2)^2/2C_1C_2(C_1 + C_2)$.

11.14   A sphere of radius a has a total charge Q which is distributed uniformly throughout its volume with charge density ρ.

    (a) Express ρ in terms of Q and a.

    (b) The electric field E and the potential V are functions only of the distance r measured radially from the center. For an external field point ($r > a$), express E and V as a function of r.

    (c) Repeat for an internal field point ($r < a$).

(d) Calculate the energy of the spherical charge distribution by imagining that the charge is built up by assembling successive spherical shells.

(e) Verify the result in (d) by integrating the energy density over the volume of the sphere $r = 0$ to $r = a$, and also from $r = a$ to $r = \infty$—that is, over all space external to the sphere.

11.15   In the classical theory of electromagnetism, the electron is represented by a charge e which is uniformly distributed over the surface of a sphere of radius a. According to the theory of relativity, the energy of an electron at rest is m_0c^2, where c is the speed of light and m_0 is the rest-mass of the electron.

(a) Equate the rest energy of the electron to the electrostatic energy of the field of the electron and show that a, the so-called classical radius of the electron, is given by

$$a = \frac{1}{8\pi\varepsilon_0} \frac{e^2}{m_0c^2}$$

(b) Calculate the numerical value of a.

11.16   A transmission line is made up of two coaxial hollow metal cylinders. The radius of the inner cylinder is a, while that of the outer one is b. The medium between the cylinders is air.

(a) Calculate the capacity per unit length of the coaxial line.

(b) Calculate the electrostatic energy density, assuming that a constant potential difference V is maintained between the cylinders.

(c) By integrating the result found in part (b) over the appropriate volume, calculate the electrostatic energy of the charged system per unit length of line.

(d) Check the result in (c) by calculating the energy from the capacitance of the system.

11.17   Four point charges of the same magnitude each equal to 1 μ coul are brought from a large distance and are positioned at the corners of a square whose side 1 m. Three of the charges are positive, and the fourth is negative. What is the potential energy of the charge distribution?

11.18   A long straight cylindrical conductor carries a steady current of 50 amp. The radius of the conductor is 2 mm. Calculate the volume density of the magnetic energy for points within the body of the conductor as well as for external points. Assume the current is distributed uniformly over the cross section of the cylinder.

11.19   Two thin coaxial cylindrical conductors form a transmission line. The radius of the inner cylinder is a, while that of the outer one is b. The space between the conductors is air. If the wall thickness of the conductors is negligible, the inductance per unit length of the line is $(\mu_0/2\pi) \log (b/a)$. The inner cylinder carries a current I. The current in the outer cylinder has the same magnitude but is directed in the opposite sense.

(a) Compute the volume energy density of the magnetic field at any point in the space between the cylinders.

(b) From the result found in (a), evaluate the magnetic energy associated with unit length of the line.

(c) Verify the answer to (b) by utilizing the given value of the inductance.

Chapter 12.
Time-varying Currents

12.1   Introduction

In our study of currents and fields we have ignored the possibility of radiation from the source. The term radiation implies a loss of energy from the source by the propagation of an electromagnetic disturbance. In subsequent chapters we shall see that the modifications of the various field relations developed so far enable us to predict the transmission of energy through space by progressive wave motion.

The electric and magnetic fields discussed up to this point have been fields produced by static charges or by steady or "slowly varying" currents. The phrase "slowly varying" means that the time rate of change of current must be low enough so that, in times comparable to the time required by an electromagnetic signal to reach a distant field point, the current changes in the source are negligible. In more quantitive terms, currents are slowly varying if, as in (5.15) (which expresses the law of conservation of charge), dq/dt may be set equal to zero with negligible error. In alternating-current circuits the time variation is characterized by a frequency f or an angular frequency $\omega = 2\pi f$. In free space an electromagnetic wave has a wavelength $\lambda = c/f$, where c is the speed of light. The current in such a circuit may be regarded as slowly varying if the power radiated from the circuit is negligible. In practice, this criterion can be met if l, the largest dimension of the circuit, is very much smaller than the wavelength λ—that is, if $l \ll \lambda$ or $f \ll c/l$. At 60 cycles/sec (power-line frequency), $\lambda = 5 \times 10^6$ m, and the inequalities are

(ABOVE) The Cambridge Electron Accelerator. Time-varying currents in this synchrotron accelerate particles to energy levels of 6 Bev. (Courtesy Massachusetts Institute of Technology–Harvard University.)

(RIGHT) The path of a 30 Mev electron making about 30 revolutions. The electron-positron pairs involved were produced by high-energy X rays from the Berkeley synchrotron. (Courtesy Lawrence Radiation Laboratory, University of California.)

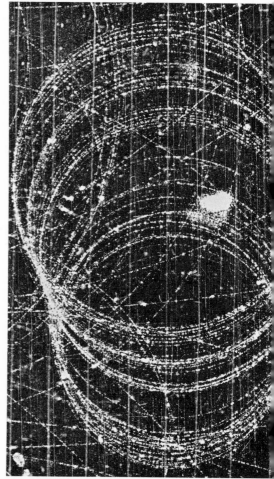

automatically satisfied. At 10^6 cycles/sec (low radio frequency), $\lambda = 300$ m, and the inequality is again satisfied if circuit dimensions are of laboratory size. At 100 megacycles/sec (10^8), $\lambda = 3$ m, and the wavelength is comparable to laboratory-circuit dimensions. In this chapter we shall be concerned primarily with time-varying currents which may be classified as "slow."

Time-dependents currents may possess either a periodic or a nonperiodic variation. The examples to be presented here will involve the application of constant or sinusoidal emfs to simple arrangements of circuit parameters. In each case the purpose of the analysis will be to determine the form of the time dependence of charges and currents.

12.2   Response of *R-L* and *R-C* Circuits to a Constant emf—Growth of Current or Charge

Figure 12.1 shows a series circuit consisting of an inductance L, a resistance R, a constant emf $\mathcal{E}$, and a switch S. The inductor and the seat of emf have negligible resistance, and the resistor is noninductive. Let i denote the current at any time t after closing the switch. If R obeys Ohm's law, the equation of the circuit is

$$\left(\mathcal{E} - L\frac{di}{dt}\right) = iR$$

or
$$\mathcal{E} = L\frac{di}{dt} + iR \tag{12.1}$$

Upon rearrangement and separation of variables, (12.1) becomes

$$\frac{di}{\left(i - \dfrac{\mathcal{E}}{R}\right)} = -\frac{R}{L}\,dt \tag{12.2}$$

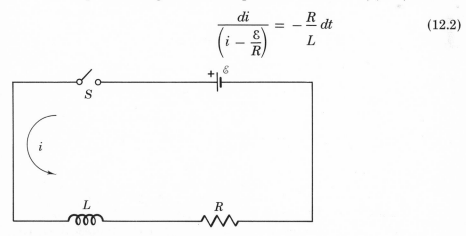

Figure 12.1   Response of an *R-L* circuit.

Integration yields

$$\ln \left(i - \frac{\mathcal{E}}{R} \right) = -\frac{R}{L}t + k \qquad (12.3)$$

Whence
$$\left(i - \frac{\mathcal{E}}{R} \right) = e^k e^{-(R/L)t} \qquad (12.4)$$

where k is a constant of integration to be evaluated by considering the initial conditions—namely, that when $t = 0$, $i = 0$. When this condition is substituted in (12.4), we find that e^k is $-\mathcal{E}/R$. Hence

$$i = \frac{\mathcal{E}}{R} (1 - e^{-(R/L)t}) \qquad (12.5)$$

As t increases, the exponential term approaches zero and the transient state represented by (12.5) approaches the final steady-state value $I = \mathcal{E}/R$. A plot of the current i as a function of the time t is given in Fig. 12.2. The time constant of the circuit is defined

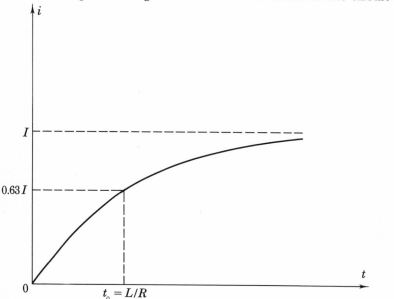

Figure 12.2 Growth of current in an R-L circuit.

as the instant at which the absolute value of the exponent in (12.5) is equal to unity—that is, $t_0 = L/R$. At this time, $i = I(1 - 1/e)$; in other words, the current has attained about 63 per cent of its final value. Although the steady-state value I is independent of the inductance L, for a given R the current rises to its final value more slowly if L is large.

Next we consider the R-C circuit shown in Fig. 12.3. We assume that initially the capacitor is uncharged—that is, at $t = 0$,

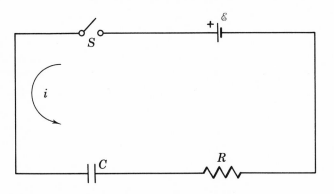

Figure 12.3 Response of an R-C circuit.

the charge q on the capacitor C is zero. At any instant after S is closed, the circuit equation is given by

$$\mathcal{E} = q/C + iR \tag{12.6}$$

If the capacitor is being charged, $i = dq/dt$. Hence

$$\mathcal{E} = q/C + R\frac{dq}{dt} \tag{12.7}$$

As before, this equation can be cast in the form

$$\frac{dq}{(q - \mathcal{E}C)} = -\frac{dt}{RC} \tag{12.8}$$

which upon integration yields

$$q = \mathcal{E}C(1 - e^{-t/RC}) \tag{12.9}$$

where the constant of integration has been evaluated by using the initial condition $q = 0$, when $t = 0$. As t increases, the charge q on the capacitor increases and approaches the steady-state value $Q = \mathcal{E}C$. The plot in Fig. 12.4 shows the variation of q with t. In this circuit, the time constant $t_0 = RC$. During this time the charge acquired by the capacitor is $Q(1 - e^{-1})$, or $0.63Q$.

The charging current may be obtained either by differentiating both sides of (12.6) with respect to t and by solving the resulting differential equation, or by differentiating q in (12.9) di-

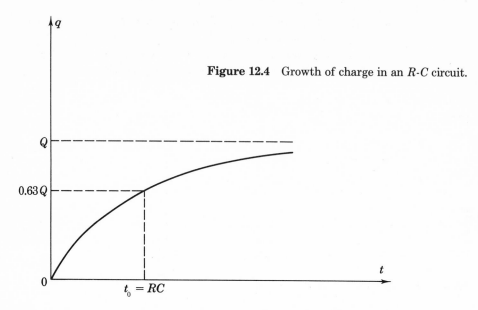

Figure 12.4   Growth of charge in an R-C circuit.

rectly. In either case, the instantaneous charging current is

$$i = \frac{\mathcal{E}}{R}e^{-t/RC} = Ie^{-t/RC} \qquad (12.10)$$

which starts with the initial value $I = \mathcal{E}/R$ and approaches zero as t increases.

12.3   Response of R-L and R-C Circuits upon Removal of the emf—Decay of Current or Charge

When the current in the circuit of Fig. 12.1 has attained the steady value I, let the applied emf $\mathcal{E}$ be shorted out. The circuit equation now becomes $0 = L(di/dt) + iR$. This equation may also be solved for i by the steps presented in Section 12.2. The result is

$$i = Ie^{-(R/L)t} \qquad (12.11)$$

Similarly, when the charge on the capacitor in Fig. 12.3 has reached its steady value Q, let the external emf be removed by short-circuiting its terminals. The equation of the circuit now becomes $0 = q/C + iR$, since the applied $\mathcal{E} = 0$. The charge remaining on the capacitor at any instant is given by

$$q = Qe^{-t/RC} \qquad (12.12)$$

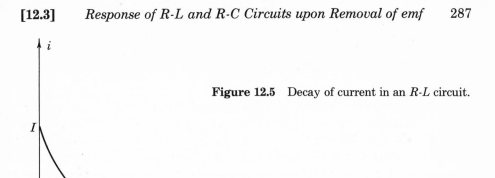

Figure 12.5   Decay of current in an *R-L* circuit.

The graphs of the decaying current or charge in the *R-L* and *R-C* circuits appear in Figs. 12.5 and 12.6 respectively. In either case the time constant is t_0, which means that i or q drops to $(1/e)$th of its initial value in the time t_0.

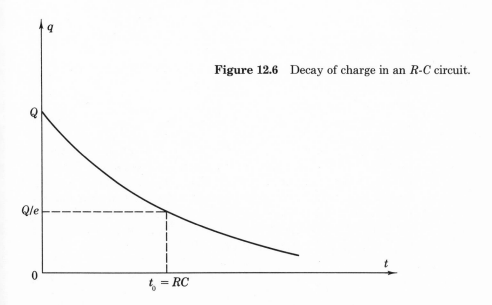

Figure 12.6   Decay of charge in an *R-C* circuit.

12.4   Electrical Oscillations

In the preceding section we ignored the effect of circuit inductance in considering the discharge of a capacitor. We shall now
discuss the case in which a charged capacitor, with an initial
charge Q, is discharged through a resistanceless coil of inductance
L. Figure 12.7 represents the charged capacitor, a switch, and the

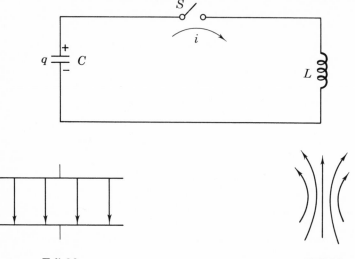

E-field   B-field

Figure 12.7 Oscillating L-C circuit.

coil. When the switch is closed, the capacitor begins to discharge.
At any time thereafter, the circuit equation is

$$q/C - L\frac{di}{dt} = 0 \tag{12.13}$$

In writing the above equation it has been assumed that the direction of flow of charge is in the clockwise sense, away from the
positively charged plate. Since initially the current is increasing,
the electric field induced in the coil is directed so that the terminal connected to the switch is at the higher potential. On the
other hand, the current $i = -(dq/dt)$, because the capacitor is
discharging. With the aid of this relation we get

$$\frac{d^2q}{dt^2} + \frac{q}{LC} = 0 \tag{12.14}$$

This is the differential equation of harmonic motion without dissipation. Its solution is

$$q = c_1 \sin (\omega t + c_2) \qquad (12.15)$$

where c_1 and c_2 are arbitrary constants and

$$\omega^2 = \frac{1}{LC} = 4\pi^2 f^2 \qquad (12.16)$$

where f is the natural frequency of the L-C circuit. As initial conditions we have: $q = Q$ at $t = 0$, and $(dq/dt) = 0$ at $t = 0$. Upon substitution of these initial conditions in (12.15), we obtain

$$q = Q \sin \left(\omega t + \frac{\pi}{2}\right) = Q \cos \omega t \qquad (12.17)$$

The solution indicates that the charge on the capacitor varies periodically with the characteristic angular frequency $\omega = 1/\sqrt{LC}$ or a natural frequency $f = (1/2\pi) \sqrt{1/LC}$. Immediately after the switch S is closed, the capacitor begins to discharge through the coil, the charge q being reduced to zero in one-quarter of a period, or $\pi \sqrt{LC}/2$ sec. In the next quarter-period, the lower plate becomes positively charged, then the direction of flow reverses, and the initial state is restored at the end of the period. The process repeats itself, and in the absence of heat or radiative losses, the back-and-forth surge of charge would continue indefinitely. The name *electrical oscillation* is given to this process in which there is energy transfer between the electric and magnetic fields. Initially the electrostatic energy $Q^2/2C$ resides in the capacitor. After a quarter of a period, the current has reached its maximum value I, and the energy of the system appears as magnetic energy $LI^2/2$. At any other instant the respective energies are: $q^2/2C$ and $Li^2/2$. With the aid of (12.16) and (12.17) one may readily verify that their sum is constant, as indicated by the equality

$$(q^2/2C + Li^2/2) = Q^2/2C = LI^2/2$$

A mass m suspended from a spring of force constant k represents the corresponding mechanical analog (see Fig. 12.8). In this case the equation of motion is $(d^2y/dt^2) + (k/m)y = 0$, with a corresponding solution $y = Y \cos (\omega t)$, which represents simple harmonic motion of angular frequency $\omega = \sqrt{k/m}$. In a formal way, the inductance L and capacitance C of the electrical circuit correspond respectively to the mass m and elastance $1/k$ of the mechanical analog. Since q corresponds to y, the magnetic energy

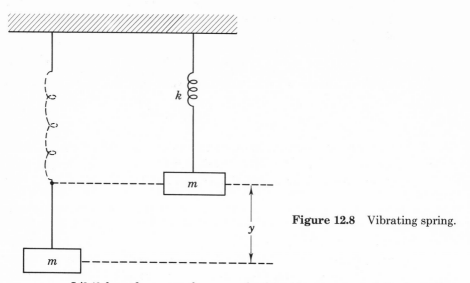

Figure 12.8 Vibrating spring.

$Li^2/2$ has the same form as the kinetic energy $mv^2/2$. A similar resemblance exists between the energy of charge $q^2/2C$ and the potential energy of the spring $ky^2/2$.

In all physical systems the resistive effect is unavoidably present. The differential equation in this case contains the additional term $R(dq/dt)$. The equation is of the form

$$L\frac{d^2q}{dt^2} + R\frac{dq}{dt} + \frac{q}{C} = 0 \qquad (12.18)$$

The solution is more involved and will not be attempted here. However, the result indicates that the current oscillates with a frequency given by

$$f = \frac{1}{2\pi}\sqrt{\frac{1}{LC} - \frac{R^2}{4L^2}} \qquad (12.19)$$

Also, the amplitude of the current decreases with the time in accordance with the factor $e^{-Rt/2L}$. The dissipative effect is illustrated by the damping of the oscillatory current, as implied in Fig. 12.9. As seen in (12.19), the oscillation frequency of the R-L-C circuit approaches the natural frequency of the L-C circuits as $R^2/4L^2$ becomes negligible. In addition, f is real only if $(1/LC)$ $> (R^2/4L^2)$. In fact, the solution of (12.18) is oscillatory if this inequality does hold. On the other hand, if $(1/LC) = (R^2/4L^2)$, the solution reduces to an exponential decay and the circuit is said to be *critically damped*. If $(1/LC) < (R^2/4L^2)$, the system is *overdamped*. See the behavior of q with time in Fig. 12.9.

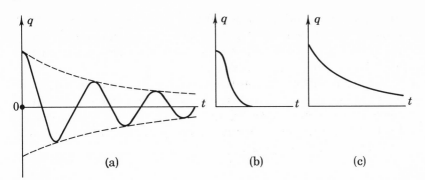

Figure 12.9 The R-L-C circuit. (a) The discharge of the capacitor is oscillatory. The oscillations are damped if $R^2 < 4L/C$. The discharge becomes aperiodic when $R^2 \geqq 4L/C$. The diagrams in (b) and (c) show the critically damped and overdamped cases respectively.

In the oscillatory circuits discussed so far, we have had almost complete separation of the electric and magnetic fields. The electric field was essentially localized to the space between the capacitor plates and was associated with the charges on the plates. Furthermore, at low oscillation frequencies, the electric field at points between the plates was in phase with the charge on the plates. Similarly, the presence of an alternating current in the inductor gave rise to a time-varying magnetic field, within and in the immediate vicinity of the inductor. Except for joulean heat losses, the energy stored in the electric field during one-quarter of a cycle was transferred into magnetic energy, which in turn was almost completely restored to the capacitor during the next quarter-cycle. Circuit elements, such as the capacitor and the inductor described above, are known as "lumped" parameters, because the electric and magnetic fields associated with them do not overlap in space but are localized in the region of the element. (There is a negligibly weak magnetic field in the gap between the plates. This originates from the time variation of the electric displacement.) In the mechanical analog of the vibrating spring we also find separation of energies. Here there is periodic interchange between the kinetic energy possessed by the mass and the potential energy of the spring.

In the following chapter we shall study the mechanics of wave motion as set up in a one-dimensional medium such as a string under tension. If one end of the string is given a periodic disturbance, there results a traveling wave which transmits energy from one end to the other. In this case, the kinetic and potential energies are not isolated in space. Instead, each element of the string possesses mass and is subject to restoring forces. Consequently, every element of the string possesses periodically varying potential and kinetic energy—that is, the two types of energy exist in the same region of space.

Similar requirements must be met if electromagnetic disturbances are to be propagated. In the problem of the parallel wires to be discussed in Chapter 14, we encounter electric and magnetic fields which exist in the same region of space. Such a system is capable of propagating electrical disturbances.

12.5   Alternating Currents

In the first part of this chapter we introduced the transient behavior of a few simple circuits. There the discussion was devoted to the growth and decay of charge and current when a constant emf was suddenly applied to or removed from the circuit. Since the applied emf was not dependent on the time, the steady-state value of the current approached a constant value.

We shall now turn to a problem in which the applied emf is a periodic function of the time. Although there are many types of periodic function, we shall limit our treatment to the special case of sinusoidal or cosinusoidal functions, because of their importance in numerous applications. Sinusoidal variations play a role in the theory of mechanical and electrical oscillations, in power distribution systems, and in the study of electromagnetic waves. The analytical representation of a simple harmonic oscillation is familiar enough. In the equation

$$y = A \cos (\omega t - \theta) \tag{12.20}$$

the dependent variable y represents an oscillatory quantity which is a function of the time t. The formula contains three constants, A, ω, and θ, which describe the oscillation. The quantity A is the amplitude or the largest positive value of y. The instantaneous phase angle $(\omega t - \theta)$ contains the angular velocity ω and θ, which is the value of the phase angle when $t = 0$. The angular frequency is associated with the period T and the frequency f by the relation $\omega = 2\pi/T = 2\pi f$. The period T represents the time between two successive maxima, and the frequency f is the number of oscillations per second. These characteristic parameters are shown in Fig. 12.10.

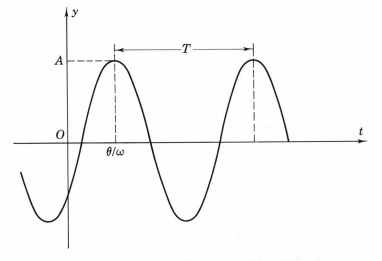

Figure 12.10   Sinusoidal variation as a function of the time.

The equation for a sinusoidal current may be taken as

$$i = I_m \sin (\omega t - \theta) \qquad (12.21)$$

where I_m is the maximum value of the time-varying current. In many measurements it is useful to describe the magnitude of the current by specifying its effective or root-mean-square (rms) value. The effective value of a time-varying current is that steady current which, when maintained in an unvarying resistance R for a time interval $(t_2 - t_1)$, will produce the same amount of heat as that produced by the time-varying current in the same resistance over the same time interval. If the effective value is denoted by I, then, from the above definition, we have

$$I^2 R(t_2 - t_1) = \int_{t_1}^{t_2} i^2 R \, dt$$

Whence the square of the effective current is

$$I^2 = \frac{1}{(t_2 - t_1)} \int_{t_1}^{t_2} i^2 \, dt \qquad (12.22)$$

The right-hand side of (12.22) represents the mean value of i^2. Hence I may alternately be labeled as the root-mean-square value of i.

In general, the effective value depends on the time interval.

We compute below the effective value of the current described by (12.21) over a period. By definition.

$$I^2 = \frac{I_m^2}{T} \int_0^T \sin^2 (\omega t - \theta)\, dt$$

In terms of the double angle, the integrand may be written as $\tfrac{1}{2}[1 - \cos 2(\omega t - \theta)]$. Since the integral of the cosine over a period vanishes, the evaluation reduces to

$$I^2 = \frac{I_m^2}{2T} \int_0^T dt = \frac{I_m^2}{2}$$

Or
$$I = \frac{I_m}{\sqrt{2}} = 0.707 I_m \tag{12.23}$$

Accordingly, the effective value of a sinusoidal current over a cycle is the peak value divided by $\sqrt{2}$. The same result is obtained if the integration is carried over an integral number of quarter-cycles. According to (5.3), the average value of i over the time interval $(t_2 - t_1)$ is defined by

$$I_{\text{avg}} = \frac{1}{(t_2 - t_1)} \int_{t_1}^{t_2} i\, dt$$

Over half a cycle, the average value is computed from

$$I_{\text{avg}} = \frac{I_m}{T/2} \int_0^{T/2} \sin (\omega t - \theta)\, dt = \frac{2 I_m}{\pi} \tag{12.24}$$

The average current over an integral number of cycles is zero.

12.6   A Sinusoidal Voltage Applied to Individual Circuit Elements

When a potential difference of the form $v = V_m \sin \omega t$ is applied to a purely resistive element R, the instantaneous current is determined from $v = iR$, or

$$i = \frac{V_m}{R} \sin \omega t = I_m \sin \omega t \tag{12.25}$$

This is the steady-state value of the current which is established after the transients are over. If Ohm's law is valid, the current in R is also sinusoidal, with a maximum value $I_m = V_m/R$. When the functions representing v and i are compared, it is seen that these quantities are in phase—that is, the difference between their respective phase angles is zero. Figure 12.11 shows a plot of v and i as a function ωt for the special case of a purely resistive circuit.

v or i

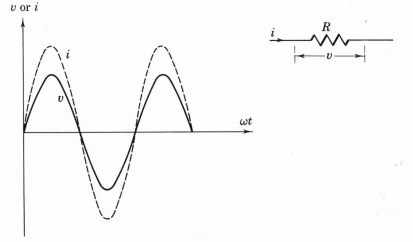

Figure 12.11 Phase relation between potential difference v and current i in a purely resistive element.

When a potential difference $v = V_m \sin \omega t$ is applied to a capacitance C, the form of the steady-state current is derived by differentiating the instantaneous charge $q = vC$ with respect to the time. The steps are indicated below:

$$i = \frac{dq}{dt} = C\frac{dv}{dt} = CV_m\omega \cos(\omega t)$$

or
$$i = \frac{V_m}{X_C} \sin\left(\omega t + \frac{\pi}{2}\right) \qquad (12.26)$$

where X_C, called the *capacitative reactance*, is defined as

$$X_C \equiv \frac{1}{C\omega} \qquad (12.27)$$

The maximum current is equal to V_m/X_C. Inspection of the phase angles of v and i reveals that the current is $\pi/2$ radians or 90° out of phase with the impressed voltage. Relative to the voltage, the current reaches its peak value a quarter of a period earlier. To describe this phase relationship we say that the current *leads* the impressed voltage by 90°. (See Fig. 12.12.)

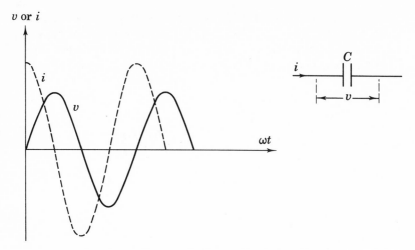

Figure 12.12   Phase relation between potential difference v and current i in a purely capacitative element.

Finally, we treat the case of a purely inductive element. The equation of the circuit is

$$v - L \frac{di}{dt} = 0$$

where $v = V_m \sin \omega t$ is the impressed potential difference, and L is the inductance of the element. The expression for the current is found by integrating the circuit equation. The result is

$$i = -\frac{V_m}{L\omega} \cos (\omega t) = \frac{V_m}{X_L} \sin \left(\omega t - \frac{\pi}{2} \right) \qquad (12.28)$$

where X_L, called the *inductive reactance*, is defined as

$$X_L \equiv L\omega \qquad (12.29)$$

The maximum value of the current is V_m/X_L. The sinusoidal function representing the current indicates again that the current is $\pi/2$ radians or 90° out of phase with the impressed voltage, relative to which the current reaches its maximum value a quarter of a period later. However, in this case the current *lags* the impressed voltage by 90°. (See Fig. 12.13.)

The tabulation below summarizes the results developed in this section. For each of the three single elements, the impressed potential difference $v = V_m \sin \omega t$ is chosen as reference. The resistance R and the reactances X_C and X_L are grouped under the heading of impedance. The subsequent sections will be concerned with combinations of individual elements. In such cases,

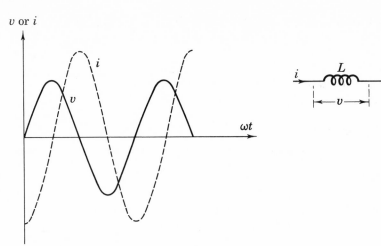

Figure 12.13 Phase relation between potential difference v and current i in a purely inductive element.

the amplitude of the current is again given by V_m/Z. The quantity Z, called the *circuit impedance,* is determined by the values of R, X_C, and X_L associated with the individual circuit components. The relations used to define R, X_C, X_L, and Z involve the ratio of voltage to current. Hence these quantities are expressed in ohms.

Circuit Element Quantity	R	C	L
Instantaneous current i	$\dfrac{V_m}{R}\sin \omega t$	$\dfrac{V_m}{X_C}\sin\left(\omega t + \dfrac{\pi}{2}\right)$	$\dfrac{V_m}{X_L}\sin\left(\omega t - \dfrac{\pi}{2}\right)$
Peak value of i	V_m/R	V_m/X_C	V_m/X_L
Impedance	R	$X_C = \dfrac{1}{C\omega}$	$X_L = L\omega$
Phase relations i relative to v	In phase	i leads v by $\pi/2$ radians	i lags v by $\pi/2$ radians

12.7   Complex Numbers in Circuit Applications

Circuit problems involving sinusoidally varying quantities can often be analyzed conveniently by the use of complex numbers. A complex number is a quantity composed of two real numbers

x and y and the imaginary *unit j*. The latter is a number such that $j^2 = -1$. A complex number **z** has the form

$$\mathbf{z} = x + jy \tag{12.30}$$

We shall summarize some of the properties of such numbers, which, as in the case of vectors, will be designated by boldface type.

A number **z** can be associated with a point $P(x, y)$ in the x,y plane, as indicated in Fig. 12.14. The x coordinate of P is termed

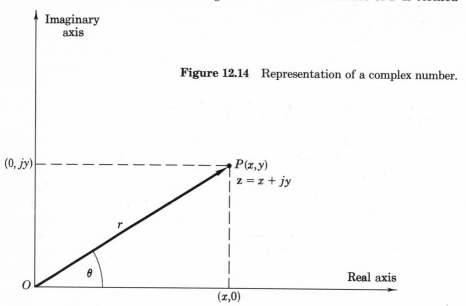

Figure 12.14   Representation of a complex number.

the *real* part of the complex number **z**, while the coordinate y is called the *imaginary* part. The numbers $x + j0 = x$ represent real numbers and are denoted by points on the x-axis. Correspondingly, the numbers $0 + jy = jy$ are referred to as *imaginary* numbers and are represented by points on the y-axis.

The length of the line OP joining the origin to P, here denoted by r, is referred to variously as the *absolute value* or the *modulus* of **z** and is denoted by $|\mathbf{z}|$. The terms amplitude and magnitude are also used in referring to $|\mathbf{z}|$. It follows that $r = |\mathbf{z}| = \sqrt{x^2 + y^2}$. The polar coordinates of the point P are (r, θ). The angle θ is called the argument (arg **z**) of the complex number and is measured by $\tan^{-1}(y/x)$. In polar form, **z** can be written as

$$\mathbf{z} = x + jy = r(\cos\theta + j\sin\theta) \tag{12.31}$$

Two complex numbers $z_1 = x_1 + jy_1$ and $z_2 = x_2 + jy_2$ are equal, provided $x_1 = x_2$ and $y_1 = y_2$—that is, the real and imaginary parts are independent. Complex quantities can be added, subtracted, multiplied, and divided (division by zero is excluded), according to the algebraic rules which are valid for real numbers. The negative of $z = x + jy$ is $-x + j(-y)$, and its reciprocal

$$z^{-1} = (x + jy)^{-1} = \frac{(x - jy)}{(x^2 + y^2)}$$

Of importance is the *complex* conjugate of z, denoted as z^* and obtained by replacing $+j$ by $-j$. Thus $z^* = (x + jy)^* = (x - jy)$.

Complex numbers can be represented in another form, which is of considerable usefulness in applications. From Taylor series expansions of $\cos\theta$, $\sin\theta$, and $e^{j\theta}$, one can deduce the Euler formula

$$e^{j\theta} = \cos\theta + j\sin\theta \qquad (12.32)$$

By comparison with the result in (12.31), it follows that the exponential $e^{j\theta}$ is a complex number whose absolute value is unity and whose argument is θ. The exponential form of z corresponding to the relation in (12.31) is

$$z = re^{j\theta} \qquad (12.33)$$

Similarly, the complex conjugate of z becomes

$$z^* = re^{-j\theta} \qquad (12.34)$$

The exponential factor $re^{j\theta}$ can be looked upon as the result of an operation which rotates the length r through the angle θ in the positive (counterclockwise) sense. In a like manner, $re^{j(\theta+\phi)}$ is the result obtained when r is rotated through an angle $(\theta + \phi)$. (Consult Fig. 12.15.) It is interesting to observe that if $\theta = \pi/2$, then $e^{j\theta} = j$. In other words, multiplication by j causes a rotation of $\pi/2$. Similarly, multiplication by j^2, j^3, and j^4 gives rise to rotations of π, $3\pi/2$, and 2π respectively.

If, instead of the point $P(x, y)$, the line segment directed from the origin to point $P(x, y)$ is regarded as a representation of the complex quantity, then the operation of adding complex numbers is equivalent to the process of adding vectors in a plane. When $z_1 = (x_1 + jy_1)$ and $z_2 = (x_2 + jy_2)$ are added, the sum $z = (x_1 + x_2) + j(y_1 + y_2)$. The x and y components of the resultant of two vectors is also found by summing the x components and the y components of the individual vectors.

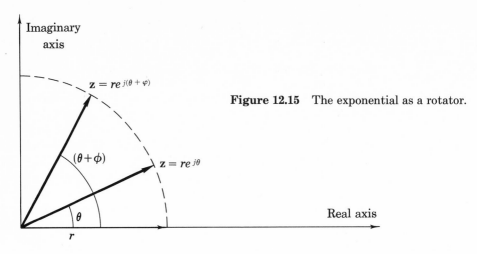

Figure 12.15   The exponential as a rotator.

12.8   A-C Circuit Containing Resistance and Capacitance

In the remainder of this chapter the term alternating current (abbreviated a-c) will be applied to circuits in which the instantaneous currents and voltages vary sinusoidally with the time. Figure 12.16 is a diagrammatic representation of a series combination of a resistance R and a capacitance C. An alternating emf v is applied to the terminals of the RC (resistance, capaci-

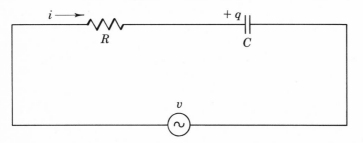

Figure 12.16   An a-c circuit containing resistance and capacitance.

tance) combination. The circuit equation is obtained by equating the applied emf to the sum of the potential drops across R and C at some instant of time. This yields

$$iR + q/C = v$$

in which q represents the instantaneous charge on the capacitor.

Differentiation of both sides of the above relation with respect to the time t results in

$$R\frac{di}{dt} + \frac{i}{C} = \frac{dv}{dt} \tag{12.35}$$

The application of complex numbers to the solution of a-c circuit problems will be illustrated by solving the specific equation appearing in (12.35). To see just how the method works, let i_1 denote the solution of (12.35) when $v = V_m \cos \omega t$ and let i_2 denote the solution when an emf of the form $v = V_m \sin \omega t$ is applied. Next, (12.35) is rewritten for each emf and its associated circuit current. The resulting pair of equations is

$$R\frac{di_1}{dt} + \frac{i_1}{C} = \frac{d}{dt}(V_m \cos \omega t)$$

$$R\frac{di_2}{dt} + \frac{i_2}{C} = \frac{d}{dt}(V_m \sin \omega t)$$

After multiplying each term of the last equation by j, the modified equation is added to the first. The sum is given by

$$R\frac{d\mathbf{i}}{dt} + \frac{\mathbf{i}}{C} = \frac{d}{dt}(V_m \cos \omega t + jV_m \sin \omega t) \tag{12.36}$$

in which the complex current $\mathbf{i}$ is substituted for the quantity $(i_1 + ji_2)$. The algebraic steps leading to (12.36) indicate that when the complex emf

$$\mathbf{v} = V_m(\cos \omega t + j \sin \omega t) = V_m e^{j\omega t} \tag{12.37}$$

replaces the actual emf, one obtains a complex current $\mathbf{i}$, whose real part i_1 arises from the $\cos \omega t$ term of the applied emf while the imaginary part i_2 is the current due to the $\sin \omega t$ term.

To proceed with the solution of (12.35), we assume that the complex current $\mathbf{i}$ has the form $\mathbf{I}_m e^{j\omega t}$. This is reasonable, since the current must have the same angular frequency ω. In (12.35) we substitute the complex $\mathbf{v}$ in place of v. Upon performing the indicated differentiations and simplifying, we find that (12.36) is reduced to

$$\mathbf{i} = \frac{\mathbf{v}}{\left(R + \dfrac{1}{j\omega C}\right)} = \frac{\mathbf{v}}{\mathbf{z}} \tag{12.38}$$

where $\mathbf{z}$ is called the complex *impedance*. It is defined by

$$\mathbf{z} \equiv \left(R + \frac{1}{j\omega C}\right) \tag{12.39}$$

The complex impedance $\mathbf{z}$ can be expressed in various ways. In terms of the capacitive reactance $X_C \equiv 1/C\omega$, the result in (12.39) assumes the form

$$\mathbf{z} = \left(R - j\frac{1}{C\omega}\right) = R - jX_C = Ze^{-j\phi} \qquad (12.40)$$

where

$$Z = \sqrt{R^2 + X_C^2} \qquad (12.41)$$

and

$$\phi = \tan^{-1}\frac{1}{CR\omega} = \tan^{-1}\frac{X_C}{R} \qquad (12.42)$$

Finally, we express the right-hand side of (12.38) in exponential form. Thus

$$\mathbf{i} = \frac{V_m e^{j\omega t}}{Ze^{-j\phi}} = \frac{V_m}{Z}e^{j(\omega t + \phi)} \qquad (12.43)$$

If we take the imaginary part of $\mathbf{v}$ as the actual emf, the circuit current will be the imaginary part of $\mathbf{i}$ as given in (12.43). That is, if

$$v = V_m \sin \omega t \qquad (12.44)$$

$$i = \frac{V_m}{Z} \sin (\omega t + \phi) \qquad (12.45)$$

which indicates that the peak value of the current is

$$I_m = \frac{V_m}{Z} \qquad (12.46)$$

In Fig. 12.17 current and voltage curves are plotted as a function of ωt. The current leads the applied voltage by the angle ϕ defined in (12.42). If the circuit is purely capacitive, $R = 0$, $\tan \phi = \infty$, and $\phi = \pi/2$. Similarly, if the circuit is purely resistive, $X_C = 0$, $\tan \phi = 0$, and $\phi = 0$. These deductions for the limiting cases agree with the results found in Section 12.6. For the actual circuit, $0 < \phi < \pi/2$.

The complex current $\mathbf{i}$ and voltage $\mathbf{v}$ are plotted in the diagram of Fig. 12.18. The magnitudes of $\mathbf{i}$ and $\mathbf{v}$ are equal to I_m and V_m respectively. The complex quantities $\mathbf{i}$ and $\mathbf{v}$ make a fixed angle ϕ with each other, and as time goes on the pair may be considered to rotate about the origin O in the counterclockwise direction with angular velocity ω. At any angle ωt, the projections of I_m and V_m on the imaginary axis generate the curves shown in Fig. 12.17. The analytical expressions for the curves are given by (12.44) and (12.45).

v or *i*

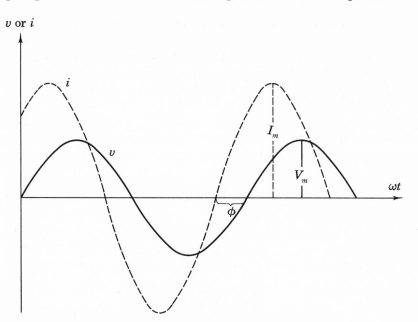

Figure 12.17   Phase relations between *v* and *i* in an *R-C* circuit.

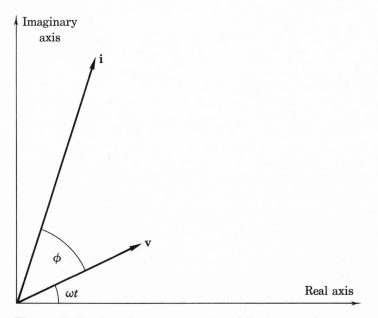

Figure 12.18   Complex representation of the impressed potential difference and the current in an *R-C* circuit.

It may be worthwhile to review the notation used in the above discussion. The symbols v and i represent the instantaneous values of actual voltage and current, while the symbols $\mathbf{v}$ and $\mathbf{i}$ (in boldface type) are their complex counterparts. Either the real or the imaginary parts of $\mathbf{v}$ and $\mathbf{i}$ may serve as the actual circuit quantities. The symbol $\mathbf{z}$ denotes the complex impedance whose absolute value is Z. The maximum values or the amplitudes of $\mathbf{v}$ and $\mathbf{i}$ are written as V_m and I_m. These are related by $V_m = I_m Z$.

12.9   A-C Circuit Containing Resistance and Inductance

Figure 12.19 represents a series arrangement of a resistance R, a pure inductance L, and an applied alternating emf v, which is imposed on the terminals of the R-L circuit. This case will also

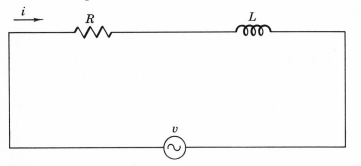

Figure 12.19   An a-c circuit containing resistance and inductance.

be treated by the method of complex quantities. The circuit equation is

$$v - L\frac{di}{dt} = iR$$

or

$$L\frac{di}{dt} + iR = v \tag{12.47}$$

As before, we write $\mathbf{v}$ for the complex emf $V_m e^{j\omega t}$ and represent the complex current $\mathbf{i}$ by $I_m e^{j\omega t}$. With these substitutions, (12.47) can be put in the form

$$(R + jL\omega)\mathbf{i} = \mathbf{v}$$

or

$$\mathbf{i} = \frac{\mathbf{v}}{\mathbf{z}} \tag{12.48}$$

where the complex impedance is represented by any one of the following expressions:

$$\mathbf{z} = (R + jL\omega) = (R + jX_L) = Ze^{j\phi} \qquad (12.49)$$

As in Section 12.6, the inductive reactance X_L is defined as $L\omega$. The absolute value of $\mathbf{z}$ is

$$Z = \sqrt{R^2 + X_L^2} \qquad (12.50)$$

and the phase difference between $\mathbf{v}$ and $\mathbf{i}$ is given by

$$-\phi = \tan^{-1} \frac{L\omega}{R} = \tan^{-1} \frac{X_L}{R} \qquad (12.51)$$

The current $\mathbf{i}$ may be expressed in the exponential form as

$$\mathbf{i} = \frac{V_m e^{j\omega t}}{Ze^{j\phi}} = \frac{V_m}{Z} e^{j(\omega t - \phi)} \qquad (12.52)$$

If the imaginary part of $\mathbf{v}$ is assumed to be the applied emf, the imaginary part of $\mathbf{i}$ describes the resulting circuit current. Thus, if

$$v = V_m \sin \omega t \qquad (12.53)$$

then $$i = \frac{V_m}{Z} \sin (\omega t - \phi) \qquad (12.54)$$

The phase relations between $\mathbf{v}$ and $\mathbf{i}$ are depicted in Fig. 12.20,

v or i

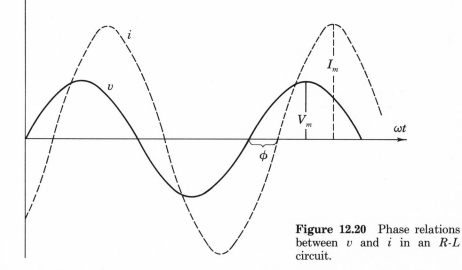

Figure 12.20 Phase relations between v and i in an *R-L* circuit.

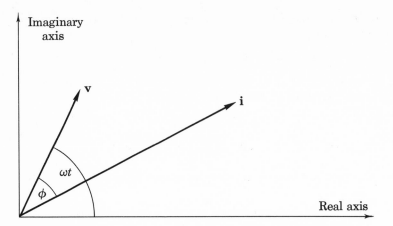

Figure 12.21 Complex representation of the impressed potential difference and the current in an *R-L* circuit.

which reveals that the current lags the impressed voltage by the angle ϕ. (See Fig. 12.21 for the complex representation.) As the impedance is varied from a pure resistance to a pure inductive reactance, the phase difference ϕ changes from 0 to $\pi/2$.

12.10   A-C Circuit Containing Resistance, Capacitance, and Inductance

When a sinusoidal emf v is applied to a series combination containing a resistance R, a capacitance C, and an inductance L (see Fig. 12.22), the equation of the circuit may be written down

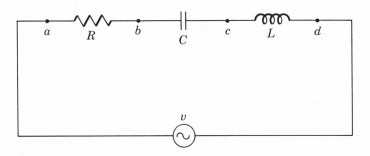

Figure 12.22 An a-c circuit containing resistance, capacitance, and inductance.

by equating the net instantaneous emf to the sum of the instantaneous potential differences across C and R—that is,

$$v - L\frac{di}{dt} = \frac{q}{C} + iR$$

Upon rearrangement and differentiation with respect to time, we find

$$L\frac{d^2i}{dt^2} + R\frac{di}{dt} + \frac{i}{C} = \frac{dv}{dt} \tag{12.55}$$

To obtain the steady-state solution, once again we substitute in (12.55) the complex quantities

$$\mathbf{i} = \mathbf{I}_m e^{j\omega t} \qquad \text{and} \qquad \mathbf{v} = V_m e^{j\omega t}$$

When the indicated operations are performed, the expression for the complex current is

$$\mathbf{i} = \frac{\mathbf{v}}{\mathbf{z}} \tag{12.56}$$

where
$$\mathbf{z} = \left[R + j\left(L\omega - \frac{1}{C\omega} \right) \right]$$

$$= R + j(X_L - X_C) = Ze^{j\phi} \tag{12.57}$$

The absolute value of $\mathbf{z}$ equals

$$Z = \sqrt{R^2 + (X_L - X_C)^2} \tag{12.58}$$

with the customary abbreviations $X_L = L\omega$ and $X_C = 1/C\omega$. The phase angle may be evaluated from

$$\phi = \tan^{-1}\frac{X_L - X_C}{R} \tag{12.59}$$

Utilizing the exponential forms for $\mathbf{v}$ and $\mathbf{z}$, we can describe the complex circuit current by

$$\mathbf{i} = \frac{V_m}{Z} e^{j(\omega t - \phi)} \tag{12.60}$$

If the imaginary part

$$v = V_m \sin \omega t \tag{12.61}$$

is taken as the applied emf, the actual circuit current is

$$i = I_m \sin (\omega t - \phi) \tag{12.62}$$

12.11   Impedance and Voltage Diagrams for the Series Circuit

Impedance diagrams which display graphically the relation between R, X_C, X_L, and Z facilitate the solution of numerical problems. A typical diagram for the series circuit appears in Fig. 12.23. Starting from the origin O, the magnitude of the resist-

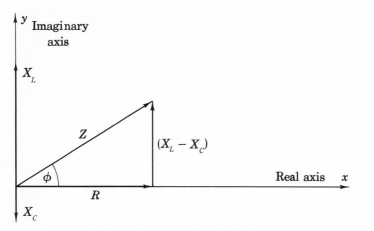

Figure 12.23   Impedance diagram for a series R-C-L circuit.

ance is drawn to scale along the positive x-axis (real axis), which also serves as a reference line for measuring phase differences. Appropriate lengths representing the reactances X_L and X_C are drawn from the origin respectively along the positive and negative y-axis (imaginary axis). As required by the analytical results given previously in (12.58) and (12.59), the impedance Z is determined by adding R, X_L, and X_C vectorially, whereas the ratio $(X_L - X_C)/R$ gives the tangent of the phase angle ϕ.

The diagram in Fig. 12.23 is frequently referred to as the vector impedance diagram. Unlike space vectors, such as velocities, forces, current densities, fields, and the like, resistances, reactances, and impedances are not vectors but scalars. In this connection, the term vector is used synonymously with the term complex quantity in so far as the process of addition is concerned. Complex quantities and vectors in a plane obey the same rule for addition. Other operations which apply to complex quantities do not have counterparts in vector algebra. Because of its long-established adoption in circuit analysis, the term vector will be used to denote a complex current, voltage, or impedance, particularly in conjunction with graphical solutions which depict the phase relationships and magnitudes.

In laboratory practice it is customary to measure the effective (rms) values of currents and potential differences. As already proved for sinusoidal variations, the effective values of such quantities are found by multiplying the corresponding peak values by the factor $\frac{1}{2}\sqrt{2}$. Consider again the circuit diagram in Fig. 12.22. If we denote the effective values of the current and the voltage by the symbols I and V, then V_{ab}, the effective value of the voltage across the resistance R, is IR, and this voltage is in phase with the current in R. Similarly, $V_{bc} = IX_C$ and $V_{cd} = IX_L$. In the case of the reactive elements, the current in the capacitor leads V_{bc} by $90°$, while that in the inductor lags V_{cd} by $90°$. To construct the voltage diagram, the voltage IR is plotted to scale along the x-axis, which now may serve as the reference line for the specification of the out-of-phase voltages IX_L and IX_C. The magnitudes of IX_L and IX_C are plotted respectively along the positive and negative y-axis. The vector voltage diagram is shown in Fig. 12.24. The impressed voltage

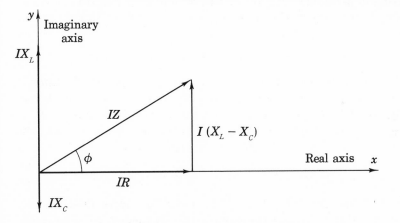

Figure 12.24 Voltage diagram for a series *R-C-L* circuit.

$V = IZ$ and the phase angle ϕ are found by referring to the voltage triangle. In the series arrangement, the current I has the same value in all elements, so that the lengths of the vectors in the voltage diagram differ from those plotted in the impedance diagram by the scale factor I.

In terms of the instantaneous voltages, it is valid to write

$v = v_{ab} + v_{bc} + v_{cd}$. Such an equality does not hold for the effective values—that is, $V \neq V_{ab} + V_{bc} + V_{cd}$. The paradoxical behavior is accounted for on the basis of the phase differences which exist between the effective values. As seen from the vector diagram of voltages, the correct relation is

$$V^2 = I^2 R^2 + I^2 (X_L - X_C)^2$$

12.12   Power in A-C Circuits

Consider a two-terminal network composed of resistive and reactive elements. Let v denote the instantaneous potential difference applied to the terminals and i the instantaneous current. Then the instantaneous power $P(t)$ supplied to the network is vi. The energy W delivered to the network in a time interval $(t_2 - t_1)$ is

$$W = \int_{t_1}^{t_2} P(t) \, dt = \int_{t_1}^{t_2} vi \, dt$$

This expression is valid in general for any form of functional time dependence of v and i. In particular, if v and i are sinusoidal functions of the time as given by (12.61) and (12.62), the instantaneous power is expressed by

$$P(t) = vi = V_m I_m \sin \omega t \sin (\omega t - \phi)$$

The quantity of importance is the average power P, which is defined as the energy furnished divided by the time interval during which this energy was delivered. In symbols, $P = W/(t_2 - t_1)$. With the aid of trigonometric transformation, the instantaneous power vi can also be expressed as

$$vi = \frac{V_m I_m}{2} \cos \phi - \frac{V_m I_m}{2} \cos (2\omega t - \phi)$$

This form shows that the power input fluctuates about the average value $(V_m I_m / 2) \cos \phi$ with the frequency 2ω. The implication is that during part of the cycle the external emf furnishes power to the network, while during the remainder of the cycle the network returns power to the generator. The average power over a time interval equal to the period of oscillation T is also calculated from

$$P = \frac{1}{T} \int_0^T vi \, dt = \frac{V_m I_m}{T} \int_0^T \sin \omega t \sin (\omega t - \phi) \, dt$$

As might be expected from the preceding discussion, the integration yields

$$P = \frac{I_m V_m}{2} \cos \phi$$

or, in terms of the effective values,

$$P = VI \cos \phi \tag{12.63}$$

The quantity $\cos \phi$ is called the power factor of the network. Its value may range from unity, for a purely resistive network ($\phi = 0$), to zero, for a purely reactive network ($\phi = \pm\pi/2$). The result in (12.63) for the average power will remain unchanged if the average is calculated over a time interval equal to an integral number of periods. In practice, it is understood that the average is taken over a time interval which is long compared to one period, and which therefore is very nearly the same as the average over an integral number of periods. The average power may be considered as the product of the effective current I and $V \cos \phi$, the component of the effective voltage in phase with the current.

12.13   Impedances in Series and Parallel

Because of the linear form $\mathbf{v} = \mathbf{iz}$, the equivalent impedance of series and parallel connections may be calculated by the same rules that are valid for combining resistance [see (5.44) and (5.45)] provided that impedances are treated as complex numbers. Thus the equivalent impedance $\mathbf{z}$ of several impedances $\mathbf{z}_1, \mathbf{z}_2, \mathbf{z}_3, \ldots$ connected in series is

$$\mathbf{z} = \mathbf{z}_1 + \mathbf{z}_2 + \mathbf{z}_3 + \cdots \tag{12.64}$$

Similarly, if impedances $\mathbf{z}_1, \mathbf{z}_2, \mathbf{z}_3, \ldots$ are connected in parallel, $\mathbf{z}$, the equivalent network impedance, is calculated from

$$\frac{1}{\mathbf{z}} = \frac{1}{\mathbf{z}_1} + \frac{1}{\mathbf{z}_2} + \frac{1}{\mathbf{z}_3} + \cdots \tag{12.65}$$

As an example of the method we shall obtain the equivalent impedance of the arrangement shown in Fig. 12.25. Applying relation (12.65), the equivalent complex impedance $\mathbf{z}$ is

$$\mathbf{z} = \frac{\mathbf{z}_1 \mathbf{z}_2}{\mathbf{z}_1 + \mathbf{z}_2}$$

where $z_1 = R + jL\omega$ and $z_2 = 1/jC\omega$. A somewhat laborious algebraic manipulation leads to the result

$$z = \frac{R + j[L\omega(1 - LC\omega^2) - R^2C\omega]}{D} \tag{12.66}$$

where the denominator D is given by

$$D = R^2C^2\omega^2 + (1 - LC\omega^2)^2 \tag{12.67}$$

Since the equivalent impedance is now known, the line current is determined by dividing z into $V_me^{j\omega t}$.

12.14   Frequency Response

The frequency dependence of the reactances X_L and X_C has already been pointed out. With increasing angular frequency ω, $X_L \to \infty$ and $X_C \to 0$, since X_L varies directly and X_C inversely with ω.

The series and parallel arrangements considered so far reveal that the complex impedance is dependent on the angular frequency of the applied emf. The frequency response of a circuit often has important consequences.

Consider the series R-L-C circuit. As ω is continuously increased from zero, the absolute value of the impedance $Z = \sqrt{R^2 + (X_L - X_C)^2}$ as given by (12.58) is minimum at a particular frequency ω_0 which makes $X_L = X_C$—that is, $L\omega_0 = 1/C\omega_0$. The characteristic angular frequency ω_0 is called the *resonance frequency*. Its square is given by

$$\omega_0^2 = \frac{1}{LC} \tag{12.68}$$

Since $\omega = 2\pi f$, the oscillation frequency at resonance is

$$f_0 = \frac{1}{2\pi}\sqrt{\frac{1}{LC}} \tag{12.69}$$

In a series circuit, at resonance the impedance is purely resistive—that is, $Z = R$. Consequently the impressed voltage is in phase with the current I. As can be seen from the relation

$$I = \frac{V}{\sqrt{R^2 + (X_L - X_C)^2}} \tag{12.70}$$

at resonance the effective value of the current attains a maximum, since the denominator reaches a minimum for $X_L = X_C$. The maximum value is V/R, which implies that the value of the current at resonance increases with decreasing circuit resistance. In the vector diagrams given in Figs. 12.23 and 12.24, the resonance condition implies that the reactance vectors have equal magnitudes. Correspondingly, IX_C, the voltage across the capacitor, is numerically equal to IX_L, the voltage across the inductor. Another interesting observation is that at resonance the potential difference across either reactance equals $(L\omega_0/R)$ times the impressed voltage. Consequently the voltage appearing across either reactance may be many times higher than the impressed voltage.

The phase angle ϕ is defined by $\tan \phi = (X_L - X_C)/R$ and therefore varies with ω. At very low frequencies ($\omega \doteq 0$) the impedance is high and essentially capacitive. Therefore $\phi \doteq -\pi/2$, and the current leads the applied voltage. As ω is gradually increased toward ω_0, the angle ϕ approaches zero from the negative side. At resonance, $\phi = 0$ and the power factor $\cos \phi$ is unity. Upon increasing ω beyond ω_0, ϕ becomes positive, and at very high frequencies the impedance becomes predominantly inductive, the current lags the voltage more and more, and the phase angle approaches $+\pi/2$. It is clear that as the frequency of the generator driving the circuit is varied, both the magnitude and the phase of the current also vary.

The parallel circuit shown in Fig. 12.25 possesses a different

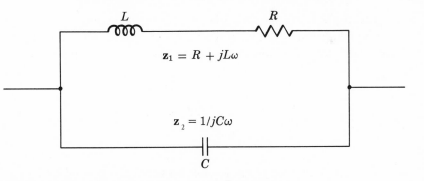

Figure 12.25 A parallel arrangement of impedances.

frequency response. In this case there are several possibilities in specifying a resonant frequency. In general, the frequency which makes the power factor unity is different from the frequency which makes the circuit impedance a maximum. In turn, both of these characteristic frequencies are different from $\omega_0 =$

$1/\sqrt{LC}$. If the impedance is evaluated for the limiting case where $R = 0$, the result in (12.66) reduces to

$$\mathbf{z} = j\frac{L\omega}{(1 - LC\omega^2)}$$

whose absolute value is

$$|\mathbf{z}| = \frac{L\omega}{(1 - LC\omega^2)} \tag{12.71}$$

In (12.71), if $\omega^2 = \omega_0^2 = 1/LC$, the impedance becomes infinite. In practice, this limiting case is nearly realized if R, the resistance of the inductance (or coil), is small relative to its reactance X_L—that is, if Q, which is defined by the ratio $L\omega/R$, is high. A high Q parallel circuit presents a high impedance to frequencies near ω_0 and thus discriminates against currents whose frequencies lie close to the resonance frequency. On the other hand, we saw that the series circuit at resonance presents a low-impedance path for currents having frequencies near ω_0. The parallel and series arrangements act as filters by rejecting or by enhancing particular frequencies. Such frequencies are selected by "tuning" or adjusting the circuit parameters L or C.

12.15   Numerical Examples

Example 1. In the circuit below, the dashed portion (terminals l, m) includes a coil whose resistance is 16 Ω and whose inductance is 0.050 henry. A sinusoidal emf of effective value equal to 100 v

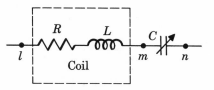

and an angular frequency ω of 480 radian/sec is applied to the terminals l and n of the series combination.

(a) What is the peak value of the emf?

$$V_m = \sqrt{2}\, V = 1.41 \times 100 = 141 \text{ v}$$

(b) Calculate the reactive inductance of the coil.

$$X_L = L\omega = 0.050 \times 480 = 24\ \Omega$$

(c) What is the impedance of the coil?

$$Z = \sqrt{R^2 + X_L^2} = \sqrt{256 + 576} = 8\sqrt{13} = 28.8 \ \Omega$$

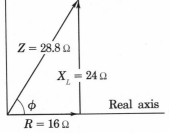

(d) By what angle does the current in the coil lag the voltage appearing across its terminals?

From the accompanying impedance diagram for the coil, we see that $\tan \phi = 24/16 = 1.50$, so that $\phi = 56.3°$.

(e) Beginning with very low values, the variable capacitance is increased gradually until the current in the circuit is 5.00 amp. For this adjustment, determine the circuit impedance and the capacitative reactance.

The impedance is calculated from $Z = V/I = 100/5.00 = 20 \ \Omega$. Now $Z^2 = R^2 + (X_L - X_C)^2$. Hence $(X_L - X_C)^2 = 400 - 256$. Whence $X_C = 12$ or $36 \ \Omega$. The second answer corresponds to the smallest value of C. If the capacitance is increased further, there will be a second value of $X_C = 12 \ \Omega$ when the current is again 5.00 amp and the impedance is $20 \ \Omega$. When $X_C = 36 \ \Omega$, the current (real axis) leads the impressed voltage. For the second adjustment $X_C = 12 \ \Omega$, the current lags the impressed voltage. Consult the impedance diagrams below.

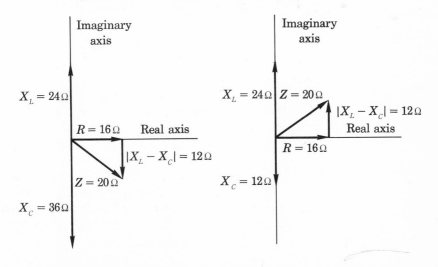

(f) What is the effective voltage across the capacitor for each adjustment?

$V_C = X_C I$. Case 1, $36 \times 5 = 180$ v. Case 2, $12 \times 5 = 60$ v.

(g) For what value of X_C will the current be in phase with the applied voltage? What is the value of the current under this circumstance?

The current will be in phase with the voltage when $Z = R$—that is, when $X_L = X_C = 24$ Ω. In this case, $I = 100/16 = 6.25$ amp.

Example 2. A sinusoidal emf of fixed frequency and amplitude is applied to the points a and c, as shown in the accompanying diagram.

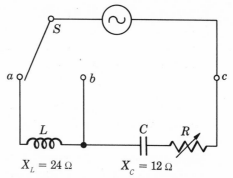

$X_L = 24$ Ω $X_C = 12$ Ω

(a) Consult the data given in the diagram and evaluate the particular value of R which makes the power factor of the circuit equal to 0.80.

The power factor is $\cos \phi$, which equals R/Z. Hence

$$0.80 = \frac{R}{\sqrt{R^2 + (X_L - X_C)^2}}$$

whence $R = 16$ Ω.

(b) The circuit is modified by throwing the switch S, which thereby applies the emf to the points b and c. The resistance R is varied so that the rate of heat produced is a maximum. Calculate the value of R which satisfies this condition.

Power delivered to the circuit is $P = VI \cos \phi$. We need to express P in terms of the single variable R. To do this note that $\cos \phi = R/Z$, and that $I = V/Z$. Upon substitution in the expression for the average power, we find

$P = V^2R/Z^2$ or $P = V^2R/(R^2 + X_C^2)$. Upon differentiating P with respect to R and setting the derivative equal to zero, we find that P is maximum when $R = X_C = 12 \, \Omega$.

Example 3. When the inductive reactance of a certain coil is plotted as a function of the angular frequency ω, the resulting graph is a straight line whose slope is equal to $5.0 \times 10^{-3} \, \Omega$ sec/radian. The coil is placed in series with a fixed capacitor and the combination is then connected across a generator whose angular frequency can be varied from 100 to 10,000 radian/sec.

The sinusoidal emf of the generator has the effective value of 30 v for all frequencies. When ω is adjusted to 5000 radian/sec, the current in the coil reaches its highest rms value of 0.30 amp.

(a) What is the capacitance of the capacitor?

The slope of the X_L vs ω plot is the inductance of the coil—that is, $L = 5.0$ millihenry. By the statement of the problem, the circuit is at resonance when $\omega = 5000$ radian/sec. Hence, $LC = 1/\omega_0^2$, or $C = 1/L\omega_0^2 = 8.0 \times 10^{-6}$ farad or 8.0 μf.

(b) What is the resistance of the coil?

At resonance, $R = Z = V/I = 30/0.30 = 100 \, \Omega$.

Time-varying Currents:
Problems

12.1 Starting with (12.6), obtain an expression for the power delivered by the seat of constant emf. Integrate this expression over the time necessary to establish the steady state. Compare the result with that given in (11.15).

12.2 A capacitance C_1 is charged to a potential difference V_1. The terminals of the charged capacitor are then connected to a second, uncharged capacitor of capacitance C_2 through a connecting lead of resistance R. Deduce an expression for the instantaneous voltage across the first capacitance at any time after the connection is made.

12.3 A 4 μf capacitor is initially charged to a potential difference of 100 v and is then placed in series with an open switch S, a resistance R, and a seat of emf, as shown in the diagram. The + and − signs on C indicate the polarity of its initial charge.

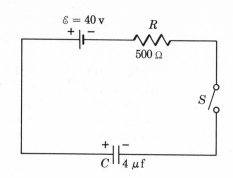

Let the switch S be closed and kept closed until the steady state is reached. Transcribe the table below and fill in the blanks. Show your calculations.

Time	Current in R	Charge on C	Energy in C
Just as S is closed			
When the steady state is reached			

12.4 A coil (resistance R Ω, inductance L henry) is connected to a source of constant emf, $\mathcal{E}$ volt, and negligible internal resistance.

Reproduce the table below. For the values of the instantaneous current i specified at the heading of each column, fill out the blanks with the appropriate values expressed explicitly in terms of numerical and circuit constants $\mathcal{E}$, L, and R. Give the units of the quantity appearing in each row. In each case indicate the relation from which each result is obtained.

Quantity ↓ Current i →	0	$\mathcal{E}/2R$	$\mathcal{E}/R$	Units
Time rate of increase of i				
Rate of increase of stored magnetic energy				

12.5 A steady current of 2.0 amp is established in the circuit represented by the adjoining diagram. Suppose that at the time $t = 0$, the constant emf $\mathcal{E}$ is short-circuited so that at all subsequent

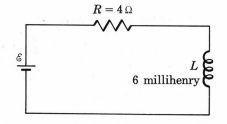

times there is no external emf acting in the circuit, which is otherwise complete.

(a) At the instant when the current in the circuit has dropped to 0.50 amp, what is the time rate of decay of the current?

(b) When the instantaneous current is 0.50 amp, what is the power delivered by the inductor?

(c) If e and i represent respectively the values of the induced emf and the current at any time t, what is the physical significance of the integral $\int_0^\infty ei\, dt$? Substitute the appropriate value for e and carry out the integration, using i as the variable of integration.

12.6   A coil has an inductance of L henry and a resistance of 5 Ω. When the current in the coil has reached the steady value of 20 amp, the constant external emf is suddenly replaced by a noninductive resistance of 25 Ω.

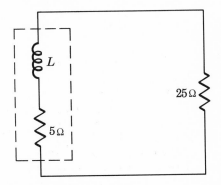

(a) When the circuit current has dropped to 6.0 amp, the current is decreasing at the rate of 10,000 amp/sec. Determine the value of L.

(b) Write down an integral to represent the energy dissipated in the entire circuit while the current changes from 20 amp to its equilibrium value. Evaluate the integral.

(c) What fraction of the initial magnetic energy stored in the coil is dissipated in the 25 Ω resistor over the period specified in (b)?

12.7   The pulsating current i has the time dependence shown in the diagram. During the rising portion (0–3 sec) the current is represented by $i = 0.4t$ amp, where the time t is expressed in seconds.

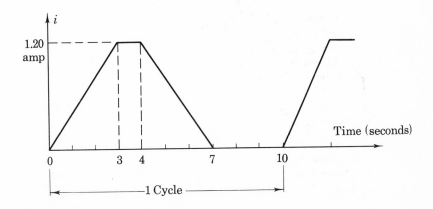

(a) What is the average value of the current over the duration of a single pulse—i.e., from $t = 0$ to $t = 7$ sec? Hint: Use the symmetry of the wave form.

(b) What is the average value over a cycle?

(c) How much heat is produced by the pulsating current in a 10 Ω resistor over the interval $t = 0$ to $t = 4$ sec?

12.8   A battery whose emf is 2 v is being charged by a time-varying current i (in amperes) described by

$$i = 5 \sin \left(\frac{2\pi}{T} t \right), \text{ for } 0 \leq t \leq \frac{T}{2};$$

$$i = 0, \text{ for } \frac{T}{2} \leq t \leq T$$

where t is the time in seconds and T is the period equal to 1/60 sec. As a result, v, the instantaneous terminal potential difference of the battery, is a function of the time, as shown in the graph.

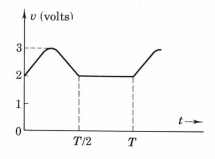

(a) What is the internal resistance of the battery?

(b) Calculate the energy converted into heat within the battery over the time interval $t = 0$ to $t = T/2$ sec.

(c) The average value of the charging current over the interval $t = 0$ to $t = T$ is $(5/\pi)$ amp. How much electrical energy is converted into chemical energy in the interval $t = 0$ to $t = T$ sec?

12.9   A 1 μf capacitor and a 2 μf capacitor are given charges of 50 μcoul and 300 μcoul respectively by connecting them individually across batteries having different emfs.

Later, as shown in the diagram, the positive and negative terminals of the charged capacitors are connected through a 50 Ω resistor while an open switch S, a resistor R, and an emf of 100 v are placed in series with the remaining terminals x and y.

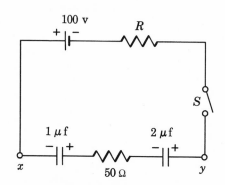

(a) What is the potential difference across the terminals x and y while S remains open?

(b) Immediately upon closing S, the current in the 50 Ω resistor is 2 amp. What is the value of R?

12.10 In the circuit as shown (with the switch S in the open position), the capacitor is charged to a potential difference of 20 v with the indicated polarity. At the instant a constant emf of 120 v is applied to the circuit by closing S, the current in the circuit is 0.10 amp.

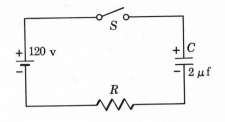

(a) Calculate the value of R.

(b) If $C = 2$ µf, what is the time rate of change of the potential difference across the capacitor when the current in the circuit is 0.10 amp?

(c) By how much will the energy stored in the capacitor have changed when the steady state is reached with the switch in the closed position?

12.11 A resistor and an uncharged capacitor are connected in series.

(a) Show graphically how the potential difference across the capacitor varies with the time if the series combination is connected to a constant-current source such as is approximated by an electrostatic generator.

(b) Refer to the curve in (a) and by a suitable calculation show how the slope of the curve at a given instant depends on the resistance or capacitance of the combination.

(c) Sketch a second graph showing the time variation of the capacitor voltage for the case in which a constant-potential source is applied to the series combination.

12.12 In the circuit shown, a constant potential of 100 v is maintained across the points a and b. With the switch S open, the equilibrium value of the charge on each capacitor is the same.

The switch S is now closed. When the steady state is again reached, the combined electrostatic energy of the two capacitors is 6800 µjoule. Find the capacitance of each capacitor.

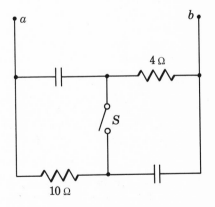

12.13 With the switch S in the open position as shown in the diagram on page 322, the charge on the 3 µf-capacitor is 315 µcoul when the steady state is reached in the network.

(a) Determine the magnitudes of ε and i, and the emf of and the current in the battery, whose internal resistance is 6 Ω.

(b) Let the switch S be closed. What is the emf of self-induction in the coil (inductance 6.5 millihenry; resistance 13 Ω) immediately after the switch is closed?

(c) How much energy is dissipated in the 13 Ω resistor in the time necessary to re-establish the steady state with S in the closed position?

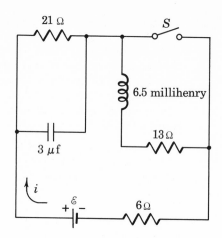

12.14 Refer to the diagram of the circuit shown at the right.

(a) Calculate the potential difference across each capacitor when the current in the seat of emf is steady.

(b) Suppose the connection XY is cut. What will be the potential difference across each capacitor when the steady state is again reached?

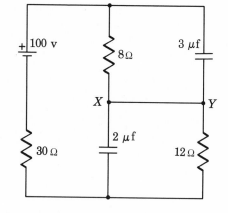

12.15 When a capacitor with an initial charge Q is allowed to discharge through a resistance, the charge q remaining on the plates after an elapsed time t is given by

$$q = Qe^{-t/RC}$$

Consider the arrangement at the right. Assume that initially the circuit has attained the steady state so that the voltage across C, as read by the electrostatic voltmeter (ESV), is equal to ε. When

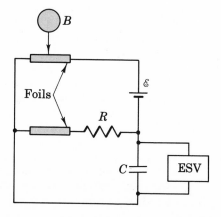

a small ball B is allowed to fall, the two metal foils are fractured in succession, thereby breaking first the battery circuit and then the capacitor circuit. For $R = 10^5$ Ω and $C = 2.5$ μf, the voltmeter reading after passage of the ball is observed to be $\mathcal{E}/e$. ($e =$ base of natural logarithms.) The battery and foils have negligible resistance.

How long does it take for the ball to traverse the distance between the foils?

12.16   In the circuit diagram, the coil has an inductance $L = 2$ henry, but its resistance is negligible. In the parallel arrangement, $R = 10$ Ω and $C = 5$ μf. A constant potential of 50 v is maintained across the points a and b. The instantaneous values of the currents at any time t after closing the switch S are indicated on the diagram.

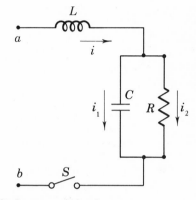

(a) What is the charge on the condenser when i_2, the current in the resistor, is 2 amp?

(b) Show that any time t after closing S, the current in the resistor, i_2, must satisfy the equation

$$L\left[RC\frac{d^2i_2}{dt^2} + \frac{di_2}{dt}\right] + i_2R = 50$$

(c) How much energy is stored in the circuit when the steady state is reached?

12.17   A variable resistance and a fixed capacitance are connected as shown. A sinusoidal voltage is applied to the combination across points 1 and 2. The current in R leads the applied voltage by 60°.

What will be the numerical value of the angle of lead if the angular frequency of the applied voltage is doubled and the value of the resistance is reduced to half its initial value?

12.18   The numerical values of voltages and currents furnished in this problem represent effective (or rms) values of the corresponding sinusoidal time variations. In the series circuit shown in the diagram on page 324, the constant frequency a-c generator has a terminal voltage of 130 v, and its impedance is negligible.

(a) The variable capacitor C is adjusted so that the current is

10 amp and lags the applied voltage. What is the capacitative reactance?

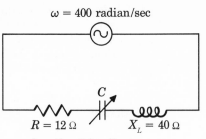

$\omega = 400$ radian/sec

$R = 12\ \Omega$ C $X_L = 40\ \Omega$

(b) For the condition specified in part (a) evaluate tan ϕ, where ϕ is the difference in phase between the voltage and the current. An appropriate impedance diagram should accompany your solution.

(c) The capacitance is changed to a lower value. For this adjustment the phase difference has the same numerical value as in part (b), but now the current leads the applied voltage. What is the new value of C if the angular frequency of the generator is 400 radian/sec?

12.19   An inductor, a capacitor, and a 3 Ω resistor are connected in series. A sinusoidal emf of variable angular frequency ω is applied to the combination. The circuit is tuned by increasing ω from zero to the resonant angular frequency ω_0. Under this adjustment the capacitative reactance is 2.0 Ω.

(a) Now suppose that ω, the angular frequency of the generator, is increased to $2\omega_0$. By the use of an appropriate impedance diagram, calculate the value of tan ϕ, where ϕ is the difference in phase between the applied voltage and the current.

(b) For the situation described in part (a), state explicitly whether the current leads or lags the applied voltage.

(c) If the effective (or rms) value of the applied voltage is 6.0 v in all cases, what is the average power delivered to the series combination when (1) $\omega = \omega_0$ and (2) $\omega = 2\omega_0$?

12.20   In the circuit shown, $C = 2$ μf, and the coil has a resistance of 300 Ω and an inductance of 0.5 henry. G is a variable-frequency generator which has a sinusoidal emf of amplitude equal to 120 $\sqrt{2}$ v.

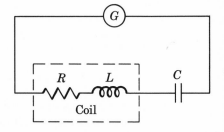

G

R L C

Coil

(a) For what frequency of the generator is the applied emf in phase with the current?

(b) Remembering that the 300 Ω resistance is all contained in the winding of the coil, calculate the rms voltage across the terminals of the coil for the generator frequency specified in part (a). By means of a vector diagram find the tangent of the angle by which the terminal voltage of the coil leads the current.

12.21 A sinusoidal voltage of fixed frequency and rms value equal to 156 v is applied to the series arrangement in which $R = 5 \ \Omega$ and $X_L = 10 \ \Omega$ at the particular frequency.

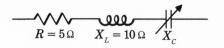

(a) The circuit is tuned by varying the capacitance. What is the rms value of the current at resonance? Include an impedance diagram for this case.

(b) By further adjustment of the capacitance, the line current is set equal to 12.0 amp (rms), with the line current leading the impressed voltage. Calculate the value of X_C for this case. Include an impedance diagram.

(c) What additional information is necessary to determine the fixed frequency of the generator?

12.22 In the circuit shown, $R = 50 \ \Omega$, $L = 0.5$ henry, $C = 2 \ \mu f$. The a-c generator G has an emf of constant amplitude, but its frequency can be varied.

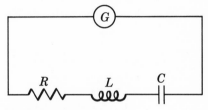

(a) For what value of the frequency of the generator is the power supplied to the circuit a maximum? Sketch a vector impedance diagram for this case.

(b) There are two generator frequencies for which the power supplied to the circuit has one-half the maximum value referred to in part (a). Calculate the value of the impedance of the circuit for either one of these two frequencies.

12.23 A resistor and a capacitor are connected in series across the terminals of an a-c generator which has a sinusoidal emf of 208 v (rms) and an angular frequency of 120π radian/sec. The rms current in the resistor is 8 amp and the power factor is 5/13.

(a) Calculate the reactance of the capacitor at the given frequency. Include a vector diagram in the solution of this part.

(b) A coil of negligible resistance is placed in series with the capacitor and the resistor. When the series combination of the three elements is connected to the terminals of the same generator, the line current is observed to be 20.8 amp. Calculate the inductive reactance of the coil.

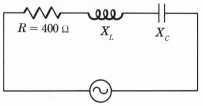

12.24 A sinusoidal voltage of fixed amplitude and variable angular frequency ω is applied to the series circuit shown.

(a) When ω is adjusted to 50 radian/sec, $X_L = 100$ Ω, $X_C = 400$ Ω, and the rms value of the line current is 0.250 amp. What is the rms value of the applied voltage at this value of ω? Include an impedance diagram in your solution.

(b) As ω is gradually raised above its value in part (a), the rms value of the current again becomes equal to 0.250 amp. Determine this value of ω. Include an impedance diagram.

12.25   Calculate the impedance of a coil and a capacitor connected in parallel for the special case where the resistance of the coil is negligible. Plot a graph showing the frequency response of this arrangement.

12.26   Calculate the complex impedance of the following networks. In each case express the impedance so that the resistive (real) and inductive (imaginary) parts are separated.

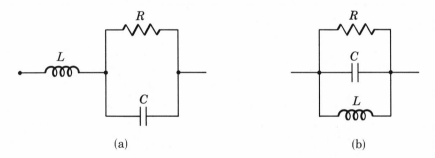

(a)   (b)

Chapter 13.
Mechanical Waves

13.1   Introduction

Although we are primarily concerned with the study of electromagnetic waves, it is helpful to approach the subject of wave
motion by considering a few examples of mechanical waves.
Technically, the term "wave motion" is used to describe the
characteristics of a disturbance which travels in a given region
and transmits energy. The traveling configuration, or the propagated disturbance, is often referred to as a "wave."

Mechanical waves may be excited under conditions where a
deformation produced in the medium gives rise to some sort of
restoring force. Water waves are among the most readily recognized examples of surface-wave phenomena. Waves may also exist in taut wires, in strings and cables, and in membranes, rods,
and other elastic solid media. They may be generated within the
body of either liquids or gases.

The disturbance varies from case to case. In the case of a
string under tension, the propagated disturbance may be a side-
wise displacement of an element of the string. In the case of a
metal rod, it may be the deformation initiated at one end by an
impulsive blow. In a gas, the traveling configuration may be a
condensation—that is, a region where both the density and the
pressure have values in excess of the values found in the undisturbed gas.

To visualize the process responsible for the propagation of
mechanical waves, it is convenient to divide the medium into
elementary segments and to regard each segment as coupled to

neighboring ones by some sort of elastic force. Owing to this connection between adjacent parts, a disturbance or a pulse initiated at some point is transmitted from one element to another. In an extensive medium the pulse will eventually be found in regions remote from the source of the disturbance. The time required for the pulse to cover a given distance is determined by the pulse velocity, which for small disturbances is governed solely by the physical properties of the medium.

It is well established that electric and magnetic fields may be propagated in free space, in dielectric media, along conductors, or within cavities. Investigations carried out in the realm of radio, radar, optics, X rays, and γ rays have demonstrated conclusively that such phenomena exhibit common characteristics. They are referred to collectively as electromagnetic waves. An introductory discussion of such waves will be presented subsequently. In this chapter we shall present physical concepts which underlie wave motion in general and shall acquaint the reader with the terminology and the simpler aspects of the mathematical machinery necessary for the treatment of wave phenomena.

13.2   Transverse Waves in a Stretched String

As an illustration of mechanical waves in one dimension, we consider the propagation of a pulse along a flexible string which is subject to a tension T. Let m denote the mass of the string per unit length of the string. An exaggerated representation of the pulse appears in Fig. 13.1. If a pulse is to travel along the string, the string should be at least somewhat extensible. In our treatment of the problem here we shall assume that the tension in the string does not depart significantly from its normal value T. This assumption is valid if the displacement is sufficiently small—that is, if the traveling configuration does not possess large kinks.

The wave is described by specifying the displacement y of any point P from its equilibrium position. (See Fig. 13.1.) This displacement depends on two independent variables: the time t, and the distance x of P from the origin O. The problem is to determine the functional dependence of y on x and t.

To solve the problem we must formulate the equation of motion of a small portion of the string. In Fig. 13.2, let AB denote

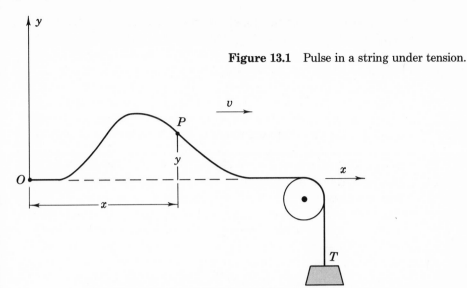

Figure 13.1 Pulse in a string under tension.

such a segment. At a fixed instant of time t, let x and y represent the coordinates of P, the midpoint of AB. The force on the end B is equal to the tension T, which acts at an angle α_2 with the x-axis. At the other end A, the force has the same magnitude but is directed at an angle α_1. At a given instant, the slope of a small segment AB centered at P is represented by $(\partial y/\partial x)|_P$. The partial-derivative notation is used since the displacement y is in general a function of two variables x and t, but t is held

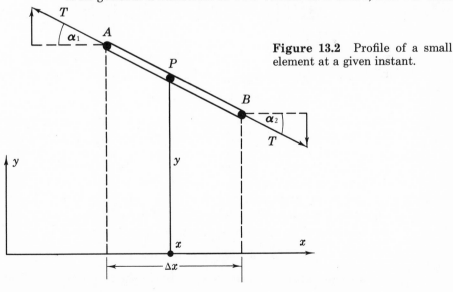

Figure 13.2 Profile of a small element at a given instant.

constant in evaluating the slope. Since the string is flexible, the tension will always act along the tangent to the string at a given point.

The net force on AB in the y direction is

$$T(\sin \alpha_2 - \sin \alpha_1) \cong T(\tan \alpha_2 - \tan \alpha_1) \qquad (13.1)$$

The last approximation is valid, since, as before, it is to be assumed that the displacement at any x is sufficiently small so that the angle α does not exceed a few degrees. The replacement of the sine of the angle by the tangent involves the neglect of $(\partial y/\partial x)^2$ relative to unity. This may be seen from the steps which follow:

$$\sin \alpha = \frac{\tan \alpha}{\sec \alpha} = \frac{\tan \alpha}{\sqrt{(1 + \tan^2 \alpha)}}$$

$$= \frac{\partial y/\partial x}{\sqrt{1 + (\partial y/\partial x)^2}} \doteq \frac{\partial y}{\partial x} = \tan \alpha \qquad (13.2)$$

We can also determine what approximation is involved in the initial assumption regarding the constancy of the tension. If the string obeys Hooke's law, a change in the tension will be directly proportional to a change in the length. If Δs denotes the arc length AB, an increase in the length of an element Δx may be calculated from

$$\Delta s - \Delta x = \left[\sqrt{1 + \left(\frac{\partial y}{\partial x}\right)^2} - 1 \right] \Delta x \doteq \frac{1}{2}\left(\frac{\partial y}{\partial x}\right)^2 \Delta x \qquad (13.3)$$

Hence, the change in the tension depends on $(\partial y/\partial x)^2$ and may therefore be neglected.

In terms of the slopes at the points A and B, the right-hand side of (13.1) can be written as

$$T(\tan \alpha_2 - \tan \alpha_1) = T\left[\frac{\partial y}{\partial x}\bigg|_B - \frac{\partial y}{\partial x}\bigg|_A \right] \qquad (13.4)$$

The slope $\partial y/\partial x$ is a function of x. By inspection of Fig. 13.3 it is seen that the slope at a point B may be found by adding to $(\partial y/\partial x)|_A$, the slope at point A, the change in the slope incurred in going from A to the neighboring point B. Thus

$$\frac{\partial y}{\partial x}\bigg|_B = \frac{\partial y}{\partial x}\bigg|_A + \left[\frac{\partial}{\partial x}\left(\frac{\partial y}{\partial x}\right) \right]_{P'} \Delta x \qquad (13.5)$$

where the last term on the right denotes the change in the slope,

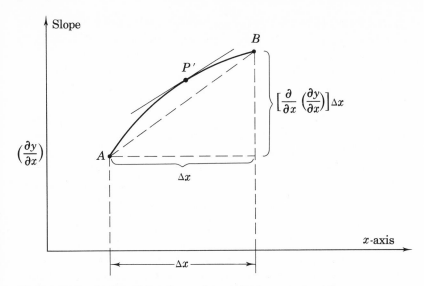

Figure 13.3   A plot of the slope of a small element at neighboring elements of the string.

and the rate of change of the slope (quantity in brackets) is to be evaluated at some point P' intermediate between A and B. By subtracting the slope at A from that at B, the unbalanced force in the y direction becomes

$$T\left[\frac{\partial}{\partial x}\left(\frac{\partial y}{\partial x}\right)\right]_{P'} \Delta x$$

This force may now be equated to the mass ($m\,\Delta s$) of the element times its acceleration. Hence

$$T\left[\frac{\partial}{\partial x}\left(\frac{\partial y}{\partial x}\right)\right]_{P'} \Delta x = m\,\Delta s\frac{\partial^2 y}{\partial t^2} \doteq m\,\Delta x\,\frac{\partial^2 y}{\partial t^2} \qquad (13.6)$$

As Δx is made to shrink, P', the point at which the derivative in the square brackets is evaluated, approaches P and in the limit relation (13.6) becomes

$$\frac{\partial^2 y}{\partial t^2} = \frac{T}{m}\frac{\partial^2 y}{\partial x^2} \qquad (13.7)$$

This is the partial differential equation of wave motion for the case in which the displacement is a function of a single space coordinate x and of the time t.

The type of wave motion contemplated here is a particular example of a group known as *transverse* waves. The term transverse is used to describe waves in which the quantity that serves as a measure of the disturbance (in this example y, the displacement of each element of the string) is at right angles to the direction in which the wave travels. In the present illustration, this direction is the x-axis, which coincides with the undisturbed string.

We wish to find out how the various segments of the string move. To do so it is necessary to solve (13.7)—that is, to determine the dependence of y on x and t. A discussion of the solution of the second-order partial differential equation cannot be taken up here. A mathematical analysis indicates that the general solution is of the form

$$y = f\left(t - \frac{x}{v}\right) + g\left(t + \frac{x}{v}\right) \tag{13.8}$$

where f and g are arbitrary functions of the arguments $[t - (x/v)]$ and $[t + (x/v)]$ respectively, and where v is a positive constant.

Let us examine the physical significance of the solution in (13.8). Consider the function $y_1 = f[t - (x/v)]$. Its value at the point $x = x_1$ and at the time $t = t_1$ is given by

$$y_1\bigg|_{\substack{x=x_1 \\ t=t_1}} = f\left(t_1 - \frac{x_1}{v}\right) \tag{13.9}$$

At a later time $t_2 = (t_1 + \Delta t)$, and at a point $x_2 = x_1 + v\,\Delta t$, the function f assumes the value

$$f\left[(t_1 + \Delta t) - \frac{x_1 + v\,\Delta t}{v}\right] = f\left(t_1 - \frac{x_1}{v}\right) = y_1\bigg|_{\substack{x=x_2 \\ t=t_2}} \tag{13.10}$$

In other words, the displacement y_1 evaluated at x_2 and t_2 has the same value as the displacement evaluated at x_1 and t_1, provided $(x_2 - x_1)$, the distance between the two points, is set equal to the product of the constant v and the time difference $(t_2 - t_1)$. This means that during the time interval $(t_2 - t_1)$ the particular value of y has been propagated from x_1 to x_2 with a velocity equal to v. (See Fig. 13.4.)

On the other hand, at a fixed point x_1, the displacement y_1 will take on successively different values, depending on the time. In this case y_1 would describe the motion of a particle of the string. It is essential to realize that the concept of wave motion is to be associated with the propagation of the disturbance along the string with velocity v and not with the movement of individual elements.

While $f[t - (x/v)]$ represents a disturbance moving in the posi-

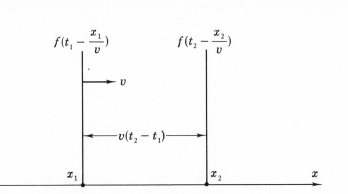

Figure 13.4   The propagation of a given displacement.

tive x direction, $g[t + (x/v)]$ corresponds to a wave propagation in the negative x direction. (Verify this assertion by reasoning based on the content of Fig. 13.4.) Note that in this case, with an increase in the time t, the positional coordinate x must change in a way that leaves the argument $[t + (x/v)]$ unchanged.

When the solution of the form (13.8) is substituted in the differential equation (13.7), we obtain the relation between velocity and the characteristics of the string. This connection is

$$v^2 = \frac{T}{m} \tag{13.11}$$

Thus, waves of any shape travel along the string with a constant velocity which can be calculated from the linear density and the tension. If terms of the order of $(\partial y/\partial x)^2$ are retained in the formulation, the velocity v is no longer independent of the wave form, which for larger displacements would change with the time.

13.3   Properties of Simple Harmonic Waves

The general solution $y = f[t - (x/v)]$ is an arbitrary function and does not specify that the wave motion be periodic. However, special periodic solutions, such as those represented by simple harmonic waves, are of considerable importance in physical problems. We shall discuss some of the properties of such waves.

As a special case, let the cosine of the argument $[t - (x/v)]$ be selected as a solution of the wave equation—that is, let the displacement y be written as

$$y = A \cos \left[\omega \left(t - \frac{x}{v} \right) \right] \qquad (13.12)$$

This form of the solution represents a periodic wave traveling in the positive x direction. In relation (13.12) A is called the *amplitude* and ω is a constant having the dimensions of reciprocal time. In the discussion which follows, sinusoidal or cosinusoidal functions of the argument $[t - (x/v)]$ will be referred to as harmonic waves.

A simple model may help clarify the physical content of (13.12). Consider a linear array of particles situated on the x-axis (see Fig. 13.5). Let us imagine that the particle at the origin O

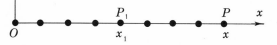

Figure 13.5   The motion of individual particles on the x-axis.

is capable of oscillating along the y-axis with simple harmonic motion described by

$$y = A \cos \frac{2\pi}{T} t$$

where T is the period of the motion. Let us assume further that all particles are able to perform identical vibrations and that each particle is coupled to the ones adjacent to it. If the particle at O is set into oscillation, each particle along the line will respond successively. For instance, the particle P_1 at a distance x_1 from O will start vibrating at a later time. The time delay is measured by x_1/v, where v is the wave velocity. Hence the particle at x_1 will take on the same displacements as those assumed by the particle at O at a later time. The motion at x_1 will lag behind that at O by the time interval (x_1/v). Accordingly,

$$y \bigg|_{x_1} = A \cos \left[\frac{2\pi}{T} \left(t - \frac{x_1}{v} \right) \right]$$

describes the vibrations of P_1. More generally, the displacement of any particle P, at a distance x from O, can be predicted from

$$y = A \cos \left[\frac{2\pi}{T} \left(t - \frac{x}{v} \right) \right]$$

which has the same form as the expression for the harmonic wave given by (13.12), provided $2\pi/T$ is identified with ω. If the linear array extends indefinitely along the $+x$-axis, a given displacement appearing at the origin will advance along the $+x$-axis, and in due time the particles of the entire array will be executing oscillatory motions.

It has already been emphasized that y, the displacement of any particle, is determined by the two independent variables x and t. At a specified time the individual displacements obey the relation

$$y = f(x) \Big|_{t=\text{Const}}$$

A plot of this function is called the *wave form* or *wave profile*. In the case of the harmonic waves described by (13.12) the wave form, as obtained by setting $t = 0$, is represented by

$$y = A \cos \omega \left(-\frac{x}{v} \right) = A \cos \omega \left(\frac{x}{v} \right)$$

Now, the period of the cosine function is 2π; hence, from (13.12) it follows that at any time t

$$2\pi + \omega t - \frac{\omega x}{v} = \omega \left(t - \frac{x + \lambda}{v} \right) \qquad (13.13)$$

where λ is the *wavelength*, or the distance between two equal successive displacements of the same sign. Upon simplification, (13.13) yields

$$\omega = \frac{2\pi v}{\lambda} \qquad (13.14)$$

Consequently the formula for the wave form becomes

$$y = A \cos \frac{2\pi}{\lambda} x \qquad (13.15)$$

A plot of this function is seen in Fig. 13.6. The maxima of the profile are referred to as *crests*, the minima as *troughs*.

On the other hand, at a specified x, y varies in time, and

$$y = f(t) \Big|_{x=\text{Const}}$$

describes the motion of a single particle at a fixed position. For

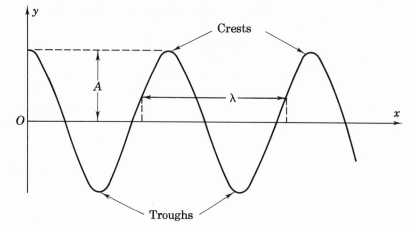

Figure 13.6   The wave profile, showing the displacement of all particles at a given instant $t = 0$. The wave is described by $y = A \cos 2\pi[(t/T) - (x/\lambda)]$.

the special case of harmonic waves and for the particle at $x = 0$, from (13.12) we obtain

$$y = A \cos \omega t \qquad (13.16)$$

which again states that the motion of a given particle is simple harmonic. The oscillation curve is plotted in Fig. 13.7, where T is the *period* of the motion, or the elapsed time between two equal successive displacements in the same direction. The quan-

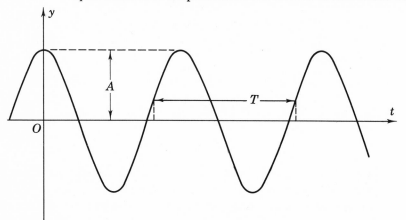

Figure 13.7   The displacement of a particle at the origin as a function of the time t. The wave is described by $y = A \cos 2\pi[(t/T) - (x/\lambda)]$.

tity ω in (13.16) is called the *angular frequency* and may be written as

$$\omega = \frac{2\pi}{T} = 2\pi f \tag{13.17}$$

where f is the *frequency*, or the number of oscillations per unit time, and is equal to $1/T$. Combining (13.14) and (13.17), we obtain

$$v = f\lambda = \frac{\lambda}{T} \tag{13.18}$$

This relation, here deduced from formulas descriptive of harmonic waves, is a formal definition of the velocity of the waves for any type. It can be seen that v can be written down directly as the ratio of the distance λ covered by a particular displacement to the time T required to cover the distance.

The expression for y given by (13.12) can now be written in a variety of equivalent forms. Two of the most useful ones are:

$$y = A \cos 2\pi\left(\frac{t}{T} - \frac{x}{\lambda}\right) \tag{13.19}$$

$$y = A \cos (\omega t - kx) \tag{13.20}$$

where k, defined by $\quad\quad k \equiv 2\pi/\lambda \tag{13.21}$

is variously called the *wave vector* or the *propagation constant*. The quantity $1/\lambda$, representing the number of waves per unit distance, is known as the *wave number*. In the angle $(\omega t - kx)$, or the argument of the cosine, the order for the time t and the positional coordinate x is arbitrary. The order of these terms in (13.20) or, more generally, in (13.8) may be reversed.

In (13.19) and (13.20), the argument of the cosine is referred to as the *phase angle*, or just the *phase*, of the wave. If the displacement is not zero at the origin at time $t = 0$, an additional term e must be included in the angle. Hence, more generally,

$$y = A \cos (\omega t - kx + e) \tag{13.22}$$

The angle e is called the *initial phase* or *epoch*.

For a given wave, the displacements at two points x_1 and x_2 at any time t are described by

$$y_1 = A \cos (\omega t - kx_1)$$

$$y_2 = A \cos (\omega t - kx_2)$$

The quantity $k(x_2 - x_1)$, obtained by taking the difference between the corresponding phase angles, is called the *phase difference* between the two displacements. Likewise, for two similar wave trains emitted by two sources at distances r_1 and r_2 from a fixed point,

$$y' = A \cos (\omega t - kr_1)$$

$$y'' = A \cos (\omega t - kr_2)$$

And $$k (r_2 - r_1) = \frac{2\pi}{\lambda} (r_2 - r_1) \qquad (13.23)$$

again represents the *phase difference* between the two wave trains in terms of the path difference.

If the wave form is not cosinusoidal but consists of a repetitive pattern, the concepts defined by (13.17) and (13.18) are still applicable.

In light of the foregoing discussion, the velocity v, which appears in the harmonic wave solution represented by (13.12), denotes the speed with which a displacement of a given magnitude is propagated. Since the fixed magnitude is specified by the value of the phase angle, the velocity v is appropriately referred to as the *phase velocity* of the wave.

In this approach we have considered the amplitude of the wave as being constant. Actually, this characteristic is an idealization approximated at large distances from a source which produces waves in a nonabsorbing medium. Whenever there is absorption of energy by the medium in which the waves are traveling, the wave amplitude diminishes with distance from the source.

A continuous surface which at a given instant is the locus of all points in the same phase of vibration is called a *wave front*. A disturbance which starts from a small source and travels in all directions with the same phase velocity represents a wave in which the surfaces of constant phase are concentric spheres. In this instance the wave front is said to be *spherical*. The solution as illustrated in (13.8) is not applicable to spherical waves but represents a plane wave. The term *plane wave* implies that the wave fronts are parallel planes perpendicular to the direction of propagation. The wave described by (13.12) is such a wave, since displacements at all points of the y,z plane have the same phase at a given instant. The wave motion has the additional property that the displacement, which lies in the y,z plane, is parallel to a particular direction—namely, the y-axis. This property is described by saying that the wave is *linearly polarized*. Thus the expression $y = A \cos \omega[t - (x/v)]$ is the analytical representation for a transverse, linearly polarized, plane harmonic wave of constant amplitude and constant frequency.

In mathematical operations it is often advantageous to express the displacement in the complex notation. From the identity

$$A e^{j(\omega t - kx)} = A \cos (\omega t - kx) + jA \sin (\omega t - kx) \qquad (13.24)$$

we can see that instead of using just the real part of the complex expression on the right, we may use the left-hand complex displacement. This form simplifies the operations of differentiation and integration. However, it must be remembered that in the result physical significance is to be attached either to the real part or to the imaginary part separately.

13.4 Energy and Intensity of Waves

When the string is traversed by a wave, both kinetic and potential energy are associated with each element of the string. In the special case of harmonic waves described by (13.20), the kinetic energy per unit length is

$$K = \frac{1}{2} m \left(\frac{\partial y}{\partial t}\right)^2 = \frac{1}{2} m \omega^2 A^2 \sin^2 (\omega t - kx) \qquad (13.25)$$

where $(\partial y/\partial t)$ is the velocity in the y direction at any point P.

From the content of (13.7) the restoring force per unit length is $T(\partial^2 y/\partial x^2)$. The increase in the potential energy of an element is the negative of the work done by the restoring force. By differentiating the displacement y with respect to the time, one finds that $T(\partial^2 y/\partial x^2) = -m\omega^2 y$. Hence, using η as a "dummy" variable of integration, V, the potential energy per unit length, may be evaluated from

$$V = -\int_0^y T \frac{\partial^2 \eta}{\partial x^2} \, d\eta = m\omega^2 \int_0^y \eta \, d\eta = \frac{1}{2} m\omega^2 y^2$$

or $\qquad V = \frac{1}{2} m\omega^2 A^2 \cos^2 (\omega t - kx) \qquad (13.26)$

Combining the results found in (13.25) and (13.26), we obtain the total energy per unit length of the string. If W denotes the sum of the kinetic and potential energy per unit length, the sum as given by

$$W = K + V = \frac{1}{2} m\omega^2 A^2 \qquad (13.27)$$

indicates that the total energy density is constant. This result is to be expected, since dissipative effects have been neglected. Physically, the passage of a wave deforms a medium, and damping effects of varying degrees are to be expected.

A direct calculation of the time average of the kinetic and potential energies as given by (13.25) and (13.26) leads to the result that, in each case, the time average is equal to $\frac{1}{4}m\omega^2A^2$.

The total energy associated with the displaced portion of the string is propagated. The flow of energy is described by the wave *intensity*, which in general is defined as the average power transmitted per unit area perpendicular to the direction of propagation. In our example of transverse waves traveling in the $+x$ direction with speed v along the string, the expression for the *intensity* I may be deduced from the following reasoning. Consider an elementary volume whose cross-sectional area is a and whose length is $v\,dt$. If w is the energy per unit volume, then $(wav\,dt)$ is the energy associated with the elementary volume. This energy will flow across the end area a in the time dt. Hence I, or the amount of energy passing through the area per unit time, is

$$I = vw \qquad (13.28)$$

The energy density w may be found from the result in (13.27) by replacing the linear density m by the volume density ρ. Accordingly, the expression for the intensity I of the harmonic wave becomes

$$I = \frac{1}{2} \rho v \omega^2 A^2 \qquad (13.29)$$

The calculation emphasizes that the intensity is proportional to the square of the amplitude.

Expressions for V and K (potential and kinetic energies per unit length) may also be written down for a more general case of traveling waves. As before, the evaluation of K follows at once from the transverse velocity of a point and the approximation that $ds \cong dx$. Thus

$$K = \frac{1}{2} m \left(\frac{\partial y}{\partial t}\right)^2 = \frac{1}{2} m \left(\frac{\partial f}{\partial u}\right)^2$$

where $(\partial f/\partial u)$ stands for the partial derivative of the general solution f with respect to the argument $[t - (x/v)]$, here denoted by u.

The calculation of the potential energy associated with an element of the string depends on a knowledge of the particular forces which bring about the deformation. In the case of the string, let us compute the potential energy of an element by considering the increase in its length. As given by (13.3), the potential energy is $\frac{1}{2}(\partial y/\partial x)^2\, dx$. Therefore, the amount of work done is $T/2(\partial y/\partial x)^2\, dx$. Hence, the potential energy per unit length is $V = (T/2)(\partial y/\partial x)^2$. Setting $y = f[t - (x/v)] = f(u)$, then $(\partial y/\partial x) = -(1/v)(\partial f/\partial u)$. Consequently, utilizing the relation $v^2 = T/m$, we obtain

$$V = \frac{T}{2v^2}\left(\frac{\partial f}{\partial u}\right)^2 = \frac{1}{2}m\left(\frac{\partial f}{\partial u}\right)^2$$

These expressions for V and K when integrated over the length give the potential and kinetic energy of the string. We observe that the present calculation of V is based on the approximate difference between the arc length ds and the unstretched length of the element dx. This approximation is of an order higher than that retained in deriving the wave equation or in writing the expression for K. In these relations it was assumed that $ds \cong dx$. With these stipulations it is seen that for the general case of a progressive wave described by $f[t - (x/v)]$, the kinetic and potential energies per unit length are equal.

13.5   Boundary Conditions

In this section we shall investigate the reflection of plane transverse harmonic waves at the boundary between two strings 1 and 2 having different linear densities m_1 and m_2 ($m_1 > m_2$). (See Fig. 13.8.) The strings are attached at the origin O and are subject to the same tension T.

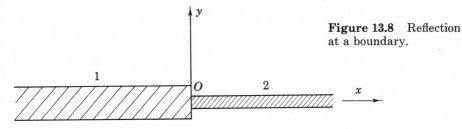

Figure 13.8 Reflection at a boundary.

A wave described by

$$y_1 = A_1 \cos (\omega t - k_1 x)$$

is traveling along string 1 in the $+x$ direction. At the junction O, this wave is partly transmitted and partly reflected. The reflected wave moving to the left in string 1 is represented by

$$y_1' = A_1' \cos (\omega t + k_1 x)$$

while for the wave which progresses along string 2

$$y_2 = A_2 \cos (\omega t - k_2 x)$$

Thus, the three wave trains have the same frequency $\omega/2\pi$ but different amplitudes, wavelengths, and phase velocities v_1 and v_2. From the relation $v = \sqrt{T/m}$, it follows that

$$k_1 = \frac{2\pi f}{v_1} = \omega \sqrt{\frac{m_1}{T}} \quad \text{and} \quad k_2 = \omega \sqrt{\frac{m_2}{T}}$$

At the junction O, the transverse displacements of strings 1 and 2 must be the same. Analytically, this is equivalent to

$$(y_1 + y_1')\Big|_{x=0} = y_2 \Big|_{x=0} \tag{13.30}$$

where the subscripts indicate that the displacements are to be evaluated at the boundary $x = 0$.

Furthermore, at O, the transverse force measured by $T \sin \alpha \doteq T \tan \alpha = T(\partial y/\partial x)$ must have the same value for both strings. This requirement is expressed by

$$\left(\frac{\partial y_1}{\partial x}\right)_{x=0} + \left(\frac{\partial y_1'}{\partial x}\right)_{x=0} = \left(\frac{\partial y_2}{\partial x}\right)_{x=0} \tag{13.31}$$

in which the constant tension T appearing on both sides has been canceled.

Equations (13.30) and (13.31), which are referred to as *boundary conditions*, make it possible to obtain relations between the amplitudes of the various progressive waves. By substituting the values of the displacements y_1, y_1', and y_2 in (13.30) and upon performing the indicated operations in (13.31) we find

$$A_1 + A_1' = A_2 \tag{13.32}$$

$$k_1(A_1 - A_1') = k_2 A_2 \tag{13.33}$$

The ratio A_1'/A_1 is defined as the *reflection coefficient R*. After appropriate manipulations of (13.32) and (13.33) to eliminate A_2, the coefficient R assumes the form

$$R = \frac{A_1'}{A_1} = \frac{(k_1 - k_2)}{(k_1 + k_2)}$$

or, upon expressing k_1 and k_2 in terms of m_1 and m_2,

$$R = \frac{\sqrt{m_1} - \sqrt{m_2}}{\sqrt{m_1} + \sqrt{m_2}} \tag{13.34}$$

This result indicates that if $\sqrt{m_1} < \sqrt{m_2}$, then R is negative, so that the incident and reflected amplitudes have opposite signs. In this situation the reflected wave suffers a phase change of 180°. The assumed inequality between the linear densities also implies that $v_1 > v_2$. That is, when the phase velocity in medium 1 exceeds that in medium 2, a phase change takes place upon reflection at the boundary. On the other hand, if $\sqrt{m_1} > \sqrt{m_2}$, R is positive and A_1 has the same sign as A_1'. In this case ($v_1 < v_2$); there is no phase change upon reflection.

13.6   Longitudinal Waves in a Fluid

As a second illustration, we shall discuss the propagation of sound waves in a compressible fluid such as air. Let us assume that the fluid is contained in a pipe and that the disturbance which progresses along the pipe is associated with the oscillatory motion of gas molecules, the movement of the particles being along the direction of travel of the wave. Waves having this character are called *longitudinal waves*.

Before considering the analytical aspects of the problem, it is worthwhile to examine somewhat qualitatively the underlying ideas associated with this kind of wave motion.

In Fig. 13.9, let one end of the pipe be provided with a piston

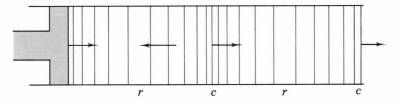

Figure 13.9   The condensations c and rarefactions r travel to the right. The arrows indicate the direction of motion of gas particles.

which oscillates periodically, and let the pipe extend along the x-axis indefinitely. As the piston moves to the right, the layer of the fluid adjacent to the piston is displaced. We shall assume that the entire layer moves as a whole. As a consequence of the motion of the piston, adjacent layers of the gas are compressed. In Fig. 13.9, the successive layers are represented by parallel lines. On the expansion stroke, the layers near the piston move to the left and there is an expansion of the adjacent layers. In the figure, such regions of condensation and rarefaction are labeled c and r, and the propagation of a particular condensation or rarefaction constitutes the wave.

In the region of a condensation the particles are moving in the direction of the propagation, while in a rarefaction the movement of particles is in a direction opposite to that in which the wave travels. (The motion of a layer may be identified with the mass movements of the molecules contained in it. This movement is in addition to the random thermal motion.) In a harmonic longitudinal wave, each layer or particle is displaced from an equilibrium position and undergoes oscillations. For example, the particle at x at the time t may have a displacement along the x-axis given by $\xi(x, t) = A \cos (\omega t - kx)$.

The traveling disturbance may be described in terms of ξ, the displacement of a given layer, or in terms of density or pressure fluctuations. The change in the density $\Delta\rho$ as measured from the mean value ρ, divided by ρ, is called the *condensation*; the difference in pressure, measured from the equilibrium pressure of the gas, is called the *excess pressure* and will be denoted by p.

In Fig. 13.10, let the x-axis coincide with the axis of the tube and let x denote the position of an element of the fluid in the undisturbed state. The portion GH of the fluid in the equilibrium state has a volume $A\,dx$, where A is the sectional area of the tube and dx is the thickness of the element. At fixed time t, let $\xi(x, t)$ denote the displacement of the left-hand boundary at G, and let $\xi(x + dx, t)$ denote the displacement of the right-hand boundary at H. In the disturbed condition the corresponding boundaries are located at G' and H'. With the aid of the diagram it is seen that dV, the increase in the volume of $G'H'$ over that of GH, is given by

$$dV = [\xi(x + dx, t) - \xi(x, t)]A = (\Delta\xi)A = \left(\frac{\partial\xi}{\partial x}dx\right)A$$

provided the thickness of GH is small enough so that $\Delta\xi$ may be

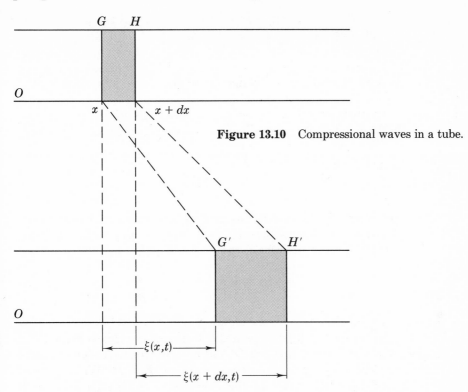

Figure 13.10   Compressional waves in a tube.

replaced by $(\partial\xi/\partial x)\,dx$. Referred to the original volume $V = A\,dx$, the fractional increase in volume is

$$\frac{dV}{V} = \frac{\partial\xi}{\partial x} \qquad (13.35)$$

As before, certain restrictions are to be imposed. First, there shall be no dissipation in the medium or at the walls. Next, $\partial\xi/\partial x$ must be small relative to unity—that is, $\Delta\xi$, the change in the displacement, is to be a small fraction of the thickness dx, as can be seen from the relation $\Delta\xi = (\partial\xi/\partial x)\,dx$. The representation in Fig. 13.10 is exaggerated for clarity.

The isothermal compressibility k is defined as the rate of change of volume with the hydrostatic pressure per unit volume at a specified temperature. In symbols,

$$k = -\frac{1}{V}\left(\frac{\partial V}{\partial P}\right)_T \qquad (13.36)$$

where the subscript T means that the partial derivative is to be evaluated at constant temperature. At a fixed temperature the gas law has the form $PV = C = $ Constant, and the isothermal compressibility defined in (13.36) reduces to $1/P$ when the derivative is evaluated. The isothermal modulus of volume elasticity, or the bulk modulus B, is defined as the reciprocal of k—that is, $B = 1/k = P$.

Accordingly, the decrease in pressure to be associated with the increase in volume prescribed by (13.35) is expressible in terms of k. With the aid of the relation $dV = (\partial V/\partial P)_T \, dP$, the compressibility k may be written as

$$k = -\frac{1}{p}\frac{dV}{V}$$

where dP, the change in the hydrostatic pressure, has been replaced by the excess pressure p. In conjunction with the value of (dV/V) given in (13.35), the excess pressure may be expressed as

$$p = -\frac{1}{k}\left(\frac{dV}{V}\right) = -\frac{1}{k}\frac{\partial\xi}{\partial x} \qquad (13.37)$$

The force acting on the element $G'H'$ is to be taken as $-A \, dp$, where dp is the difference in the values of the excess pressure at points on the end surfaces G' and H'. The negative sign indicates that the excess pressure decreases from G' to H'. Writing $dp = (\partial p/\partial x) \, dx$, the force on the element of volume then becomes $-A(\partial p/\partial x) \, dx$. Also, the mass of the gas in the volume of interest is $A(\rho + d\rho) \, dx$, or, if we neglect products of differentials, $A\rho \, dx$. Hence, the equation of motion is

$$-A\left(\frac{\partial p}{\partial x}\right) dx = (\rho A \, dx)\frac{\partial^2\xi}{\partial t^2}$$

where $\partial^2\xi/\partial t^2$ represents the acceleration of an element of the fluid having the displacement $\xi(x, t)$. Upon reduction, the above relation yields

$$\frac{\partial^2\xi}{\partial t^2} = -\frac{1}{\rho}\left(\frac{\partial p}{\partial x}\right) \qquad (13.38)$$

The right-hand side of (13.38) can be expressed as a function of the displacement $\xi(x, t)$ by differentiating p as given by (13.37). This leads to the wave equation

$$\frac{\partial^2\xi}{\partial t^2} = \frac{1}{k\rho}\frac{\partial^2\xi}{\partial x^2} \qquad (13.39)$$

It is possible to eliminate ξ by differentiating (13.37) twice with respect to t, and (13.38) once with respect to x. Assuming the order of differentiation to be immaterial, we obtain

$$\frac{\partial^2 p}{\partial t^2} = \frac{1}{k\rho} \frac{\partial^2 p}{\partial x^2} \tag{13.40}$$

which is the wave equation for the excess pressure. The partial differential equations developed above again indicate the possibility of wave motion that can be described in terms of particle displacement or excess pressure. Considering only motion along the $+x$ direction, as before, we can write the solutions of (13.39) and (13.40) as

$$\xi(x, t) = f\left(t - \frac{x}{v}\right) \tag{13.41}$$

and

$$p(x, t) = h\left(t - \frac{x}{v}\right) \tag{13.42}$$

where the phase velocity v is given by

$$v^2 = \frac{1}{k\rho} \tag{13.43}$$

The compressibility k is the reciprocal of the bulk modulus B. Writing (13.43) in terms of the bulk modulus, we obtain

$$v^2 = \frac{B}{\rho} \tag{13.44}$$

The change in the volume of a gas produced by a change in pressure depends on whether the compression is isothermal or adiabatic. A compression results in a temperature rise, and an expansion results in a temperature drop. Therefore, as the compressional wave progresses through the gas, the regions of condensation will be warmer than the adjacent regions of rarefaction unless heat is removed from the first and added to the second. Although conduction of heat from a condensation to a rarefaction is to be expected, the amount transferred will depend on the conductivity of the gas and on the distance between a condensation and a rarefaction. This distance is half a wavelength. The heat conductivity of gases is low. In addition, at low frequencies the distance between high- and low-temperature regions is large. At higher frequencies, this distance grows smaller, but the compressions and rarefactions follow each other rapidly. Hence, in general, the heat flow out of a condensation is insufficient to preserve constancy in temperature, and the process must be considered an adiabatic one.

For an isothermal compression, the bulk modulus was evaluated from the ideal gas law $PV = mRT =$ Constant and was found to equal P. (Here P is the actual pressure, not the excess pressure p.)

The corresponding gas law for an adiabatic compression is $PV^\gamma = mRT$, and the bulk modulus becomes γP. (Here γ is the ratio of specific heat at constant pressure to the specific heat at constant volume.) As was explained above, the passage of the wave involves an adiabatic process, and the expression for the speed of compressional waves is more appropriately written as

$$v = \sqrt{\frac{\gamma P}{\rho}} \tag{13.45}$$

13.7   Other Types of Wave

In the preceding sections two typical examples of wave motion were discussed, one dealing with transverse waves in a string, the other with longitudinal waves in a gas. More generally, both longitudinal and transverse waves will be propagated in media possessing bulk and shear elasticity.

Wave motion of a complicated nature may also exist along the surface of liquids. We shall cite several illustrations of this type. In the case of tidal waves, the wavelength λ is long relative to h, the depth of the liquid; the phase velocity of such waves is given by $\sqrt{gh}$, where g is the acceleration due to gravity. When the surface of a body of water is disturbed by winds or by an impact of some sort, the force of gravity and the surface tension act as restoring forces. In this instance the elements of the liquid execute elliptical motions, and the expression for the phase velocity is found to be

$$v = \sqrt{\frac{g\lambda}{2\pi} + \frac{2\pi\sigma}{\lambda\rho}} \tag{13.46}$$

where ρ and σ are the density and surface tension respectively.

There is a novel feature in the relation represented by (13.46), in that the phase velocity is seen to depend on the wavelength λ. If λ is sufficiently large, the second term in (13.46) may be neglected; then the expression becomes applicable to the case of waves excited by winds on the surface of deep water. On the other hand, if λ is small enough, the term involving the surface tension predominates and the first term in (13.46) becomes negligible. Thus for deep sea waves

$$v = \sqrt{\frac{g\lambda}{2\pi}} \tag{13.47}$$

and for ripples

$$v = \sqrt{\frac{2\pi\sigma}{\lambda\rho}} \tag{13.48}$$

Relation (13.47) illustrates a type of wave motion in which the longer wavelengths travel with higher speed. The converse is true in the case of surface waves, which obey (13.48). In either case, different wavelengths are propagated with different phase velocities. A medium in which the phase velocity is a function of wavelength is described as *dispersive*. Important effects are encountered in connection with the propagation of electromagnetic waves through dispersive media.

13.8   Phase, Group, and Signal Velocity

The dependence of phase velocity on wavelength means that when two wave trains of the same amplitude but slightly different frequencies are superposed, there results a single wave whose amplitude is no longer constant. To see why this is so, let us combine the two harmonic waves described by

$$y_1 = a \cos(\omega_1 t - k_1 x) \qquad \text{and} \qquad y_2 = a \cos(\omega_2 t - k_2 x)$$

By using a trigonometric identity, and recalling that $\Delta\omega$ and Δk, given respectively by $(\omega_2 - \omega_1)$ and $(k_2 - k_1)$, are small relative to either angular frequency ω or wave vector k, after simplification we obtain

$$y = y_1 + y_2 = \left\{ 2a \cos\left(\frac{\Delta\omega}{2} t - \frac{\Delta k}{2} x\right) \right\} \cos(\omega t - kx) \tag{13.49}$$

where

$$\omega = \frac{\omega_1 + \omega_2}{2} \quad \text{and} \quad k = \frac{k_1 + k_2}{2}$$

The result in (13.49) represents an amplitude-modulated wave— that is, a wave whose amplitude (as described by the quantity in braces) is not constant but varies in time and position. The wave form is shown in Fig. 13.11, where the dashed curve shows the modulation envelope of a group of waves. The propagation rate of the maximum value of the envelope is found by setting

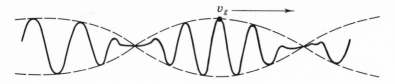

Figure 13.11   Plot of the modulated wave at a given instant.

the quantity in braces equal to $2a$. This is equivalent to setting the argument of the cosine equal to zero—that is, $x = (\Delta\omega/\Delta k)t$. The quantity $\Delta\omega/\Delta k$ represents the speed with which the maximum amplitude associated with the group of waves progresses along the $+x$ direction. It is referred to as the *group velocity*.

Now, $\Delta\omega = (d\omega/d\lambda)\,\Delta\lambda$ and $\Delta k = (dk/d\lambda)\,\Delta\lambda$. Denoting the group velocity by v_g, we transform $\Delta\omega/\Delta k$ and obtain

$$v_g = \frac{\Delta\omega}{\Delta k} = \frac{\left(\dfrac{d\omega}{d\lambda}\right)}{\left(\dfrac{dk}{d\lambda}\right)} = \frac{2\pi\,\dfrac{d}{d\lambda}\left(\dfrac{v}{\lambda}\right)}{-2\pi\,\dfrac{1}{\lambda^2}} = v - \lambda\frac{dv}{d\lambda} \quad (13.50)$$

Equation (13.50) gives the connection between v_g and v, the group and phase velocities. If there is no dispersion—that is, if v is not dependent on λ—then $dv/d\lambda = 0$. Hence v_g and v are identical.

In the previous illustrations of small-amplitude waves along a string and of compressional waves in a pipe, we derived expressions for the phase velocity which may be identified with the speed of an observer who, when traveling with a wave, detects no change in the phase of the wave. In our examples, the expressions for the phase velocity were not dependent on the wavelength but were determined by the physical properties of the medium. However, according to (13.47) and (13.48), surface waves on a liquid progress with a phase velocity which increases with λ in the case of deep sea waves but decreases with λ in the case of ripples. Now the group velocity may be looked upon as the speed of an observer who, while traveling with the wave, fails to detect a change in the amplitude of the modulation envelope. The group velocity may be greater than or less than the phase velocity. For surface waves of large λ [see (13.47)] $dv/d\lambda$ is positive, so $v_g < v$; while for ripples [see (13.48)] $dv/d\lambda$ is negative, hence $v_g > v$.

The concepts of phase and group velocity as outlined above are of limited validity. Phase velocity has meaning when the waves are periodic and are of long duration. But many physical sources emit waves for only a short time, and the corresponding wave train is of finite length. Here the wave cannot be described by a simple harmonic wave. However, it can be represented by a superposition of two or more harmonic waves. Through Fourier synthesis, a pulse or a wave with a given form may be constructed by combining harmonic waves of appropriate amplitudes and frequencies. When we re-examine the manner in which group velocity was defined, we see that the concept has meaning when the frequencies of the component waves lie within a narrow range. With this restriction, the pulse or "wave-packet" may advance over large distances without becoming deformed. Physically, this condition is nearly realized when, in (13.50), the term $\lambda\,(dv/d\lambda)$ is positive and sufficiently small so that v_g and v are not widely different. In the absence of dispersion, $dv/d\lambda = 0$. Hence phase velocity and group velocity become identical.

When electromagnetic waves pass through conducting media, $dv/d\lambda$ is negative and v_g is greater than v. Also, there are instances where the passage of electromagnetic waves through a dispersive medium gives rise to resonance effects and results in the absorption of energy over a range of wavelengths. In such cases the group velocity may attain a value in excess of c, the speed of electromagnetic waves in free space. But it is a postulate of the special theory of relativity that no *signal* can be transmitted with a speed higher than c. Thus we are led to believe that the velocity of energy propagation may not generally be associated with the group velocity. We must introduce the concept of *signal velocity*. Following the emission of a pulse from a source, wave motion transmits the energy to a receiver at a distant point. The actual speed, based on the time elapsed between the emission of the pulse and the arrival at the detector of the first impulse, is to be thought of as the signal velocity. Such a measurement yields a result which is smaller than c.

13.9   Shock Waves

The pressure variations in air associated with a compressional wave which the human ear interprets as a loud sound are of the order of $10^{-3}\,P_0$, where P_0 represents the atmospheric pressure (760 Torr). Fluctuations in pressure as low as $10^{-10}\,P_0$ can be detected by the ear as faint sound. The small excess pressures mentioned here are propagated by collisions between molecules.

Even in this range of excess pressures there is a possibility that regions of condensation, owing to their somewhat higher temperature, may move faster than regions of rarefaction. An effect of this sort gives rise to waveform distortion.

As a basic model for examining distortion, let us consider the motion of a gas produced by a piston which starts from rest and advances into a tube in which the gas is initially at rest. Immediately upon the start of the piston movement, the excess pressure distribution ahead of the piston may be represented somewhat as in the left half of the diagram in Fig. 13.12. Considering

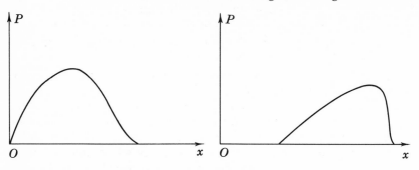

Figure 13.12   Steepening of the pressure profile.

only temperature effects and recalling that the local speed of the wave will be higher in the region of higher pressure, we find that the initial profile will be distorted in the course of time and at a later instant may assume the steep pressure front pictured in the right half of Fig. 13.12.

The formation of a profile with a nearly vertical slope is associated with the formation of a shock front. We shall demonstrate that for the simplified case of one-dimensional flow in an ideal gas, the shock front or pressure jump moves away from the piston with a supersonic speed. The value of this speed is determined by the physical properties of the quiet gas ahead of the shock wave, the nature of the thermal processes, and the speed of the piston.

Violent disturbances produced by chemical detonations, disruptive electrical discharges, and nuclear explosions set up a large-amplitude compressional pulse and create a flow of gas into the quiescent regions surrounding the source. Shock-wave phenomena studied in the laboratory indicate that the molecules involved in such a flow are confined to a relatively thin layer whose thickness is of the order of several thousand angstroms (1 angstrom $= 10^{-10}$ m). Ahead of this shock layer, the pressure, density, temperature, and flow speed remain undisturbed. In the region comprising the shock front, however, abrupt changes occur in these physical quantities. A second set of conditions exists behind the shock region.

The expression for the shock velocity resulting from the motion of a piston moving in a tube with uniform speed U_p will be developed on the basis of the conservation laws of mass, momentum, and energy. In Fig. 13.13, let P_1, ρ_1, and u_1 represent

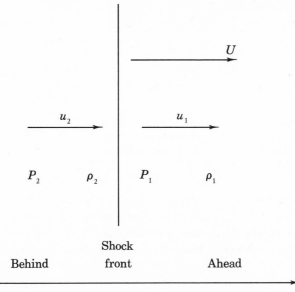

Figure 13.13 Conditions in the neighborhood of a shock layer. U denotes the speed of the shock front, while u_1 and u_2 denote the flow speed of the gas ahead of and behind the front.

the pressure, density, and speed of the gas ahead of the shock front and let P_2, ρ_2, and u_2 denote the same quantities behind the shock front. Also, let U stand for the speed of the shock front. The conservation conditions are expressed conveniently in terms of v_1 and v_2, the speeds of the gas relative to the shock front; that is, $v_1 = u_1 - U$ and $v_2 = u_2 - U$ respectively for the regions ahead of and behind the front. Consider a thin rectangular volume element centered about the shock front (see Fig. 13.14). The mass per unit time entering and the mass per unit time leaving the slab through the surface S perpendicular to the x-axis (direction of flow) are $\rho_2 v_2 S$ and $\rho_1 v_1 S$ respectively. Then, if mass is to be conserved, we have

$$\rho_2 v_2 = \rho_1 v_1 \tag{13.51}$$

Next we write the momentum equation. The momentum trans-

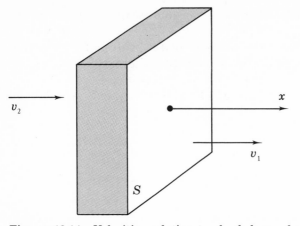

Figure 13.14 Velocities relative to shock layer, from the viewpoint of an observer moving along with the front with speed U. The flow speeds are v_1 and v_2, given respectively by $v_1 = u_1 - U$ and $v_2 = u_2 - U$ for the regions ahead of and behind the front.

fer from the left per unit time is $(\rho_2 v_2 S)v_2$. Similarly, the momentum per unit time leaving the slab is $(\rho_1 v_1 S)v_1$. But the impulse given to the elementary volume is $(P_2 - P_1)S$. Equating the impulse to the time rate of change of momentum, we have

$$(P_2 - P_1)S = \rho_1 v_1^2 S - \rho_2 v_2^2 S$$

or
$$P_1 + \rho_1 v_1^2 = P_2 + \rho_2 v_2^2 \qquad (13.52)$$

The energy conservation as expressed through the Bernoulli relation is applied to a compressible fluid. For an adiabatic process (no gain or loss of heat) the pressure P and the density are related by $P = K\rho^\gamma$, where K and γ are constants. Applying the Bernoulli theorem to this case, we have

$$\int_{P_0}^{P_1} \frac{dP}{\rho} + \frac{1}{2} v_1^2 + gh_1 = \int_{P_0}^{P_2} \frac{dP}{\rho} + \frac{1}{2} v_2^2 + gh_2$$

where P_0 refers to the pressure at a standard state. Upon carrying out the integration, and assuming that the gravitational potential energy is unchanged, we find

$$\frac{\gamma P_1}{(\gamma - 1)\rho_1} + \frac{1}{2} v_1^2 = \frac{\gamma P_2}{(\gamma - 1)\rho_2} + \frac{1}{2} v_2^2 \qquad (13.53)$$

From the basic conditions represented by (13.51, (13.52), and (13.53), various other relations can be derived. Solving for v_1 from the equality in (13.51), and substituting its value in

(13.52) and (13.53), we obtain two relations for v_2^2. Upon equating the results, we can solve for the ratio of the pressure behind the shock to the pressure ahead of it, in terms of the densities on both sides of the shock. The resulting expression is

$$\frac{P_2}{P_1} = \frac{\rho_2 - \rho_1\mu^2}{\rho_1 - \rho_2\mu^2} = \frac{(\rho_2/\rho_1) - \mu^2}{1 - (\rho_2/\rho_1)\mu^2} \tag{13.54}$$

where

$$\mu^2 \equiv \frac{\gamma - 1}{\gamma + 1} \tag{13.55}$$

By inverting (13.54) we solve for the density ratio

$$\frac{\rho_2}{\rho_1} = \frac{P_2 + P_1\mu^2}{P_1 + P_2\mu^2} = \frac{(P_2/P_1) + \mu^2}{1 + (P_2/P_1)\mu^2} \tag{13.56}$$

For air, the ratio of the specific heats $\gamma = 1.40$; hence, $\mu^2 = \frac{1}{6}$. Now, strong shocks are characterized by a large P_2/P_1 ratio. As seen from (13.56), $\rho_2/\rho_1 \rightarrow 1/\mu^2 = 6$ as $P_2/P_1 \rightarrow \infty$. Hence, for air, the density behind the shock front can be at most six times the density ahead of it.

The pressure ratio given by (13.54) can be reduced further by expressing it in terms of the *Mach number M* for the flow relative to the shock front. This number is defined as the ratio of the relative velocity v_1 to c_1, the speed of sound in the undisturbed gas. In symbols,

$$M_1 = \frac{v_1}{c_1} \tag{13.57}$$

where c_1 is given by

$$c_1 = \sqrt{\frac{\gamma P_1}{\rho_1}} \tag{13.58}$$

With the aid of (13.57) and (13.58), the momentum relation in (13.52) may be recast in the form

$$\frac{P_2}{P_1} = 1 + \gamma M_1^2 \left(1 - \frac{\rho_1}{\rho_2}\right) \tag{13.59}$$

Utilizing the value of ρ_2/ρ_1 from (13.56), we find

$$\frac{P_2}{P_1} = (1 + \mu^2)M_1^2 - \mu^2 = 1 + \frac{2\gamma}{\gamma + 1}(M_1^2 - 1) \tag{13.60}$$

which implies that the pressure ratio is roughly proportional to the square of the Mach number, since $\mu^2 = \frac{1}{6}$.

Using the formulas derived so far, we can predict the quantities on one side of the shock layer in terms of quantities on the other side plus one other quantity, such as the Mach number, the pressure, or the density on the first side. As a final calculation, let us determine the shock velocity U for the case where the piston continues to move with uniform velocity so that the gas speed u_2 behind the shock is equal to the speed of the piston. Assume that the gas speed u_1 ahead of the piston is zero. This condition implies that $v_1 = -U$ and that $v_2 = u_2 - U$, as before.

To solve, we must eliminate the P's and the ρ's in order to arrive at an equation in terms of v_1 and v_2. To do this, divide (13.52) by ρ_2; use (13.51) and (13.58) and solve the resulting relation for P_2/ρ_2 after eliminating P_1. Also, solve (13.53) for P_2/ρ_2 and combine with the preceding result. Substitute the values of v_1 and v_2 specified in the assumption. This substitution yields a quadratic in U whose solution for $U > 0$ is

$$U = (\gamma + 1)\frac{u_2}{4} + \sqrt{c_1^2 + \frac{(\gamma + 1)^2 u_2^2}{16}} \qquad (13.61)$$

We recall that c_1 is the speed of sound in the undisturbed region and that u_2 is the constant speed of the piston. Thus the shock wave travels with supersonic speed, since U is greater than c_1. Taking $\gamma = 1.4$, we see that U is *at least* equal to 1.2 u_2—that is, the shock wave travels at a higher speed than the piston. For high piston speeds, $u_2 \cong c_1$, (13.61) gives $U = 1.8\, c_1$, which means that the pulse will travel roughly at twice the speed of sound. On the other hand, as the piston speed u_2 decreases, the shock speed U approaches c_1.

Mechanical Waves: **Problems**

13.1   By direct substitution in the one-dimensional wave equation, show that an arbitrary function of the argument $[t - (x/v)]$ is a solution of the wave equation.

13.2   Explain why $g[t + (x/v)]$ represents a wave which travels in the negative x direction.

13.3 Starting with the expression for the kinetic energy density (energy per unit length) for the special case of harmonic waves along a string, calculate

(a) The time average of the kinetic energy density at a given point over a time interval which is much longer than the period of the wave.

(b) The space average of the kinetic energy density at a given instant over a length which is much longer than the wavelength.

(c) Compare the results obtained above.

13.4 A string of linear density m and of length l is maintained under tension T. Let the string be fastened at both ends so that at these points the displacement y is zero—that is, for boundary conditions take $y = 0$ at $x = 0$, and $y = 0$ at $x = 1$. If the displacement at any point is harmonic, the wave motion may be represented by the complex form

$$y = Ae^{i(\omega t - kx)} + Be^{i(\omega t + kx)}$$

Apply boundary conditions to the above solution and prove that the frequencies of the waves which may be propagated along the string are limited to a discrete set given by

$$f_n = \frac{n}{2l}\sqrt{\frac{T}{m}}$$

where n is a positive integer.

13.5 Strings of linear density $m_1 = 0.09$ kg/m and $m_2 = 0.25$ kg/m are attached and kept under tension. Calculate the coefficient of reflection at the boundary between the two strings when waves are reflected from (a) the denser string and (b) the less dense string.

13.6 Starting with the expression $\xi = A\cos(\omega t - kx)$ for the displacement of a particle in a harmonic compressional wave, obtain expressions for (a) the excess pressure and (b) the condensation.

13.7 Use the ideal gas law $PV^\gamma = C$ and show that the adiabatic bulk modulus is given by γP.

13.8 The velocity of sound waves in a gas is directly proportional to the square root of the absolute temperature. Explain why. Also, compute the value of the velocity of sound in air at $300°$K, utilizing the information given below:

$$\gamma_{air} = 1.40$$
$$\text{mean gram molecular weight} = 29$$
$$\text{gas constant } R = 8.31 \text{ joule/deg}$$

13.9   The phase velocity of propagation of surface waves is given by $v = (a\lambda + b\lambda^{-1})^{1/2}$, where a and b are constants (see p. 348 for their meaning). For what value of the wavelength is the velocity a minimum? What is the minimum value of the velocity?

13.10   (a) A rocket transmitter radiates 10 w in spherical waves. What is the energy density in the wave reaching the earth when the rocket is 400,000 km away? The waves have a speed of 3.00×10^8 m/sec.

(b) Compare the result in (a) with the energy density in a wave at a distance of 400 km from a radio station. Assume that the source radiates 100,000 w in a spherical wave.

13.11   A transverse wave travels along a string whose linear density of mass is 2.00×10^{-3} kg/m. The tension in the string is 2.88×10^{-3} new. The wave is described by

$$y = A \sin\left[(\omega t - kx) - (\pi/2)\right]$$

where lengths are expressed in meters and time in seconds.

(a) Sketch the wave profile (wave form) in the vicinity of the origin ($x = 0$) at the time $t = 0$.

(b) The string is excited by a generator whose frequency is 24 per second. Evaluate the constants ω and k.

13.12   A harmonic transverse wave traveling in the $+x$ direction is represented by

$$y = A \sin \omega\left(t - \frac{x}{v}\right)$$

where the time t is expressed in seconds and the distance x in meters. For a certain wave train of the above type, the wave form or profile at $t = 0$ is given by $y = 10 \sin(-2\pi x/400)$. At a later time $t = 0.5$ sec, the wave is represented by

$$y = A \sin\left(\frac{\pi}{2} - \frac{2\pi x}{400}\right)$$

Find the period of oscillation, the amplitude, and the velocity of the wave disturbance.

13.13   A plane wave traveling in the positive x direction is defined by

$$y = 5 \sin(t - 0.001x)$$

Find, at a given instant, the phase difference in degrees between two particles in the medium 50π units apart. What is the period of the motion?

13.14   Two identical source particles A and B, 10 cm apart, are executing simple harmonic motions with a frequency of 10 per second and equal amplitude. They vibrate in phase and send out waves whose velocity is 170 cm/sec.

(a) What is the difference in phase of the two waves arriving at a point C which is 4 cm from A and 6 cm from B?

(b) Find the ratio of the resultant amplitude at C to the amplitude of one of the sources. (Assume that plane waves are propagated with undiminished amplitude, and that the vibrations from the two sources are in the same direction.)

13.15   A standing wave pattern is produced on a cord by the superposition of two identical wave trains moving in opposite directions. If the individual wave trains are of the form $y_1 = A \sin(\omega t - kx)$ and $y_2 = -A \sin(\omega t + kx)$, their sum is represented by

$$y = y_1 + y_2 = -2A \sin kx \cos \omega t$$

(a) If the cord coincides with the x-axis, for what discrete values of x will the total displacement y be equal to zero for all time? Express your answer in terms of the wavelength. (The zeros of y are known as the nodes.)

(b) When the frequency of the waves is adjusted to 30 cycles/sec the cord assumes the configuration shown in the sketch—i.e., there are nodes at each end and two more nodes elsewhere. The cord is 6.0 m long and its linear density is 0.050 kg/m. Compute the speed of the transverse wave and the tension in the cord.

13.16   A sinusoidal transverse wave is propagated along a string whose linear mass density is 2×10^{-3} kg/m. The wave is described by

$$y = 5 \times 10^{-4} \sin\left[30\pi\left(t - \frac{x}{10}\right) + \frac{\pi}{6}\right]$$

where lengths are expressed in meters and time in seconds. Determine:

(a) The frequency of the source.
(b) The wavelength of the motion.
(c) The tension in the string.

13.17   A transverse harmonic wave train moving in the $+x$ direction is represented by

$$y = A \sin \omega\left(t - \frac{x}{v}\right)$$

At the instant $t = 0$, the displacements at P and Q, two points on the x-axis less than a wavelength apart, are as follows:

Point	x (meters from the origin)	Displacement y (meters)
P	90	+ 0.04 at maximum
Q	110	+0.02 and increasing in time

Determine the value of (a) the amplitude A, and (b) the wavelength.

13.18 The excess pressure in a compressional wave in a gas obeys the relation $p = p_0 \cos(\omega t - kx)$.

(a) Obtain expressions for the particle displacement, the particle velocity, and the condensation associated with the wave.

(b) In each case compare the phase of the particular wave with that of the pressure wave.

13.19 At an angular frequency of 2000π sec^{-1}, the lower limit of audibility of the human ear corresponds to a sound-wave intensity of 10^{-12} w/m^2. At 0° C and 760 Torr, the density of air is 1.29 kg/m^3 and the speed of sound is 331 m/sec. Calculate

(a) the wavelength of the sound wave;

(b) the maximum velocity of particles in the compressional wave;

(c) the maximum displacement of particles;

(d) the energy density in the wave.

13.20 Assume that air is an ideal gas with $\gamma = 1.4$. Assume further that when a supersonic jet plane sets up a shock wave in still air the flow speed of the gas behind the front is equal to the speed of the jet plane.

(a) Calculate the speed of the shock front if the plane is traveling at 1500 km/hr in air at 0° C. The speed of sound may be taken as 331 m/sec.

(b) Calculate the density of the gas behind the front.

Chapter 14.
Electromagnetic Waves

14.1   Introduction

Electromagnetic waves, like the longitudinal or transverse waves encountered in the study of vibrations set up in material media, transfer energy from source to receiver. However, unlike waves that exist by virtue of periodic deformations in elastic media, electromagnetic disturbances—radio and light waves, for example —may be transmitted in regions free of matter. In this chapter we will discuss the nature of this mechanism as predicted by the laws of electricity and magnetism.

14.2   Review of Electromagnetic Field Relations

Experimental observations dealing with charged systems, current distributions, and time-varying currents have served as the starting point in the formulation of such generalizations as Gauss's law for the field vectors $\mathbf{D}$ and $\mathbf{B}$, the circuital law for the vector $\mathbf{H}$, and Faraday's law of induction. A summary of these field relations is given below.

1. *Gauss's law for electric fields.* Analytically, the expression

$$\int_{\substack{\text{closed} \\ \text{surface}}} \mathbf{D} \cdot d\mathbf{A} = \int_{\substack{\text{closed} \\ \text{surface}}} D_n \, dA = Q \tag{14.1}$$

represents Gauss's law in terms of the displacement vector $\mathbf{D}$ at

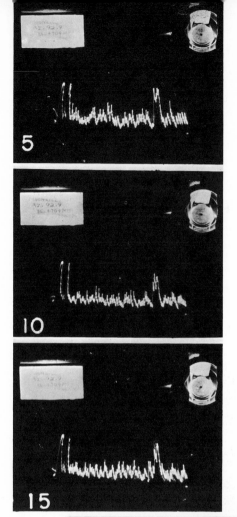

(LEFT) Oscilloscope photographs of radio wave beams that were reflected off the moon. The left portion of each wave pattern shows the outgoing signal; the right portion records the reflected (returning) pulse. These oscilloscope readings were recorded by the Diana radar of the U.S. Army Electronics Command, shortly after it made first radar contact with the moon early in 1946. (U.S. Army Photo.)

(BELOW) Photograph of the moon taken from an altitude of 3 mi by the Ranger VII Spacecraft. The picture, which covers an area about 1⅔ mi on a side, was taken by a television camera on board the Ranger VII and was transmitted to earth in the form of radio waves. (The photograph has been reduced by 40% for reproduction.) (Courtesy Jet Propulsion Laboratory, California Institute of Technology.)

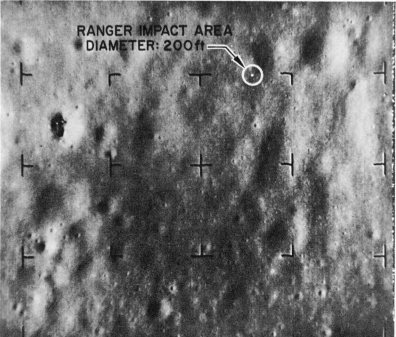

RANGER IMPACT AREA
DIAMETER: 200 ft

a point within an elementary area dA on a closed surface. In the second integral, D_n denotes the component of **D** normal to the element of area dA. The law states that the surface integral of **D** over a closed surface is equal to Q, the net free charge located within the closed surface. See (4.26).

2. *Gauss's law for the field of* **B**. The fundamental property of this field vector is described by

$$\int_{\substack{\text{closed} \\ \text{surface}}} \mathbf{B} \cdot d\mathbf{A} = \int_{\substack{\text{closed} \\ \text{surface}}} B_n \, dA = 0 \qquad (14.2)$$

The relation states that the surface integral of the normal component of **B**, integrated over a closed surface, is always zero. Refer to (7.19) and to the discussion in Section 7.3.

3. *Circuital law for the field of* **H**. The definition of the magnetic intensity given in (9.31) leads to the property

$$\oint \mathbf{H} \cdot d\mathbf{l} = \oint H_l \, dl = i \qquad (14.3)$$

This is the circuital law for the magnetic intensity as it applies to steady currents. H_l denotes the tangential component of the magnetic intensity. The law states that the line integral of the magnetic intensity around a closed path is equal to the conduction current crossing the surface which is bounded by the path of integration.

4. *The law of induction*. In accordance with (8.17), the induced emf is given by

$$\mathcal{E} = -\frac{d\Phi}{dt} \qquad (14.4)$$

This is Faraday's law which states that the emf induced in a circuit is equal to the time rate of decrease of the magnetic flux which links with the circuit. Utilizing the definitions of emf and magnetic flux (see Section 8.3), we see that the law assumes the equivalent forms

$$\oint \mathbf{E} \cdot d\mathbf{l} = -\frac{d}{dt} \int_{\substack{\text{open} \\ \text{surface}}} \mathbf{B} \cdot d\mathbf{A}$$

$$= -\int_{\substack{\text{open} \\ \text{surface}}} \frac{\partial \mathbf{B}}{\partial t} \cdot d\mathbf{A} = -\int \frac{\partial B_n}{\partial t} \, dA \qquad (14.5)$$

In (14.5), the integral on the right is carried out over the open area whose boundary is the path of integration over which the line integral of the electric intensity is evaluated.

14.3   Modification of the Circuital Law for H

While investigating the consequences of the four electromagnetic laws listed in Section 14.2, Maxwell arrived at the far-reaching observation that the circuital law given by (14.3) was not consistent with the equation of continuity in electromagnetism. The continuity relation, given by (5.15), asserts that the time rate of decrease of charge within a volume of space equals the net outward current from the surface enclosing the volume. Maxwell proposed a modification of the circuital law by introducing an additional term on the right-hand side of (14.3) in order that the relation may hold in cases involving time-varying currents or circuits containing gaps. The physical reasoning that led him to this modification will now be presented.

Consider the case of a constant current i maintained in a long straight conductor (see Fig. 14.1). The current density does not

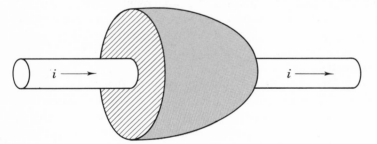

Figure 14.1   Closed surface surrounding a conduction current i.

change in time, since, by Ohm's law $\mathbf{j} = \sigma\mathbf{E}$, the electric intensity is independent of the time. It follows that there is no change in the distribution of charges, and the paths of moving charges have no terminations or beginnings. Assume that a portion of the conductor is surrounded by a closed surface consisting of a plane and a curved portion (shaped like a bell jar). Now the surface integral of $\mathbf{j}_n$, the normal component of the current density (in this case, in the body of the wire), is zero over this closed surface, since the charge within the closed surface does not change in time.

In applying the circuital law as given in (14.3), we must bear in mind that i stands for the conduction current which links with an open surface whose boundary is the path of integration. Depending on circumstances, the path of integration may surround a conductor carrying a current, or it may lie within the body of a current-bearing conductor or in a region of space such as the interior of an electrolytic cell or a vacuum tube. In any case, the current may be evaluated by integrating the normal component of the current density over the area bounded by the path l.

Figure 14.2 shows the situation where a wire carrying a con-

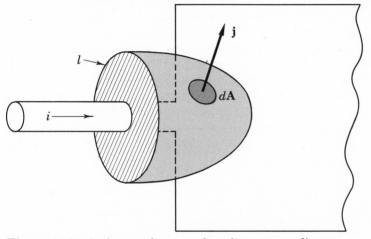

Figure 14.2   A plane and a curved surface surrounding a current. Each open surface has the same boundary l.

stant current i joins an extensive conducting medium. The closed surface surrounds the wire as well as a portion of the extensive medium. In this instance, the current may be calculated by integrating $\mathbf{j}$ over the plane or curved surface. In either case, the result is

$$i = \int_{\substack{\text{plane} \\ \text{surface}}} \mathbf{j} \cdot d\mathbf{A} = \int_{\substack{\text{curved} \\ \text{surface}}} \mathbf{j} \cdot d\mathbf{A} \qquad (14.6)$$

Moreover, if the line integral of **H** around a fixed closed path l is to have a *unique* value, the magnitude of **i** as calculated from (14.6) should yield the *same* result for any open surface which is bounded by the given path l, as shown in Fig. 14.2. The fixed path l forms the common contour of the plane as well as the curved surface. The line integral of the magnetic intensity around the path l will be single-valued so long as the same current passes through each of these surfaces. This means that the current which enters the plane surface must leave through the curved surface, as specified by (14.6). Considering the *closed* surface formed by the plane and the curved portions, it follows that

$$\underbrace{\int \mathbf{j} \cdot d\mathbf{A}}_{\substack{\text{plane} \\ \text{surface}}} + \underbrace{\int \mathbf{j} \cdot d\mathbf{A}}_{\substack{\text{curved} \\ \text{surface}}} = \underbrace{\int \mathbf{j} \cdot d\mathbf{A}}_{\substack{\text{closed} \\ \text{surface}}} = 0 \qquad (14.7)$$

where $\mathbf{j}$ is the current density directed *outward* from the surface at a point within the element of surface area $d\mathbf{A}$. In other words, the current which enters through one part of the surface (plane) must equal the current which leaves other parts of the surface (curved). If the circuital law is to yield a unique result, the condition stipulated in (14.7) must be satisfied.

However, this requirement may not always be fulfilled. Consider the situation in which a parallel-plate capacitor is suddenly connected to a source of constant emf. Let the space between the plates be evacuated. Imagine that the plate connected to the positive terminal of the seat is surrounded by a closed surface, as shown in Fig. 14.3. In this situation $\oint \mathbf{H} \cdot d\mathbf{l}$ gives i if

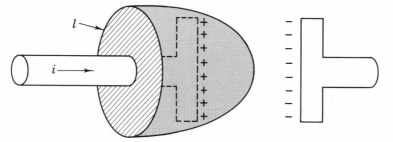

Figure 14.3   A closed surface which encloses the positive plate of a capacitor.

applied to the contour l and the plane surface but gives zero when applied to the contour l and the curved surface. In this example, charge is transferred to the capacitor plate through the connecting wire. The charging current i varies in time and represents the time rate of flow of charge into the imaginary surface. The flow terminates on the plate and charge accumulates within the closed surface, since there is no conduction current or movement of charges outward from the closed surface into the empty region. The surface charge density on the plate, and therefore the electric intensity in the region between the plates, are no longer constant, but vary with the time. If, at any time t, the net charge within the closed surface is q, the current into the surface is dq/dt, and its negative $-dq/dt$ represents the outward current across the closed surface. Expressing the outward current in terms of the current density (in the present case, in the body of the wire), we may write

$$\int_{\substack{\text{closed} \\ \text{surface}}} \mathbf{j} \cdot d\mathbf{A} = -\frac{dq}{dt} \tag{14.8}$$

which expresses the equation of continuity for charge and current given by (5.15). Therefore, in this example of a circuit containing a gap and a transient current, the net outward current over a closed surface is not zero; hence the condition imposed by the circuital law is not satisfied.

It becomes necessary to modify the form of the circuital law if its validity is to include the case of nonsteady currents. Consider again the case of the parallel-plate capacitor. The electric displacement vector **D** at a given point in the region increases with the time during the charging process. By Gauss's law, the instantaneous free charge q enclosed by the imaginary surface is given by

$$q = \int_{\substack{\text{closed} \\ \text{surface}}} \mathbf{D} \cdot d\mathbf{A} = \int_{\substack{\text{closed} \\ \text{surface}}} D_n \, dA \tag{14.9}$$

where the right-hand side represents the flux of **D** over the closed surface. Substituting this value of q into (14.8), it follows that

$$\int_{\substack{\text{closed} \\ \text{surface}}} \left(\mathbf{j} + \frac{\partial \mathbf{D}}{\partial t} \right) \cdot d\mathbf{A} = \int_{\substack{\text{closed} \\ \text{surface}}} \left(j_n + \frac{\partial D_n}{\partial t} \right) dA = 0 \tag{14.10}$$

Partial differentiation is used, since we are interested only in the time variation of **D** at a given point on the closed surface. The term $\partial D_n / \partial t$ has the dimensions of a current density and is referred to as the *displacement current density*. Equation (14.10) shows that if the time rate of change of the displacement is added to the conduction current density, and if the combined current density is integrated over the closed surface, the net "current" due to both conduction and displacement leaving the closed surface is equal to zero. But this is the requirement that must be fulfilled if the line integral of **H** around a closed path is to have a unique value.

Therefore, in order to generalize the circuital law for **H**, it is necessary to add to the conduction current i a term equal to the displacement current which is given by

$$\int_{\substack{\text{open} \\ \text{surface}}} \frac{\partial \mathbf{D}}{\partial t} \cdot d\mathbf{A}$$

The modified expression for the circuital law becomes

$$\oint \mathbf{H} \cdot d\mathbf{l} = i + \int_{\substack{\text{open} \\ \text{surface}}} \frac{\partial \mathbf{D}}{\partial t} \cdot d\mathbf{A} \tag{14.11}$$

where the integration on the right is carried out over the open area bounded by the closed path. The modified circuital relation in (14.11) satisfies the equation of continuity and is assumed to hold in general in dielectric and conducting media. When applied to circuits in which the current is steady, the surface integral on the right is zero and the equation reduces to the unmodified form. In conductors in which the current varies with the time, the contribution due to the second term is negligible unless the time variation is very rapid. On the other hand, in free space or in dielectrics where the conduction current is zero, the displacement current is of importance when $\mathbf{D}$ changes in time.

It is in this connection that the revision of the law leads to a remarkable interpretation. In the absence of conduction currents, (14.11) reduces to

$$\oint \mathbf{H} \cdot d\mathbf{l} = \int_{\substack{\text{open} \\ \text{surface}}} \frac{\partial \mathbf{D}}{\partial t} \cdot d\mathbf{A} \tag{14.12}$$

and may be interpreted to mean that a magnetic field may be brought about whenever there is a time variation of the electric displacement. From this point of view, $\partial \mathbf{D}/\partial t$ may be regarded as a property of the electromagnetic field, and no physical meaning need be attached to the *displacement currents* in a vacuum. We may therefore regard (14.11) as the counterpart of Faraday's law of induction, as given earlier by

$$\oint \mathbf{E} \cdot d\mathbf{l} = - \int \frac{\partial \mathbf{B}}{\partial t} \cdot d\mathbf{A} \tag{14.13}$$

—a relation which associates an electric field with a changing magnetic induction.

14.4 The Field Equations in Free Space

Consider a region which is free from charges and conduction currents—that is, $Q = 0$ and $i = 0$. With these restrictions, the field equations given by (14.1), (14.2), (14.5), and (14.11) reduce to

$$\int \mathbf{D} \cdot d\mathbf{A} = 0 \tag{14.14}$$

$$\int \mathbf{B} \cdot d\mathbf{A} = 0 \tag{14.15}$$

$$\oint \mathbf{H} \cdot d\mathbf{l} = \int \frac{\partial \mathbf{D}}{\partial t} \cdot d\mathbf{A} \tag{14.16}$$

$$\oint \mathbf{E} \cdot d\mathbf{l} = -\int \frac{\partial \mathbf{B}}{\partial t} \cdot d\mathbf{A} \tag{14.17}$$

In this connection, we will assume that (14.14) and (14.15) hold for time-varying fields.

Before we discuss solutions of these equations, let us explain briefly what constitutes a "solution" of the field equations. In our earlier study of electromagnetic fields, attention was centered largely on the calculation of electric fields due to static charge distributions and magnetic fields due to steady currents. Such calculations involve at most one of the integral equations, and the resulting "solution" consists of an expression for $\mathbf{E}$ or for $\mathbf{B}$ which involves one or more positional coordinates, but not the time. In the type of problem to be considered now, the currents and charges which give rise to the fields vary with time, and consequently the field quantities are also time-dependent. This time-dependence led to the modification of the circuital law by the inclusion of the displacement current, and we now have two equations: the circuital law for $\mathbf{H}$ and Faraday's law for $\mathbf{E}$. The "solutions" must now be expressions for $\mathbf{E}$ and for $\mathbf{H}$ (or $\mathbf{D}$ and $\mathbf{B}$) which simultaneously satisfy all four equations and the boundary conditions (currents and charges).

In general, a straightforward method of solving the equations, even for simple boundary conditions, is an involved and a tedious process. Rather than attempt such a procedure, we shall make a reasonable assumption regarding one of the field quantities and then examine the consequences of this assumption in the light of the field equations.

MAXWELL'S EQUATIONS

Rapid developments during the first half of the nineteenth century culminated in the formulation by James Clerk Maxwell (1831–79) of the general equations of electromagnetism.

Unlike Faraday, Maxwell came from a well-to-do family and received a formal education at Edinburgh Academy. He attended Trinity College in Cambridge and graduated with distinction. While still in his teens he displayed deep insight into the analysis of mathematical problems. In later life he held professorships at several universities, and before reaching the age of thirty-five he had made contributions to many fields of physics. Outstanding among these was the discovery of the distribution law of molecular velocities and the renowned prediction of electromagnetic waves. Maxwell's brilliant career came to an untimely end at the age of forty-eight, but not before he had won for himself a place among the most celebrated figures in the annals of theoretical physics.

In electromagnetic theory, Maxwell introduced the concept of displacement currents (Section 14.3) and deduced the field equations that bear his name [see (15.12), (15.13), (15.15), and (15.16), and the free-space relations given in (14.14) through (14.17)]. These equations are a unification of Coulomb's law of force, Ampère's investigation of the interaction of current-elements, Faraday's observations on time-varying fields, and Maxwell's own modification of the circuital law for the magnetic field. By combining these equations, Maxwell was able to forecast the existence of transverse waves in a hypothetical medium which at first was modeled after a mechanical analog. In 1864 he restated the theory without reference to specific properties of the medium. His calculations predicted for the speed of these waves a numerical value that was remarkably close to the speed of light, which was then known independently from optical experiments. Accordingly, Maxwell concluded correctly that light was an electromagnetic phenomenon.

Nearly a quarter of a century elapsed before Hertz, in 1887, confirmed Maxwell's theoretical prediction. Hertz was able to generate electromagnetic waves and measure their speed. He also succeeded in establishing their transverse nature.

Since Hertz' time, the art of producing, detecting, and utilizing electromagnetic waves has become a colossal scientific achievement. Radio, television, and radar are familiar examples of the part played by electromagnetic waves in the transmission of information. Through clear television pictures obtained at a distance of three miles from the moon's surface we have been privileged to observe the lunar landscape from our armchairs! To these successes there has recently been added a "laser" beam which bears a surprising resemblance to the "death rays" of horror fiction.

14.5   The Plane Wave Solution in Free Space

In general, it is expected that the components of the electric and magnetic fields will depend on three space coordinates and the time. We shall, however, take up the simpler case where the field vectors are a function of the single coordinate x and the time t. In this instance, it follows from (14.14) and (14.15) that the field vectors of interest are at right angles to the x-axis. To prove this, let us apply Gauss's law to the rectangular parallelopiped shown in Fig. 14.4. At a given instant, the flux of **D** leav-

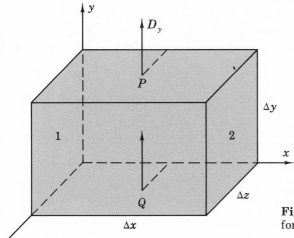

Figure 14.4   Volume element for application of Gauss's law.

ing face 2 is $D_x|_2 \, \Delta y \, \Delta z$, where $D_x|_2$ is the x component of the vector **D** at any point on face 2. Likewise, the flux leaving face 1 is $-D_x|_1 \, \Delta y \, \Delta z$.

Next, consider the faces perpendicular to the y-axis. By our assumption D_y does not depend on y or z. Hence at points P and Q, which are located on the top and bottom faces and have the same x coordinate, D_y has the same magnitude, and the flux of D_y leaving the top surface of area $\Delta x \, \Delta z$ is just equal to that which enters the bottom surface of the same area.

A similar statement can be made for the flux of D_z leaving and entering the faces perpendicular to the z-axis. Equation (14.14) requires that the net outward flux of **D** over the six faces be zero. Hence $D_x|_2 \, \Delta y \, \Delta z - D_x|_1 \, \Delta y \, \Delta z = 0$, which means that D_x, the x component of **D**, must have the same value at faces 1 and 2 and cannot vary with x. D_x must, at most, be a constant which here shall be set equal to zero, since in wave propagation constant fields are of no interest.

A similar conclusion concerning B_x may be reached by applying (14.15) to the flux of **B** over a closed surface. Furthermore, in free space $\mathbf{D} = \varepsilon_0\mathbf{E}$, and $\mathbf{B} = \mu_0\mathbf{H}$. Hence the assumed dependence of the field vectors on the single coordinate x leads to the important conclusion that the x components of the vectors may be set equal to zero. The electric and magnetic vectors must therefore lie in planes parallel to the y,z plane. In particular, the vector **D** can have only the two components D_y and D_z. And as a further simplification we shall set $D_z = 0$. This leaves the y component of **D**, which is a function of x and t.

The consequences of Faraday's law are deduced by applying the law to the rectangular circuit in the x,y plane. (See Fig. 14.5.) According to the preceding argument, $E_x = 0$. In tracing

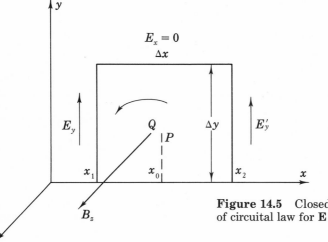

Figure 14.5   Closed path for application of circuital law for **E** (Faraday's law).

the closed path in the counterclockwise direction, E_y' may be expressed as

$$E_y' = E_y + \frac{\partial E_y}{\partial x}\bigg|_P \Delta x \qquad (14.18)$$

where the second term on the right represents the change in E_y as we pass from x_1 to x_2. Partial derivatives are used since E_y is a function of two variables x and t. In the differentiation indicated in (14.18), t is held constant. The subscript P indicates that the derivative is to be evaluated at a point P whose x coordinate x_0 lies between x_1 and x_2.

The line integral of **E** over the rectangle yields

$$\oint E_l \, dl = \left(E'_y - E_y \right) \Delta y = \frac{\partial E_y}{\partial x} \bigg|_P \Delta x \, \Delta y \qquad (14.19)$$

The flux of induction crossing the area bounded by the rectangular path is

$$\int_{\Delta x \Delta y} B_z \, dy \, dx = B_z \bigg|_Q \Delta x \, \Delta y \qquad (14.20)$$

where $B_z|_Q$ is a particular value of the z component of the induction at some point Q within the area $\Delta x \, \Delta y$. The point Q is chosen so that the value of B_z at Q lies intermediate between the largest and smallest values assumed by B_z over the area of the rectangle. By the law of induction

$$\frac{\partial E_y}{\partial x} \bigg|_P \Delta x \, \Delta y = - \frac{\partial}{\partial t} \left(B_z \bigg|_Q \right) \Delta x \, \Delta y \qquad (14.21)$$

Upon shrinking down the rectangle to some point within the area, we may write

$$\frac{\partial E_y}{\partial x} = - \frac{\partial B_z}{\partial t} = - \mu_0 \frac{\partial H_z}{\partial t} \qquad (14.22)$$

where $\partial E_y / \partial x$, H_z, and B_z assume values appropriate to the particular point. Equation (14.22) is the differential form of Faraday's law for the special case under consideration and shows that E_y gives rise to H_z, a magnetic field perpendicular to E_y.

Next we apply the circuital law for **H** to the elementary rectangle shown in Fig. 14.6. As before, H_x is equal to zero, so that only H_z need be considered in evaluating the line integral of **H** around the rectangular circuit whose sides are Δx and Δz. Tracing the rectangle in the counterclockwise direction, we have

$$\oint H_l \, dl = (H_z - H'_z) \Delta z = - \frac{\partial H_z}{\partial x} \bigg|_P \Delta x \, \Delta z \qquad (14.23)$$

(In order to determine the positive sense of the normal to the open surface, it is necessary to specify the positive sense in describing the periphery of the path. According to convention, if the periphery of the open surface is traced in the direction of rotation of a right-handed screw, the direction of advance of the screw defines the positive sense of the normal. Thus if the rectangle is traced in the counterclockwise direction, the positive normal is directed upward from the x,z plane.)

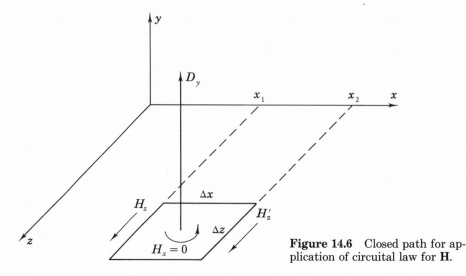

Figure 14.6 Closed path for application of circuital law for **H**.

Now, from (14.16), the result of the line integral of **H** must be equal to the time derivative of the flux of **D** through the open surface $\Delta x\, \Delta z$. The flux of **D** crossing the rectangle is given by

$$\int_{\Delta x \Delta z} D_n\, dx\, dz = D_y\bigg|_Q \Delta x\, \Delta z \tag{14.24}$$

Hence,

$$\frac{\partial}{\partial t}\left(D_y\bigg|_Q\right) \Delta x\, \Delta z = -\frac{\partial H_z}{\partial x}\bigg|_P \Delta x\, \Delta z \tag{14.25}$$

or

$$\frac{\partial D_y}{\partial t} = -\frac{\partial H_z}{\partial x} \tag{14.26}$$

The notation and explanation of the steps in arriving at the result given in (14.26) parallel those given in deducing (14.22) and will not be repeated. Since $D_y = \varepsilon_0 E_y$, (14.26) may also be written

$$\varepsilon_0 \frac{\partial E_y}{\partial t} = -\frac{\partial H_z}{\partial x} \tag{14.27}$$

This is the differential relation for the circuital law for **H** as revised by Maxwell for the special case where the electric field has one component, E_y, whose magnitude is dependent on a single positional coordinate x and the time t.

It is possible to eliminate one of the two field quantities appearing in (14.22) and (14.27) and thus obtain a differential equation which must be satisfied by either H_z or E_y. Upon differentiating (14.22) with respect to x and (14.27) with respect to t, we can eliminate H_z and obtain

$$\frac{\partial^2 E_y}{\partial t^2} = \frac{1}{\varepsilon_0 \mu_0} \frac{\partial^2 E_y}{\partial x^2} \tag{14.28}$$

The student will recognize this result as the partial differential equation of one-dimensional wave motion encountered in the earlier study of mechanical waves. The solutions of (14.28) represent transverse electric waves in free space moving along the x-axis with velocity

$$v^2 = \frac{1}{\varepsilon_0 \mu_0} \tag{14.29}$$

The other field quantities, D_y, B_y, and H_y, also satisfy the same wave equation. The form and properties of the general solution of (14.28) were discussed in Section 13.2 and will not be repeated here.

As a simple special solution of the wave equation appearing in (14.28) we select for E_y the function

$$E_y = E_0 \sin \omega \left(t - \frac{x}{v} \right) \tag{14.30}$$

where E_0, ω, and v are constants. This choice implies that the electric field is parallel to the y-axis and is a periodic function of the single coordinate x and the time t. (As before, E_x and E_z are taken as zero.)

An expression for the magnetic field may be obtained by a direct integration of (14.22), as shown by the following steps:

$$H_z = -\frac{1}{\mu_0} \int \frac{\partial E_y}{\partial x} \, dt = \frac{E_0 \omega}{\mu_0 v} \int \cos \omega \left(t - \frac{x}{v} \right) dt$$

or $$H_z = \frac{E_0}{\mu_0 v} \sin \omega \left(t - \frac{x}{v} \right) + C$$

The constant of integration C is independent of the time and represents a steady field. In the present problem we are concerned only with fields which vary in time. Hence C may be set equal to zero. The z component of the magnetic field may now be written as

$$H_z = H_0 \sin \omega \left(t - \frac{x}{v} \right) \tag{14.31}$$

where $$H_0 \equiv \frac{E_0}{\mu_0 v} \tag{14.32}$$

The remaining components of the magnetic field are zero. This can be seen by considering rectangular paths in the x,z and y,z planes.

By substituting the expressions for E_y and H_z as given in (14.30) and (14.31), we see that these field quantities are solutions of (14.27) provided

$$v^2 = \frac{1}{\mu_0 \varepsilon_0}$$

which verifies the result given in (14.29) based on the general solutions of the wave equation.

We may now conclude that the assumed electric field described by

$$E_y = E_0 \sin \omega\left(t - \frac{x}{v}\right), \qquad E_x = E_z = 0$$

satisfies the field equations provided the associated magnetic field has the components

$$H_z = H_0 \sin \omega\left(t - \frac{x}{v}\right), \qquad H_x = H_y = 0$$

with the further requirement that the constants appearing in the expressions for E_y and H_z are related by

$$H_0 = \frac{E_0}{\mu_0 v} \qquad \text{and} \qquad v^2 = \frac{1}{\mu_0 \varepsilon_0}$$

14.6   Properties of the Plane Wave Solution

We shall now investigate some of the properties possessed by this particular electromagnetic field.

1. The electric and magnetic fields represent wave motion. The fields are propagated along the positive x direction with a velocity v. Consider, for example, the electric field E_y at some point x at a given instant of time t. At a later time $(t + \Delta t)$, E_y will assume the same magnitude at a second point whose coordinate is $(x + v \Delta t)$. (See Fig. 14.7.) This statement is true because $\sin \omega[t - (x/v)]$ remains unchanged if t is replaced by $(t + \Delta t)$ and x by $(x + v \Delta t)$, as seen from the following substitution:

$$\sin \omega\left[(t + \Delta t) - \frac{x + v \Delta t}{v}\right] = \sin \omega\left(t - \frac{x}{v}\right)$$

(In passing, we recall that this property is not peculiar to sinusoi-

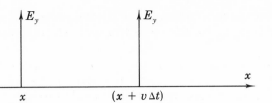

Figure 14.7 Propagation of the electric intensity E_y.

dal functions alone. Wave motion is represented by a function of the quantity $[t - (x/v)]$ or $[t + (x/v)]$.) Hence, a particular value of E_y progresses along the x-axis with a speed v and therefore E_y represents a traveling wave. Similar reasoning leads to the conclusion that the magnetic field H_z also represents a wave which advances in the positive x direction. E_y and H_z reach their maximum values at the same time and position—that is, E_y and H_z *are in phase.* Indeed, the electromagnetic disturbance must be regarded as a wave motion consisting of two mutually perpendicular vectors. The electric and magnetic fields are not to be thought of as independent sets of waves, but as different aspects of the same phenomenon.

2. In the study of wave motion, a surface passing through all points at which the wave has the same phase is called a *wave front.* (The quantity $\omega[t - (x/v)]$ is referred to as the *phase* of the wave.) The particular solutions of the field equations considered here are spoken of as *plane* waves, because, at a given instant of time, E_y has the same phase at all points of a plane perpendicular to the x-axis (direction of propagation). The plane surface of constant phase is shown in Fig. 14.8.

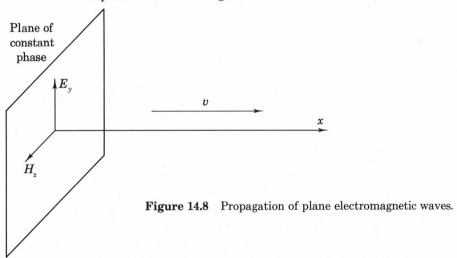

Figure 14.8 Propagation of plane electromagnetic waves.

3. The electromagnetic wave in free space is a transverse wave. The electric vector is perpendicular to the magnetic vector and both are perpendicular to the direction of propagation of the wave. (Refer again to Fig. 14.8.)

4. At a given point in space (fixed x), the electric vector is parallel to the y-axis and remains parallel to this direction while its magnitude varies in time. Similarly, the magnetic field remains parallel to the z-axis. Such a wave is described as a *linearly polarized* wave.

5. The *frequency f* and the *period T* of the wave are related to the constant ω by

$$\omega = 2\pi f = \frac{2\pi}{T} \tag{14.33}$$

6. The amplitude of the electric vector is E_0 and that of the magnetic field is H_0, which is related to E_0 by (14.32). The quantity v is the *phase velocity* of the wave. It is the velocity with which a given value of the field vector advances along the x-axis. In the present example, v has a constant value independent of the frequency of the wave. The numerical value of the phase velocity may be calculated from (14.29). The values of ε_0 and μ_0, the permittivity and permeability of free space respectively, are given by

$$\varepsilon_0 = \frac{1}{36\pi} \times 10^{-9} \text{ coul}^2\text{-new}^{-1}\text{ m}^{-2}$$

$$\mu_0 = 4\pi \times 10^{-7} \text{ coul}^{-2}\text{-sec}^2\text{-new}$$

Hence, the phase velocity of electromagnetic waves in free space is

$$v = \sqrt{\frac{1}{\mu_0\varepsilon_0}} = \sqrt{9.00 \times 10^{16} \text{ m}^2\text{-sec}^{-2}}$$

$$= 3.00 \times 10^8 \text{ m/sec}$$

The calculation indicates that the electromagnetic waves are propagated in free space with the speed of light. In the formulas of Section 14.5 the phase velocity v may be replaced by c, the speed of light in free space.

In view of the wealth of experimental evidence concerning the nature and properties of electromagnetic waves available today, this result is not startling. But in 1862, when, as a consequence of the modified circuital law, Maxwell announced the possibility of transmitting transverse waves, there were no experimental observations at his disposal. However, optical experiments carried out during the first half of the nineteenth century gave strong indication that light consisted of transverse waves. In fact, the experimentally determined value of the speed of light had been found to be approximately 3.1×10^8 m/sec. This agreed so well with the theoretically predicted speed for electromagnetic waves that, as Maxwell remarked, it was scarcely possible "to avoid the inference that light consisted of transverse undulations of the same medium, which is the cause of electric and magnetic phenomenon."

The direct verification of Maxwell's prediction came some twenty-five years later, when, in 1887, Hertz, as a forerunner of present-day developments in radio, conducted experiments with high-frequency electrical oscillations.

14.7 Flow of Energy

In connection with the study of static electric and magnetic fields, we postulated that energy was distributed throughout the region occupied by such fields. By appeal to special examples (capacitors, inductors) we demonstrated that in free space the expressions $\frac{1}{2}\varepsilon_0 E^2$ and $\frac{1}{2}\mu_0 H^2$ represent the field energy density in electric and magnetic fields respectively. We shall assume that these expressions are valid also in the case of dynamic fields where the field vectors vary in time.

As in other types of wave motion, electromagnetic waves transfer energy from the source which generates them to the receiving surfaces which intercept them. The energy absorbed from the waves may give rise to currents in conductors, may be transformed into heat, may affect photoelectric cells, or may ionize atomic systems. Accompanying the removal of energy there will be changes in the field energy associated with a given volume of space. In general, the field energy is not conserved, but it may be stated that the total field energy in a given volume decreases either because work is done on matter within the volume or because energy flows out of the boundary which encloses the volume. In particular, if no work is done on matter, the time rate of decrease of electromagnetic energy within the given volume must equal the time rate at which energy flows out of the surface enclosing the volume.

Consider a fixed elementary cylinder whose length is dx and whose end faces (each of area dA) are normal to the x-axis. (See

Fig. 14.9.) Let plane waves, as described in the preceding sections, travel with speed v along the x-axis. Then, at any instant, the energy dW, within the elementary volume, is equal to

$$dW = \tfrac{1}{2}(\varepsilon_0 E_y^2 + \mu_0 H_z^2)\, dx\, dA \qquad (14.34)$$

and the time rate of decrease of energy is

$$-\frac{dW}{dt} = -\left(\varepsilon_0 E_y \frac{\partial E_y}{\partial t} + \mu_0 H_z \frac{\partial H_z}{\partial t}\right) dx\, dA \qquad (14.35)$$

As a result of the passage of the waves, energy will flow into the volume across face 1 and out of it across face 2.

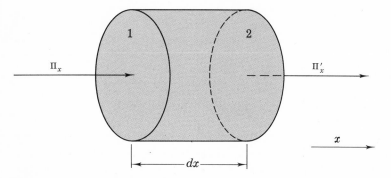

Figure 14.9   Volume element for energy-flow calculation.

At this stage it is advantageous to introduce the concept of intensity, which is defined as the time rate of flow of energy per unit area perpendicular to the direction of the wave. (In the mks system its unit is expressed as *joule per second-meter*² or watt per square meter. Thus intensity has the unit of power per unit area.) Intensity is a vector quantity, and in the special case of our problem this vector is directed along the x-axis. The intensity vector, which is named the *Poynting vector* after its discoverer, is here represented by the symbol Π. In terms of Π_x, the x component of the Poynting vector, the time rate at which energy flows into the cylinder is $\Pi_x\, dA$, while the rate at which the energy flows outward is $\Pi_x'\, dA$. If the change in the intensity vector in going from face 1 to face 2 is $(\partial \Pi_x/\partial x)\, dx$, the net amount of energy which leaves the cylinder per unit time is

$$(\Pi_x' - \Pi_x)\, dA = \frac{\partial \Pi_x}{\partial x}\, dx\, dA \qquad (14.36)$$

Equating the expressions found in (14.35) and (14.36), and dividing through by the volume of the cylinder, we obtain

$$\frac{\partial \Pi_x}{\partial x} = -\left(\varepsilon_0 E_y \frac{\partial E_y}{\partial t} + \mu_0 H_z \frac{\partial H_z}{\partial t} \right) \qquad (14.37)$$

In the right-hand side of this expression, the time derivative of one vector may be replaced by the space derivative of the other, in accordance with the field equations (14.22) and (14.27). Upon substitution, we get

$$\frac{\partial \Pi_x}{\partial x} = E_y \frac{\partial H_z}{\partial x} + H_z \frac{\partial E_y}{\partial x} = \frac{\partial}{\partial x}(E_y H_z)$$

whence
$$\Pi_x = E_y H_z \qquad (14.38)$$

The right-hand side of (14.38) is the x component of the vector product of **E** and **H** for the special case where E_y and H_z are the only nonzero components of the field vectors. More generally, the Poynting vector may be written as

$$\mathbf{\Pi} = \mathbf{E} \times \mathbf{H} \qquad (14.39)$$

which shows that the flow of energy is at right angles to the plane defined by the vectors **E** and **H**. The direction of propagation is that of the vector **E** $\times$ **H**. (See Fig. 14.10.) Since the plane defined by **E** and **H** represents a wave front, the Poynting vec-

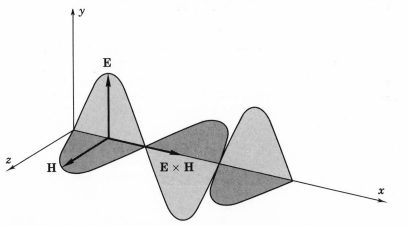

Figure 14.10 The **E** and **H** vectors in a plane electromagnetic wave, traveling along the positive x-axis. The field vectors are mutually perpendicular and are in phase. The Poynting vector **E** $\times$ **H** is directed along the direction of propagation.

tor is perpendicular to the wave front and defines the so-called *ray direction*.

In our discussion of electromagnetic waves, we have used the vector $\mathbf{H}$ instead of the vector $\mathbf{B}$. The main reason for this choice is that $\mathbf{E} \times \mathbf{H}$ denotes power per unit area and is expressed in watts per square meter (w/m^2), as may be verified by noting that in the mks system $\mathbf{E}$ is expressed in volts per meter while $\mathbf{H}$ is expressed in amperes per meter.

In the case of linearly polarized harmonic waves, the instantaneous value of Π_x may be evaluated by the use of relations (14.29) through (14.32). Accordingly,

$$\Pi_x = \sqrt{\frac{\varepsilon_0}{\mu_0}}\, E_y^2 = v\varepsilon_0 E_0^2 \sin^2 \omega\left(t - \frac{x}{v}\right) \qquad (14.40)$$

This expression shows that the Poynting vector at a given point on the x-axis varies with the time, but the flow of energy is always along the positive x-axis, which is the direction of propagation of the wave. The time average of Π_x is given by

$$(\Pi_x)_{\text{avg}} = \tfrac{1}{2}v\varepsilon_0 E_0^2 \qquad (14.41)$$

since the average value of $\sin^2 \omega(t - x/v)$ is $\frac{1}{2}$.

14.8   Plane Waves in Dielectric Media

If the region through which the waves travel is not free space but a homogeneous, isotropic dielectric in which $q = 0$ and $i = 0$, the steps carried out in finding the solutions of the field equations would be modified only by the appearance of ε and μ instead of ε_0 and μ_0. Since in a linear dielectric the relation between the field vectors is given by

$$\mathbf{D} = \varepsilon\mathbf{E} \qquad \text{and} \qquad \mathbf{B} = \mu\mathbf{H} \qquad (14.42)$$

the expressions corresponding to (14.32) and (14.29) would now be written as

$$H_0 = \frac{E_0}{\mu v} \qquad (14.43)$$

$$v^2 = \frac{1}{\mu\varepsilon} \qquad (14.44)$$

In these relations, v is the phase velocity of the wave in the medium, while μ and ε represent the permeability and permittivity of the medium, respectively.

It is seen that the phase velocity v in a dielectric is different from the velocity of electromagnetic waves in vacuum. For (14.44) may be written as

$$v^2 = \frac{1}{\mu\varepsilon} = \frac{1}{K_m\mu_0 k\varepsilon_0} = \frac{c^2}{K_m k} \tag{14.45}$$

where K_m and k are the relative permeability and dielectric constant of the medium (pure numbers), and c, the velocity in vacuum, is

$$c = \frac{1}{\sqrt{\varepsilon_0\mu_0}} \tag{14.46}$$

For a given frequency the *index of refraction n* of the medium is defined as the ratio of the phase velocity of the wave in vacuum to the phase velocity in the particular medium. Thus,

$$n = \frac{c}{v} = \sqrt{K_m k} = \sqrt{k} \tag{14.47}$$

so that the index is equal to the square root of the dielectric constant, since for dielectrics K_m is very nearly equal to unity.

Equation (14.43), which gives the connection between the amplitudes of the electric and magnetic vectors, may also be written in a more convenient form, thus

$$H_0 = \frac{E_0}{\mu v} = \frac{nE_0}{c\mu} = n\sqrt{\frac{\varepsilon_0}{\mu_0}}\,E_0 \tag{14.48}$$

where use has been made of (14.46) and (14.47) and the fact that $K_m = 1$.

Electromagnetic Waves: **Problems**

14.1   The electric intensity in a plane electromagnetic wave polarized in the z direction and traveling in glass is given by

$$E_z = A \sin 10^{15}\pi\left(t - \frac{x}{0.65c}\right)$$

where $c = 3.00 \times 10^8$ m/sec, the phase velocity of the waves in vacuum. Determine:

(a) The refractive index of the glass (the ratio c/v, where v is the velocity of the wave in glass).

(b) The wavelength of the radiation in glass.

14.2 The electric intensity E in a plane electromagnetic wave propagated in a certain direction is represented by

$$E = 100 \sin\left[\ 2\pi \times 10^6\!\left(t - \frac{10^{-10}x}{3}\right)\right]\mu v/m$$

where x is in centimeters and t in seconds.

(a) What is the least distance between two points in the medium located along the direction of propagation where, at a given instant, the electric intensity is equal to $+50$ $\mu v/m$?

(b) At a given point in the medium, what is the shortest time in which the value of E will increase from $+50$ to $+100$ $\mu v/m$?

14.3 For the case where the field quantities depend only on one space variable x and the time t, the differential form of the circuital law for H becomes

$$\frac{\partial H_z}{\partial x} = -\frac{\partial D_y}{\partial t}$$

where D_y is the y component of the displacement, and H_z is the z component of the magnetic field. Let H_z as given by

$$H_z = H_0 \sin(\omega t - kx)$$

denote the magnetic field in a plane harmonic wave in free space.

(a) Obtain an expression for E_y, the electric field intensity associated with the wave, as a function of x and t.

(b) The accompanying diagram shows how H_z varies with position at the instant $t = 0$. Reproduce the diagram and on it show how E_y varies with x at the given time $t = 0$.

14.4 For the special case where the field vectors depend only on one space variable x and the time t, Faraday's law when applied to an elementary rectangle in the x, y plane yields the relation

$$\frac{\partial E_y}{\partial x} = -\mu_0 \frac{\partial H_z}{\partial t}$$

where E_y is the y component of the electric field, and H_z is the z component of the magnetic field.

(a) For the case of plane waves in free space, take $H_z = H_0 \sin (\omega t - kx)$. Apply the relation above and obtain an expression for E_y.

(b) In a traveling plane electromagnetic wave in free space, the ratio E_y/H_z is equal to 120π Ω (mks) at any x and all the values of t. Also, $\mu_0 = 4\pi \times 10^{-7}$ mks units. From this information calculate the numerical value of the phase velocity of the waves described.

14.5 In a linearly polarized harmonic electromagnetic wave in free space (see diagram) the electric field is described by

$$E_y = E_0 \sin(\omega t - kx)$$

where $E_0 = 50$ μv/m,

$$\omega = 2\pi \times 10^8 \text{ sec}^{-1},$$

and $\qquad k = 2\pi/3 \text{ m}^{-1}$

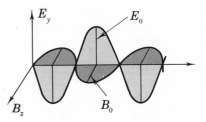

(a) Calculate the phase velocity of the wave.

(b) The above wave passes over a rectangular loop of wire located in the x,y plane as shown in the diagram. At a certain instant of time, the magnitude of the electric field E_y' over the side AD is 25 μv/m, and E_y'' over the side BC is 50 μv/m, both fields being directed along the positive y-axis. Apply

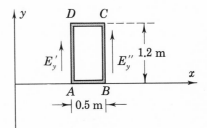

the circuital law $\oint \mathbf{E} \cdot d\mathbf{l}$ and calculate the numerical value of the emf induced in the rectangle at the particular time. The side DA (parallel to the y-axis) is 1.2 m long, while the length of AB (on the x-axis) is 0.5 m.

(c) Also obtain the emf by basing the calculations on the magnetic vector entirely.

14.6 For the wave described in Problem 14.5 above, the differential form of the generalized circuital relation is given by

$$\frac{\partial D_y}{\partial t} = -\frac{\partial H_z}{\partial x}$$

(a) Obtain an expression for the magnetic induction B_z associated with the electric field specified in Problem 14.5.

(b) Refer to the constants (in mks units) given below and obtain the numerical value of B_0, the maximum value of B_z.

$$\varepsilon_0 = \frac{1}{36\pi} \times 10^{-9} \text{ farad/m}, \qquad \mu_0 = 4\pi \times 10^{-7} \text{ henry/m}$$

14.7 For the special case where the fields depend only on one space variable x and time t, Faraday's law, when applied to an elementary rectangular circuit in the x,y plane, results in a differential relation involving E_y and B_z. (Here E_y is the y component of the electric field induced because of time variations in B_z, the z component of the induction.)

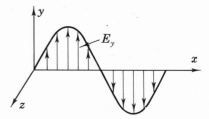

(a) Of the three relations shown below, one is the differential form of Faraday's law. Identify this relation and give the reason for your choice.

(I) $\dfrac{\partial E_y}{\partial t} = \dfrac{\partial B_z}{\partial x}$ (II) $\dfrac{\partial E_y}{\partial x} = -\dfrac{\partial B_z}{\partial t}$ (III) $\dfrac{\partial E_y}{\partial y} = \dfrac{\partial B_z}{\partial x}$

(b) If E_y is given by $E_0 \sin \omega[t - (x/c)]$, evaluate the ratio E_0/B_0 on the basis of the selection in part (a). B_0 is the amplitude of B_z.

14.8   Complete the relations below in terms of field quantities **E** and/or **H** and give the meaning of the term appearing on the right side.

(a)
$$\frac{\partial}{\partial t} \int_{\substack{\text{open} \\ \text{surface}}} \mathbf{B} \cdot d\mathbf{A} =$$

where the left-hand side represents the time rate of change of the flux of the magnetic induction vector **B**.

(b)
$$\frac{\partial}{\partial t} \int_{\substack{\text{open} \\ \text{surface}}} \mathbf{D} \cdot d\mathbf{A} =$$

where the left-hand side denotes the time rate of change of the flux of the displacement vector **D** (no conduction currents).

14.9   Consider the case of linearly polarized plane electromagnetic waves in free space where the phase velocity of the waves is $c = 3.00 \times 10^8$ m/sec. The free space values of the permittivity and the permeability are: $\varepsilon_0 = 8.85 \times 10^{-12}$ farad/m, $\mu_0 = 4\pi \times 10^{-7}$ henry/m. Prove the following:
(a) The Poynting vector may be expressed as $\varepsilon_0 c^2 \mathbf{E} \times \mathbf{B}$.
(b) The electric and magnetic field energy densities are equal.
(c) The ratio $E_y/B_z = c$.
(d) The ratio $E_y/H_z = \mu_0 c = 377 \ \Omega$.
(e) $(\Pi_x)_{\text{avg}} = 2.65 \times 10^{-3} E^2_{\text{rms}}$ w/m^2
(f) The Poynting vector is equal to the product of the energy density and the phase velocity.

14.10   Assume that a 100-watt sodium lamp behaves like a point source and radiates uniformly in all directions. Consider a field point at a distance of 1 m from the source and compute:

(a) The rms values of the electric and magnetic field strengths.

(b) The total energy density in the field.

14.11 A linearly polarized plane electromagnetic wave has a wavelength of 30 m in air. The wave is traveling along the x-axis. The electric vector in the wave has an amplitude of 10 $\mu v/m$ and is directed parallel to the y-axis. A conducting loop in the form of a square 2 m on the side is located in the x,y plane. The sides of the loop are parallel to the x- and y-axes.

(a) What is the rms value of the emf induced in the loop?

(b) What is the average power transmitted per unit area perpendicular to the direction of propagation of the wave?

14.12 Consider a long cylindrical conductor of radius r and length L. A steady current I is distributed uniformly across the cross section of the conductor whose conductivity is σ.

(a) Calculate the magnitudes of the electric and magnetic fields at the surface of the conductor.

(b) Calculate the magnitude of the Poynting vector and show that energy flows into the conductor across its surface at a rate which is equal to the rate of joulean heat production within the conductor.

14.13. A parallel plate capacitor consists of two circular plates of radius R and separation d. The charge q on the plates varies in time in accordance with $q = q_0 \sin \omega t$.

(a) Obtain an expression for the magnetic field $\mathbf{H}$ at a point P between the plates. The point P is located at a distance r from the axis of the plates. Neglect edge effects and assume that the lines of $\mathbf{H}$ are circular about the axis of symmetry.

(b) Determine the magnitude of the Poynting vector at the edge of the plates. Show that when the capacitor is being charged, the Poynting vector is directed toward the axis of the plates and that there is a flow of energy into the region between the plates.

(c) Calculate the rate of energy flow into the capacitor through the gap between the plates and compare the result with the rate of increase of field energy in the volume between the plates.

14.14 Consider a long solenoid of radius a and length l. The solenoid has n turns per unit length and is wound on a core of permeability μ_0. The current in the winding is increased with the time in accordance with $i = I_0(1 - e^{-kt})$, where I_0 and k are constants.

(a) What is the magnitude of $\mathbf{H}$ at time t?

(b) Assuming that the lines of the induced electric field are circles about the axis of the solenoid, calculate the magnitude of the induced electric field $\mathbf{E}$ at the surface of the core.

(c) Determine the magnitude and direction of $\mathbf{E} \times \mathbf{H}$ at the surface of the core.

(d) The result in (c) represents the power flowing in through unit area of the surface of the core. Calculate the power flowing into the volume of the core of length l.

(e) Compare the result obtained in (d) with the rate of increase of magnetic energy stored in the core.

14.15   Assume that electromagnetic radiation from the blast of a nuclear weapon test is estimated to be 10 calories/m² at a certain distance from the source. The radiation arrives at a receiving surface over a period of 10^{-6} sec and is uniformly distributed over the area of the receiver. If there is no radiation before or after the microsecond interval, what is the rms value of the electric vector in the radiation? (1 calorie = 4.18 joule.)

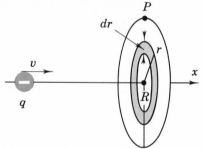

14.16   Consider an electron moving along the positive x-axis with a speed v which is small compared to the speed of light, so that the formulas developed in the text for the electric and magnetic fields are valid. Use the circuital law for $\mathbf{H}$, including the displacement current term, and find the magnetic field $\mathbf{H}$ at the point P which is located at a distance R from the x-axis. *Hint*: Calculate $\mathbf{D} \cdot d\mathbf{A}$ through a ring of radius r and thickness dr. Integrate to obtain the flux of $\mathbf{D}$ crossing the circular area of radius R. Equate the line integral of $\mathbf{H}$ to the time derivative of the flux of $\mathbf{D}$.

14.17   At a large distance from a transmitting station, the waves may be regarded as plane. Assume that all the energy radiated by the station is propagated as a sinusoidal wave of a fixed frequency and that this energy is distributed uniformly over all directions in space. If the average power radiated by the station is 50 kw, what is the maximum value of the electric field intensity at points on the surface of a sphere whose radius is 100 km?

14.18   In ordinary conductors, the contribution of the displacement current to the total current is completely negligible at low frequencies. To see why this is so, obtain the ratio of the rms values of displacement to conduction current in a medium of conductivity σ, carrying an alternating current of density j, given by $j = J \sin \omega t$. *Hint*: By the use of Ohm's law obtain an expression for $\mathbf{E}$ in terms of $\mathbf{j}$ and σ. Then, obtain an expression for the displacement current density. Take $\varepsilon \cong \varepsilon_0$.

Chapter 15.
Guided Waves

15.1   **Waves along a Pair of Parallel Wires**

Consider a pair of long parallel cylindrical conductors in air, as shown in Fig. 15.1. Such an arrangement is referred to as a transmission line. An emf $\mathcal{E}$ applied to the line at one end causes positive charges to move in the clockwise sense. The geometrical arrangement is such that there is overlapping of the electric field which arises from the charge distribution and the magnetic field

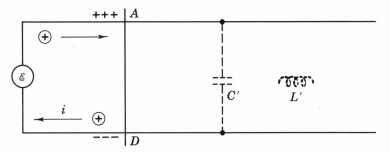

Figure 15.1   Transmission line consisting of parallel wires.

which arises from the flow of charge. Since both fields exist in the same region of space, we can no longer describe the system in terms of a "lumped" or concentrated capacitance and inductance. Instead, we shall consider the line to possess distributed capacitance and inductance. We proceed to evaluate these parameters with the aid of the diagram in Fig. 15.2.

From the dimensions and the value of the electric field indicated in the caption of the diagram, the potential difference be-

389

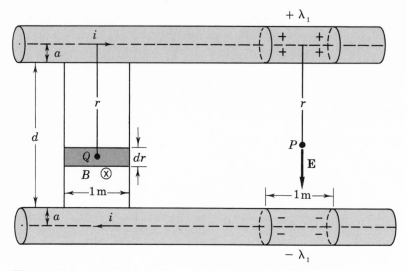

Figure 15.2 Calculation of capacitance and inductance per unit length. The electric field **E** at P is equal to $(\lambda_1/2\pi\varepsilon_0)$ $[1/r + 1/(d-r)]$. At Q, the magnetic induction **B** has the magnitude $(\mu_0 i/2\pi)[1/r + 1/(d-r)]$.

tween the wires due to the charge on both conductors is $V = (\lambda_1/\pi\varepsilon_0)$ ln (d/a). In this expression λ_1 is the charge per unit length of conductor, a is the radius of each wire, and d is the separation between the wires. It is assumed that $d \gg a$. The distributed capacitance C' is defined as the capacitance per unit length of the line—that is,

$$C' = \frac{\lambda_1}{V} = \frac{\pi\varepsilon_0}{\ln{(d/a)}} \qquad (15.1)$$

The magnitude of **B** given in the caption of Fig. 15.2 is due to the current i in each wire. Using this value of **B**, we compute by integration the flux which crosses a rectangular area whose height is d, the separation between the wires, and whose width is unity. This flux Φ' is equal to $[\mu_0 i \ln{(d/a)}]/\pi$. The distributed inductance L' is defined as the flux associated with unit length of the line divided by the current i—that is,

$$L' = \frac{\Phi'}{i} = \frac{\mu_0 \ln{(d/a)}}{\pi} \qquad (15.2)$$

In the present discussion, we shall assume that the resistance of the conductor is negligible.

We return to the diagram of Fig. 15.1. Because of the distributed inductance and capacitance associated with the line, the pulse of positive charge arising from the application of an emf travels with finite velocity and in a given time t has reached the line AD. Charges to the right of AD in either wire are still undisturbed. The imaginary line AD, which may be regarded as the leading edge of the pulse, travels to the right. If the applied emf is alternating, there will be a definite charge distribution along the lines. Consider a length dx of the pair of wires. (See Fig. 15.3.)

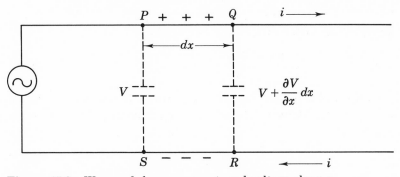

Figure 15.3 Waves of charge, current, and voltage along a transmission line from the viewpoint of distributed parameters.

At a particular instant, let the element dx carry positive charge with the current away from the generator. Correspondingly, the element on the lower wire is charged negatively with the current toward the generator.

In the $PQRS$ circuit, V, the potential difference between the wires at PS, may be denoted by $V = q/C'$, where for typographical convenience the symbol q is chosen to denote the charge per unit length, instead of λ_1 used previously. Similarly, between Q and R, the potential difference is given by $V + (\partial V/\partial x)\, dx$. From Faraday's law, the emf induced in $PQRS$ is $-L'(\partial i/\partial t)\, dx$. Hence the equation of the circuit is

$$L' \frac{\partial i}{\partial t}\, dx + \frac{\partial V}{\partial x}\, dx = 0 \tag{15.3}$$

Partial derivatives are used because V and i are functions of position and time. Replacing the second term on the left of (15.3) by $(1/C')(\partial q/\partial x)\, dx$, we obtain

$$L' \frac{\partial i}{\partial t} + \frac{1}{C'} \frac{\partial q}{\partial x} = 0 \tag{15.4}$$

which relates the time variation of current to the space variation of charge per unit length.

The time rate at which the charge increases on the segment

PQ is the difference between the current entering at P over that leaving at Q. In symbols,

$$i - \left(i + \frac{\partial i}{\partial x} \, dx \right) = -\frac{\partial i}{\partial x} \, dx = \frac{\partial q}{\partial t} \, dx$$

which yields
$$\frac{\partial q}{\partial t} = -\frac{\partial i}{\partial x} \tag{15.5}$$

We wish to eliminate i by differentiating (15.4) with respect to x and (15.5) with respect to t. The result is

$$\frac{\partial^2 q}{\partial t^2} = \frac{1}{L'C'} \frac{\partial^2 q}{\partial x^2} \tag{15.6}$$

This is recognized as the wave equation for the linear charge density q. The velocity of the wave of q traveling along the wires is given by

$$v = \frac{1}{\sqrt{L'C'}} = \frac{1}{\sqrt{\varepsilon_0 \mu_0}} \tag{15.7}$$

The last step in (15.7) is deduced by substituting the values of C' and L' as given in (15.1) and (15.2). In so doing we have taken the permittivity and permeability of the medium surrounding the line (air) to be those of free space. The quantity $1/\sqrt{\mu_0 \varepsilon_0}$ was evaluated in Section 14.6 and was found to be 3.00×10^8 m/sec.

This remarkable result states that the speed of propagation of a charge disturbance guided by a dissipationless line in free space is equal to the speed of electromagnetic waves in free space. If the wave is simple harmonic, we can represent it as

$$q = q_0 \cos \omega \left(t - \frac{x}{v} \right) \tag{15.8}$$

where ω is the angular frequency of the alternating emf impressed at the end of the line at $x = 0$. The wavelength may be obtained from $\lambda = 2\pi v / \omega$, or

$$\lambda = \frac{2\pi}{\omega \sqrt{L'C'}} \tag{15.9}$$

From (15.8), we obtain the expression for the potential difference—that is

$$V = \frac{q}{C'} = \frac{q_0}{C'} \cos \omega \left(t - \frac{x}{v} \right) \tag{15.10}$$

Also, from (15.5), we obtain the expression for the current. The result is

$$i = v q_0 \cos \omega \left(t - \frac{x}{v} \right) \tag{15.11}$$

Upon examining the form of the waves for q, V, and i, we see that all three wave trains are in phase. We can now visualize the situation of guided waves of charge and current in terms of electric and magnetic fields in the region of the wires. For this purpose it is somewhat simpler to replace the wires by metal strips, without altering the principles involved. The trace of the two conductors is shown in Fig. 15.4. At a given instant, the varia-

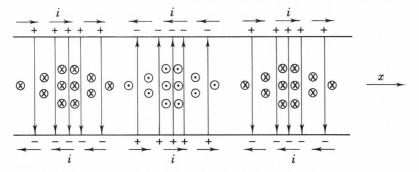

Figure 15.4 Electromagnetic wave guided by a transmission line. The solid lines represent the electric field. The magnetic field distribution is represented by circles.

tion of the **E**-field and the **H**-field with x is indicated by vertical arrows (**E** vector), by crosses (**H** in), and by dots (**H** out). The density of arrows, of crosses and of dots, is intended to convey an approximate idea of the strength of the fields. The current distributions are also indicated by small horizontal arrows above and below the charge distributions.

15.2   The Field Equations in Differential Form

Each cartesian component of a field vector is a function of position and the time. Thus E_x, the x component of **E**, is a function of x, y, z, and t. The same is true for the other components. There are many applications where it is convenient to express in differential form the field relations in (14.1), (14.2), (14.5), and (14.11). Formulas involving the derivatives of the field of **E** were developed in Section 3.6. With the aid of (3.27) and (3.35), Gauss's law appearing in (4.26) may be cast into the form

$$\mathbf{\nabla} \cdot \mathbf{D} = \frac{\partial D_x}{\partial x} + \frac{\partial D_y}{\partial y} + \frac{\partial D_z}{\partial z} = \rho \qquad (15.12)$$

where ρ is the volume density of free charge, itself a function of position and the time. By a similar transformation, Gauss's law for **B** assumes the form

$$\mathbf{\nabla} \cdot \mathbf{B} = \frac{\partial B_x}{\partial x} + \frac{\partial B_y}{\partial y} + \frac{\partial B_z}{\partial z} \equiv 0 \qquad (15.13)$$

The result in (3.43) gives the relation between the line integral of a vector around a closed path and the surface integral of the curl of the same vector over the open area bounded by the path. When we apply this relation to the circuital law for **H** given in (14.11), we find

$$\oint \mathbf{H} \cdot d\mathbf{l} = \int_{\substack{\text{open} \\ \text{surface}}} \mathbf{\nabla} \times \mathbf{H} \cdot d\mathbf{A} = i + \int_{\substack{\text{open} \\ \text{surface}}} \frac{\partial \mathbf{D}}{\partial t} \cdot d\mathbf{A} \qquad (15.14)$$

Now the conduction current i can be expressed as

$$\int_{\substack{\text{open} \\ \text{surface}}} \mathbf{j} \cdot d\mathbf{A}$$

Upon substituting this expression in the right-hand side of (15.14) and upon equating integrands, we find

$$\mathbf{\nabla} \times \mathbf{H} = \mathbf{j} + \frac{\partial \mathbf{D}}{\partial t} \qquad (15.15)$$

An identical procedure yields the differential form of Faraday's law, namely

$$\mathbf{\nabla} \times \mathbf{E} = -\frac{\partial \mathbf{B}}{\partial t} \qquad (15.16)$$

In accordance with expansion of the curl given in (3.41), it is helpful to express (15.15) and (15.16) in terms of the cartesian components of the vectors involved. Thus

$$\frac{\partial H_z}{\partial y} - \frac{\partial H_y}{\partial z} = j_x + \dot{D}_x$$

$$\frac{\partial H_x}{\partial z} - \frac{\partial H_z}{\partial x} = j_y + \dot{D}_y \qquad (15.17)$$

$$\frac{\partial H_y}{\partial x} - \frac{\partial H_x}{\partial y} = j_z + \dot{D}_z$$

Similarly,

$$\frac{\partial E_z}{\partial y} - \frac{\partial E_y}{\partial z} = -\dot{B}_x$$

$$\frac{\partial E_x}{\partial z} - \frac{\partial E_z}{\partial x} = -\dot{B}_y \qquad (15.18)$$

$$\frac{\partial E_y}{\partial x} - \frac{\partial E_x}{\partial y} = -\dot{B}_z$$

In the above relations, differentiation with respect to the time is indicated by placing a dot ($\cdot$) over the symbol.

15.3   Waves in Rectangular Wave Guides

In this section, we shall take up various aspects of the propagation of electromagnetic waves in an isotropic, homeogeneous dielectric of permittivity ε and permeability μ. The dielectric fills the interior of a long rectangular metallic tube or wave guide. A cross section of the wave guide and the orientation of the axes are shown in Fig. 15.5. We shall consider waves which are propagated in the $+x$ direction and assume that the field quantities are sinusoidal functions of the time. This variation is conveniently represented by the complex exponential $e^{j\omega t}$. Also, the

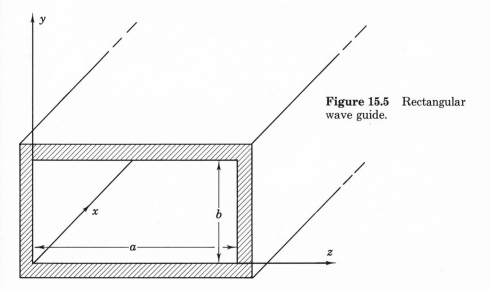

Figure 15.5   Rectangular wave guide.

dependence of the field quantities on the distance x will be restricted to the form $e^{-\gamma x}$, where γ is, in general, complex and has the form $\gamma = (\alpha + j\beta)$. The quantities α and β appearing in γ are the so-called attenuation and phase constants respectively. Accordingly, the functional form of the field quantities will have the form $e^{j\omega t - \gamma x}$. In the final solution, either the real or the imaginary part of this factor will be taken.

When solutions are obtained for the various components of **E** and **H**, it is found that two types of waves satisfy the field equations. These are known as transverse electric (TE) and transverse magnetic (TM) waves. TE waves are characterized by solutions which have a component of **H** in the direction of propagation but have no component of **E** in that direction. To illustrate, if the propagation is in the x direction, $H_x \neq 0$, but $E_x = 0$ for the TE mode of transmission. Analogous conditions apply for the TM waves. This feature is not found in the case of the propagation of unguided waves in space where neither **E** nor **H** has components along the direction in which the wave travels.

In the introductory analysis to be undertaken here, the **E**-field will be limited to a single component E_y, while E_x and E_z will be set equal to zero. With this restriction, the set of equations labeled (15.18) reduces to

$$-\frac{\partial E_y}{\partial z} = -\mu \dot{H}_x; \qquad 0 = -\mu \dot{H}_y; \qquad \frac{\partial E_y}{\partial x} = -\mu \dot{H}_z \quad (15.19)$$

From the middle equation it follows that H_y is independent of the time and constitutes a constant field which is set equal to zero since the present problem is concerned with time-varying fields only. As a result of the above simplifications, the nonzero components of the field are E_y, H_x, and H_z.

The conduction current density in the dielectric is zero. Taking into account the field components which are zero, the set of equations labeled (15.17) assumes the simpler form

$$\frac{\partial H_z}{\partial y} = 0; \qquad \frac{\partial H_x}{\partial z} - \frac{\partial H_z}{\partial x} = \varepsilon \dot{E}_y; \qquad -\frac{\partial H_x}{\partial y} = 0 \quad (15.20)$$

From these equations we conclude that H_z and H_x are not functions of y but may depend on x and z. We wish to eliminate H_x and H_z by utilizing relations (15.19) and (15.20) and to obtain an equation involving only E_y. To do this, differentiate the second equation in (15.20) with respect to t. Also, differentiate the first equation in (15.19) with respect to z and the last equation in

(15.19) with respect to x. Upon combining the results obtained above, we obtain

$$\frac{\partial^2 E_y}{\partial x^2} + \frac{\partial^2 E_y}{\partial z^2} = \mu\varepsilon\frac{\partial^2 E_y}{\partial t^2} \tag{15.21}$$

which is the two-dimensional wave equation for E_y. As a trial solution, let $E_y = E_0(z)e^{(j\omega t - \gamma x)}$, where the factor E_0 multiplying the oscillatory part depends only on z. Substitution of E_y in (15.21) gives

$$\frac{d^2 E_0}{dz^2} + k^2 E_0 = 0 \tag{15.22}$$

where

$$k^2 = \gamma^2 + \mu\varepsilon\omega^2 \tag{15.23}$$

Equation (15.22) is recognized as the differential equation of simple harmonic motion. Its solution is

$$E_0(z) = A \sin (kz + C) \tag{15.24}$$

To evaluate the constants we need to specify the boundary conditions on E_y. At the boundary surfaces located at $z = 0$ and at $z = a$, E_y is tangential to the metal walls. If the conductivity of the metal is high, E_y is damped out rapidly as the wave penetrates into the body of the metal. At these boundaries, E_y may be set equal to zero, in conformity with the general boundary conditions which require the continuity of the tangential components of **E**. With these conditions we find that in (15.24) $C = 0$, and $ka = m\pi$ where m is an integer. The factor A is also a constant, whose magnitude depends on the source producing the oscillations. Whence

$$E_0(z) = A \sin \left(\frac{m\pi}{a}z\right), \qquad m = 1, 2, 3, \ldots \tag{15.25}$$

In the notation $TE_{n,m}$, the integer n indicates the number of maxima of the field in the y direction over the height b. Similarly, the integer m indicates the number of maxima in the z direction over the width a. In the special solution under consideration, E_y is the only component of the electric field transverse to the direction of propagation. The amplitude of E_y does not depend on y but is a function only of z. It follows that for this problem, $n = 0$, but m may take on integral values. Incorporating the exponential function, we find that the expression for E_y becomes

$$E_y\Big|_{0,m} = E_0(z)e^{j\omega t - \gamma_{0,m}x} = A \sin \left(\frac{m\pi}{a}z\right)e^{j\omega t - \gamma_{0,m}x} \tag{15.26}$$

with

$$\gamma_{0,m} = \alpha + j\beta_{0,m} \tag{15.27}$$

In general, E_y is multiplied by the factor $e^{-\alpha x}$, which indicates that the wave is attenuated and that its amplitude diminishes with the distance x. We shall assume that there is no attenuation—that is, $\alpha = 0$. The propagation constant is now a pure imaginary and is equal to

$$\gamma_{0,m} = j\beta_{0,m} \tag{15.28}$$

Finally, upon adopting the imaginary part of the result in (15.26), E_y for the lowest ($n = 0$, $m = 1$) mode of transmission is represented by

$$E_y\bigg|_{0,1} = A \sin\left(\frac{\pi}{a}z\right) \sin(\omega t - \beta_{0,1}x) \tag{15.29}$$

The H_x and H_z components of the magnetic field may be obtained in a straightforward way from the first and third relation of the set labeled (15.19). Recalling that $H_y = 0$, we can list the magnetic field components as

$$H_x\bigg|_{0,1} = -\frac{A\pi}{a\mu\omega} \cos\left(\frac{\pi z}{a}\right) \cos(\omega t - \beta_{0,1}x)$$

$$H_y\bigg|_{0,1} = 0 \tag{15.30}$$

$$H_z\bigg|_{0,1} = \frac{\beta_{0,1}A}{\mu\omega} \sin\left(\frac{\pi z}{a}\right) \sin(\omega t - \beta_{0,1}x)$$

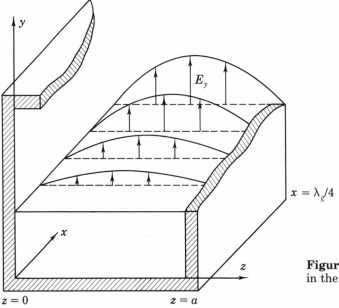

Figure 15.6   A plot of E_y in the $TE_{0,1}$ mode.

Figure 15.6 shows a plot of the **E**-field, at a given instant (t = π/ω), in planes perpendicular to the x-axis at a few values of x. The magnetic field configuration is more complicated. A typical sketch of the **H**-field appears in Fig. 15.7 in a plane perpendicular to the y-axis. The plot is based on the values H_x and H_z at the time (t = π/ω).

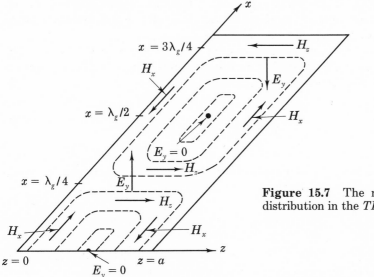

Figure 15.7 The magnetic field distribution in the $TE_{0,1}$ mode.

In (15.23) $\mu\varepsilon = 1/v^2$, where v is the phase velocity of unguided waves in the dielectric. From the boundary condition leading to relation (15.25), $k = m\pi/a$. If $\alpha = 0$, (15.23) can be transformed into

$$\frac{m^2\pi^2}{a^2} = \gamma_{0,m}^2 + \frac{\omega^2}{v^2} = -\beta_{0,m}^2 + \frac{4\pi^2}{\lambda^2} \qquad (15.31)$$

in which ω is the angular frequency of the wave and λ is the wavelength in an extensive dielectric free from boundaries. On the other hand, the phase constant

$$\beta_{0,m} = \frac{2\pi}{(\lambda_g)_{0,m}} \qquad (15.32)$$

where $(\lambda_g)_{0,m}$ is the wavelength in the wave guide associated with the mode (0, m). By combining (15.31) and (15.32), the wavelength in the guide is found to be

$$(\lambda_g)_{0,m} = \frac{\lambda}{\sqrt{1 - (m\lambda/2a)^2}} \qquad (15.33)$$

In particular, if $m = 1$,

$$(\lambda_g)_{0,1} = \frac{\lambda}{\sqrt{1 - (\lambda/2a)^2}} \tag{15.34}$$

which means that there can be propagation in the guide only if the wavelength of the unguided wave is less than twice the width of the guide. Otherwise the denominator in (15.34) becomes imaginary. Moreover $\lambda_g > \lambda$, although the wave has the same frequency inside and outside the guide.

In the more general case of TE waves where $\mathbf{E}$ has two components, E_y and E_z, the propagation constant depends on the two integers n and m as indicated by

$$\gamma_{n,m} = \sqrt{\left(\frac{n\pi}{b}\right)^2 + \left(\frac{m\pi}{a}\right)^2 - \frac{\omega^2}{v^2}} \tag{15.35}$$

If $(n\pi/b)^2 + (m\pi/a)^2 > \omega^2/v^2$, there is no propagation, since in this case $\gamma_{n,m}$ is real and therefore $\beta_{n,m} = 0$. As before, there is a critical wavelength measured by

$$(\lambda_c)_{n,m} = \frac{2}{\sqrt{(n/b)^2 + (m/a)^2}} \tag{15.36}$$

For $TE_{0,1}$ mode $(\lambda_c)_{0,1} = 2a$ as before. Hence the wave guide acts as a filter which transmits frequencies higher than the cut-off frequency $v/(\lambda_c)_{n,m}$.

15.4   Propagation Velocities in Wave Guides

The concepts of phase, group, and signal velocities were introduced in Section 13.8 in connection with the study of mechanical waves. We return to the consideration of these velocities with a slightly different notation appropriate to the case of guided waves. The term phase velocity, here denoted by v_{ph}, is the propagation rate of surfaces of equal phase. Since waves are represented by any function of the argument $(\omega t \pm \beta x)$, the surfaces of constant phase are described by setting $\omega t = \beta x$. Here β replaces k, which was used previously. Surfaces of constant phase are propagated with a speed

$$v_{\mathrm{ph}} = \frac{dx}{dt} = \frac{\omega}{\beta}$$

The term group velocity, here designated as v_{gr}, is associated with the propagation speed of the maximum amplitude of a group of waves. From (13.50), $v_{gr} = d\omega/d\beta = 1/(d\beta/d\omega)$. For guided waves $\beta = \sqrt{\omega^2/v^2 - (n\pi/b)^2 - (m\pi/a)^2}$. Upon differentiation of β we obtain the connection between the phase and group velocity of guided waves. The result is

$$v_{gr}v_{ph} = v^2 \tag{15.37}$$

In this result v is the wave speed in the unbounded, extensive dielectric, and if the dielectric is replaced by evacuated space, $v = c$, the speed of light.

An interesting feature of this relation is deduced from the observation that the wavelength in the guide, as given by (15.34), is longer than the wavelength of the free wave in vacuum. But each wave has the same frequency. Hence the phase velocity within the guide is greater than c! However, if $v_{ph} > c$, (15.37) predicts that v_{gr}, the group velocity which is the rate of energy propagation, is less than c. Hence energy is not transmitted with a velocity that exceeds the speed of light.

From (15.34) it follows that as λ, the free space wavelength in vacuum, is decreased (or as the oscillation frequency is in-

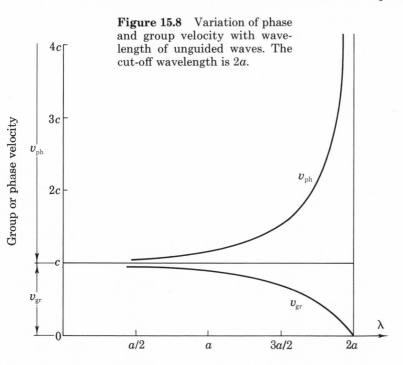

Figure 15.8 Variation of phase and group velocity with wavelength of unguided waves. The cut-off wavelength is $2a$.

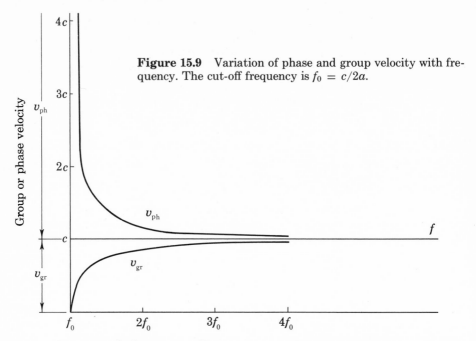

Figure 15.9   Variation of phase and group velocity with frequency. The cut-off frequency is $f_0 = c/2a$.

creased above cut-off), λ_g, the wavelength in the guide, also diminishes and approaches λ. Accordingly, the phase velocity and group velocity each approach c. On the other hand, as λ is increased toward the value $2a$, v_{ph} approaches ∞ while v_{gr} approaches zero, indicating again that no energy can flow when $\lambda > 2a$. The situation is pictured in Figs. 15.8 and 15.9.

15.5   Radiation

In this section we shall describe the process whereby an electromagnetic wave is radiated into a region of space. In the preceding sections we saw that traveling electric and magnetic fields coexisted in space and were essentially guided by conducting strips. We now turn to a qualitative examination of conditions where such waves become disengaged from conductors. The quantitative treatment of this problem is beyond the scope of this text.

We consider a modification of the arrangement discussed in connection with the parallel-wire system. Let a short length of such a transmission line (short compared to a wavelength) be deformed into a single straight conductor with a high-frequency oscillator coupled magnetically to the mid-portion. The arrangement is illustrated in Fig. 15.10 and is loosely referred to as a dipole antenna. The ends of the wire are alternately charged positively and negatively, and there is an oscillatory current in the conductor. At the instant when the charge displacement is

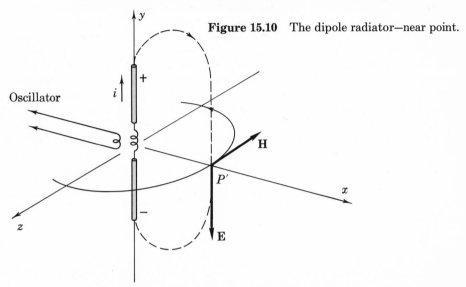

Figure 15.10   The dipole radiator—near point.

maximum, the current is zero, and conversely. The figure represents some intermediate instant when the current is directed upward and the charge at the upper end is positive.

The results of preceding sections indicate that field quantities are propagated through space with a finite velocity v. Consider now the fields at the point P', whose x coordinate x' is such that x'/v is a small fraction of the period of oscillation $2\pi/\omega$. On the basis of our experience with low-frequency currents and charges, we predict the existence at P' of an electric field **E** and a magnetic intensity **H**, oriented as shown in Fig. 15.10. Since **E** originates from the charge distribution and **H** is associated with the current, the electric vector at P' is tangent to the line of force (broken curve) in the x,y plane, while the magnetic vector is tangent to the circle in the x,z plane. Thus, at P', **E** is parallel to the y-axis, and **H** is parallel to the z-axis. Both fields exist at the same point in space. However, at the point P' the electric intensity **E** attains its maximum value when the charge displacement is maximum, while **H** attains its maximum value when the current is maximum. Hence **E** and **H** are 90° out of phase. Calculations show that for this phase difference the power delivered to the region surrounding the dipole averages to zero over a complete cycle.

THE ELECTROMAGNETIC SPECTRUM

The term "spectrum" is used to designate a range of wavelengths or frequencies. The accompanying chart shows the spectrum of electromagnetic waves, arranged according to wavelength. Starting with very long radio waves—whose wavelength compares with the distance from New York to Los Angeles—the scale extends downward to the region of gamma rays, whose wavelength compares with nuclear dimensions. Theory places no limits on the wavelength of electromagnetic radiations. Moreover, the field equations are successful in describing propagation phenomena over an immense range of wavelengths embracing more than twenty orders of magnitude. The limits of the various regions indicated on the chart are approximate and often overlap. All portions of the spectrum have been explored experimentally, and no fundamental difference has been observed between various type of waves. In vacuum, the waves are transverse, and all types are propagated with the common speed c.

The chart includes brief statements on how the various types of wave are produced and detected. Quantum physics is needed to account for the mechanism of emission from molecular, atomic, and nuclear systems.

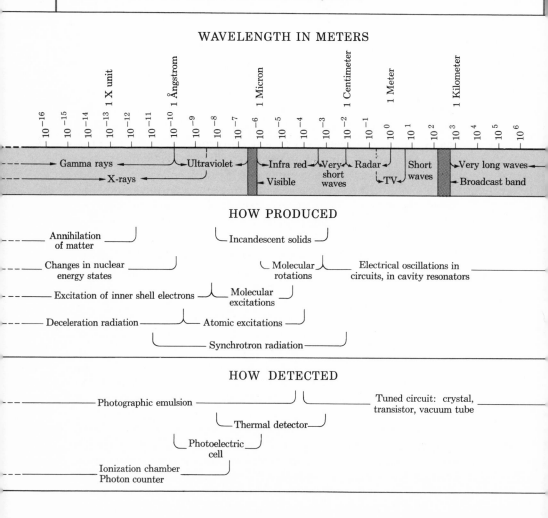

WAVELENGTH IN METERS

Next consider a distant point P, such that x/v is large compared to a period of oscillation. (See Fig. 15.11.) Because electromagnetic fields are propagated with finite velocity, the state of
affairs at P is significantly different. For this position of the field

Figure 15.11   The dipole radiator—far point P on the x-axis.

point, the time necessary for a disturbance to reach P is no longer
negligible in comparison with a period of oscillation. At a given
instant, the field vectors are not the same as those which exist
near the dipole at the specified moment, but are due to conditions
existing at the dipole at an earlier moment. Therefore there will
be a time lag of x/v sec in the behavior of the field vectors. The
electric field at P will therefore vary in time according to $E =
E_0 \sin \omega[t - (x/v)]$, where $\omega x/v$ represents the retardation in
phase.

The complete solution of the problem indicates that at the dis-
tant point P, $\mathbf{E}$ and $\mathbf{H}$ oscillate in phase. The vectors maintain
their space relations ($\mathbf{E}$ perpendicular to $\mathbf{H}$, and both perpendicular to the x-axis). Due to the phase retardation, there is now a
net flow of energy outward from the dipole. The traveling disturbance represented in part by $E_0 \sin \omega[t - (x/v)]$ is referred to
as a radiation field. The amplitude E_0 is not constant but diminishes inversely as the first power of the distance from the dipole.
At reasonably large distances from the dipole, the wave fronts
are spherical. At very large distances, they can be regarded as
plane.

If the field point is not on the x-axis but is at some point such
as Q (see Fig. 15.12), the amplitude of the electric vector (for the
same distance r from the source) is reduced by the factor $\sin \theta$,
where θ is the angle between the axis of the dipole and the radius

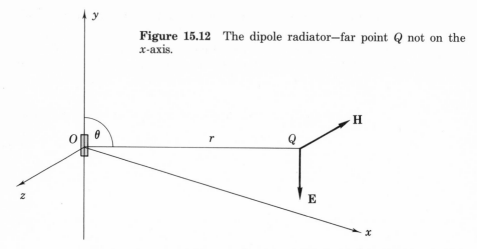

Figure 15.12 The dipole radiator—far point Q not on the x-axis.

vector to Q. Accordingly, there is no radiation along the axis of the dipole (y-axis), since $\theta = 0$ for this direction. As before, the magnetic vector is perpendicular to **E** as well as to r. Energy flows along r, which also constitutes the direction of the Poynting vector or the ray direction.

From the quantitative point of view, the source which is the simplest to deal with is the electric dipole. The dipole consists of a pair of charges of equal magnitude but of opposite sign. The charges could be situated on a pair of conductors, such as spheres, joined by a short thin conductor, the charge on which could be regarded as negligible. The charges on the terminals of the wire would vary with time. An oscillating electric dipole is shown in Fig. 15.13. For the static case **p**, the moment of the dipole was defined in Section 4.2 as $q\mathbf{l}$, where q is the magnitude of charge on one end of the wire and $\mathbf{l}$ is the fixed distance between them. In the present case, the charge q varies in time and the current i in the connecting wire is dq/dt.

There are several approaches to the problem of determining the components of the field originating from an oscillating dipole. The mathematical machinery cannot be treated at an elementary level. The details of calculation are particularly simple if the charge and current oscillations in time are harmonic and possess a frequency such that the length l is small relative to the wavelength of the emitted wave. The solution of this classical problem is found in all advanced texts.* The field components are best de-

*A particularly readable account appears in J. R. Reitz and F. J. Milford, *Foundations of Electromagnetic Theory*. Reading, Mass.: Addison-Wesley Publishing Company, Inc., 1960.

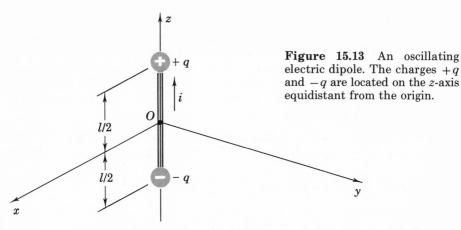

Figure 15.13 An oscillating electric dipole. The charges $+q$ and $-q$ are located on the z-axis equidistant from the origin.

scribed in spherical coordinates r, θ, ϕ. We quote the end results from Reitz and Milford. The field vectors at the point P are illustrated in Fig. 15.14.

The magnetic field has one component, H_ϕ, perpendicular to the plane containing the z-axis and the radius vector r. Its magnitude is

$$H_\phi = A \sin \theta \left[\frac{\omega}{rc} \cos \omega\left(t - \frac{r}{c} \right) + \frac{1}{r^2} \sin \omega\left(t - \frac{r}{c} \right) \right] \quad (15.38)$$

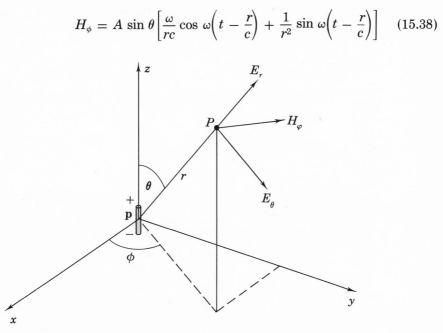

Figure 15.14 Electric and magnetic vectors in the radiation field of an oscillating dipole **p**.

where c is the speed of light, ω is the angular frequency of oscillation, and A is a constant equal to $i_0 l/4\pi$. The current i_0 is the amplitude of the instantaneous current in the connecting wire.

The electric field has two compoents, E_r in the direction of r, and E_θ which is perpendicular to r in the plane determined by r and the z-axis. The E_ϕ component is zero. The magnitudes of E_r and E_θ are

$$E_r = \frac{2A}{\varepsilon_0} \cos\theta \left[\frac{\sin \omega(t - r/c)}{r^2 c} - \frac{\cos \omega(t - r/c)}{r^3 \omega} \right] \tag{15.39}$$

$$E_\theta = -\frac{A}{\varepsilon_0} \sin\theta \left[\left(\frac{1}{r^3 \omega} - \frac{\omega}{rc^2} \right) \cos \omega(t - r/c) \right.$$

$$\left. - \frac{1}{r^2 c} \sin \omega(t - r/c) \right] \tag{15.40}$$

As mentioned before, the field may be divided into two zones—the near zone where r is small relative to the wavelength λ given by $(2\pi c/\omega)$, and the far zone where r is large compared to λ. The fields contain terms which involve $1/r^3$, $1/r^2$, and $1/r$, where r is the distance between the dipole and the field point. The inverse square and inverse cube terms die down rapidly with distance r, and therefore are important only in the near zone. On the other hand, the terms in $1/r$ are peculiar to the far zone or the radiation field. These are the field components which are responsible for the flow of energy away from the source into space.

The discussion given thus far may be extended satisfactorily to such radiating systems as radio or radar antennas. However, in optical problems involving visible light, the source of light consists of a very large number of excited atoms or molecules. Here, the radiators are of atomic dimensions and do not oscillate continuously. Instead, each radiating atom may be thought of as a dipole whose duration of oscillation is small (of the order of 10^{-8} sec). The entire assemblage therefore emits a number of wave trains of limited length. Since each atom, in its radiation, is independent of other atoms, the emitted wave trains will bear no consistent phase relation with each other; furthermore, the orientations of the equivalent dipoles representing the radiating atoms will be quite random. This situation differs markedly from the case of emission from a radio antenna. The electromagnetic wave from the latter source consists of very long wave trains produced by sustained oscillations of antenna currents.

Guided Waves: **Problems**

15.1 Suppose the parallel-wire transmission line is replaced by a coaxial cable consisting of an inner conducting cylinder of radius a and a coaxial outer conducting cylinder of radius b.

(a) Obtain expressions for the inductance and capacitance per unit length of the cable.

(b) Assume that an alternating emf is applied to the cable and obtain the wave equation which the charge density must satisfy.

15.2 Consider the traveling waves of voltage and current in the parallel-wire transmission line discussed in Section 15.1 and obtain an expression for the ratio of maximum voltage to maximum current in terms of a and d.

15.3 Assume that the electric vector in a plane wave in free space traveling in the x direction is a function of a single positional coordinate x and the time t. Assume further that the component of the electric field in the x direction is zero.

(a) Refer to the set of relations in (15.17) and (15.18) and verify that:

$$\frac{\partial E_y}{\partial x} = -\dot{B}_z, \qquad \frac{\partial E_z}{\partial x} = \dot{B}_y$$

$$\frac{\partial H_z}{\partial x} = -\dot{D}_y, \qquad \frac{\partial H_y}{\partial x} = \dot{D}_z$$

(b) Show that both E_y and E_z separately satisfy the one-dimensional wave equation as given in (14.28).

15.4 Assume that a linearly polarized wave with the electric vector parallel to the y-axis is incident at one end of the wave guide described in Section 15.3. If the frequency of the wave is less than the cut-off frequency of the guide, the incident wave cannot give rise to a traveling wave within the guide. Assume that there is no dissipation in the walls of the wave guide. Explain what happens to the incident wave.

15.5 Refer to the field components of the $TE_{0,1}$ wave described by (15.29) and (15.30). Integrate the x component of the Poynting vector over the cross section of the guide to obtain the rate of energy flow along the x direction.

15.6   What is the value of the divergence of the electric field in the space within the guide? The electric field is described by (15.29). Answer the same question for the magnetic field as given by (15.30).

15.7   In Section 15.4, evaluate $(d\beta/d\omega)$ and verify the result given in (15.37).

15.8   A wave of angular frequency ω is propagated in a region containing ions (charge e, mass m) of density N. The index of refraction is given by

$$n = \frac{c}{v_{ph}} = \left(1 - \frac{Ne^2}{m\varepsilon_0\omega^2}\right)^{\frac{1}{2}}$$

where c is the speed of light in vacuum.

(a) Express v_{ph} as a function of the wavelength, recalling that $\omega = 2\pi v_{ph}/\lambda$.

(b) From the relation

$$v_{gr} = v_{ph} - \lambda\frac{dv_{ph}}{d\lambda}$$

obtain an expression for the group velocity v_{gr}.

(c) Show that the product $v_{ph}v_{gr}$ is equal to c^2.

15.9   Examine the components of the electric and magnetic vectors in the field of the dipole oscillator and select the terms that depend on the inverse first power of the distance r.

(a) Integrate the component of the Poynting vector normal to a sphere of radius r and show that the instantaneous rate at which the dipole radiates energy is

$$\frac{i_0^2 l^2\omega^2}{6\pi\varepsilon_0 c^3}\cos^2\omega(t - r/c)$$

(b) If the charge q varies in accordance with $q = q_0 \cos \omega t$, prove that the rate of emission of energy from the dipole is proportional to the fourth power of the frequency and to the square of the amplitude of the dipole moment.

15.10   Refer to the electric and magnetic field components of the oscillating dipole. At low frequencies and at points quite close to the dipole, the terms which predominate are those whose coefficients contain (λ/r) to the highest power.

(a) Rewrite the expressions for H_ϕ, E_r, and E_θ so that the coefficients of various terms are written in terms of

$$\left(\frac{\lambda}{r}\right)^2, \quad \left(\frac{\lambda}{r}\right)^1, \quad \text{or} \quad \left(\frac{\lambda}{r}\right)^0$$

(b) Select those terms which predominate in the near zone at long wavelengths (low frequencies).

(c) Compare these terms with the results obtained for the electrostatic field of the dipole [(4.3) and (4.4)] and with the magnetic field of a current element (7.2).

15.11 As in the case of mechanical waves, traveling waves along a transmission line of finite length suffer reflection at the end of the line. Under certain conditions a standing wave pattern may be formed on the transmission line. For instance, let a line of finite length L be short-circuited at one end and left open at the output end. In this case, the superposition of incident and reflected current waves may give rise to a system of current nodes (zero current for all time) provided λ is chosen appropriately.

(a) As given in (15.11), current waves progressing along the $+x$ direction are given by

$$i = i_0 \cos (\omega t - kx)$$

where $k = 2\pi/\lambda$. Write the expression for the reflected wave, assuming that the amplitude of the reflected wave is also i_0. (Complete reflection.)

(b) Combine the reflected and incident waves and from the result show that a standing wave pattern is formed when the wavelength assumes the particular values given by

$$\lambda_m = \frac{4L}{(2m + 1)}$$

where $m = 0, 1, 2, 3, \ldots$.

Chapter 16.
Superposition,
Reflection,
and Refraction of Waves

16.1   The Principle of Superposition

When several waves are propagated in a given region, the disturbance at a given point resulting from the combined effect of the various waves is equal to the sum of the disturbances which the individual waves would produce at the given point in the absence of the others. This is a statement of the so-called *superposition principle*, which is valid when the differential equation representing the wave motion is linear. As a consequence of this linearity, the sum of two or more separate solutions of the given wave equation is also a solution.

In our study of mechanical waves we pointed out that only when small disturbances were involved was the equation describing the wave motion linear in form. However, for electromagnetic waves the corresponding wave equation is linear even without such restrictions on the magnitude of the field quantities. Hence the superposition principle is of general validity in the case of electromagnetic waves. We proceed to describe certain operations commonly used in obtaining the resultant of two or more wave motions.

412

16.2   Composition of Fields Which Vary Harmonically

The electromagnetic spectrum extends from the region of long radio waves ($\lambda \sim 10^4$ m) to the domain of gamma rays ($\lambda \sim 10^{-14}$ m). Radar, heat, and light waves are also electromagnetic in nature and have wavelengths which lie in the region extending from 10^{-2} m to 10^{-7} m. Although the sources which produce the waves differ considerably, during propagation the waves exhibit superposition effects which are observable throughout the spectrum. The superposition phenomena, such as interference and diffraction, are commonly studied in the domain of microwaves or in the region of optics. In this connection, and also in analyzing states of polarization, it becomes necessary to combine two or more linearly polarized harmonic waves which have the same frequency but different amplitudes and phases.

We consider first the case where the electric vector in each wave is parallel to a given direction in space. If the y-axis is chosen for this direction, a pair of wave trains satisfying the above requirement may be described by

$$E_{y_1} = a_1 \cos (\omega t - kx)$$

and
$$E_{y_2} = a_2 \cos (\omega t - kx - \alpha) \tag{16.1}$$

The calculation of the resultant of the two waves is based on the superposition principle, according to which the resultant electric field at a fixed point at any instant is derived by adding the individual fields. The manipulation is simplified without loss of generality if the fixed point is taken at $x = 0$. At this position the electric fields vary in time in accordance with

$$E_{y_1} = a_1 \cos (\omega t) \qquad \text{and} \qquad E_{y_2} = a_2 \cos (\omega t - \alpha) \tag{16.2}$$

There are several approaches to determining the variation of the resultant in time.

Procedure I, Graphical. Assign values to t, calculate E_{y_1} and E_{y_2} for each t and add algebraically, and plot the values of the resultant for each value of t. The curve describes the variation of the resultant field in time. Essentially the same result is achieved by plotting the individual graphs for E_{y_1} and E_{y_2} and obtaining the graph of the resultant by the addition of ordinates.

Procedure II, Analytical. The expression for the resultant

In 1955, a group of astronomers working with a radio telescope noticed that they were receiving strong bursts of radio waves from the planet Jupiter. Subsequent investigations produced interesting discoveries about linearly and circularly polarized light and about the origins of these emissions.

Early in the investigations it was discovered that the radio waves were polarized in a particularly complex way: rather than being linearly polarized, the emissions from Jupiter are circularly polarized. In linear polarization, as shown in (a), the waves vibrate in a single plane (in the drawing here, vertically). Circular polarization (b) has both vertical and horizontal components, which add vectorially to trace the path of a helix. In one wavelength of radiation, a vector describes a circle.

The possible origins of these radio emissions are shown in (c), a cross-sectional and a three-dimensional view of Jupiter and its radiation belts. In the cross section, the helices represent typical paths of high-velocity charged particles trapped in strong magnetic fields, similar to the Van Allen belts surrounding the earth, and mirrored between regions of equal field strength. These particles appear to be the source of Jupiter's linearly-polarized, long-wave radiation: vertical as at B and horizontal as at C. At A, because the belts are eccentric, a mirror point comes close to the surface of the planet. As a result, some particles are dumped into the atmosphere. Encounters of this type may be the source of Jupiter's long-wave radiation, which is circularly polarized.

(BELOW) Spectra of emissions from Jupiter—as recorded at the High Altitude Observatory, the University of Colorado, in 1962 and in 1963.

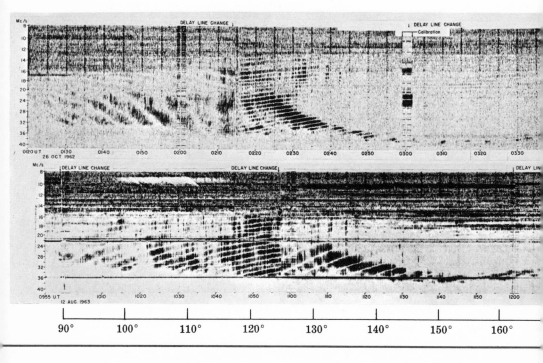

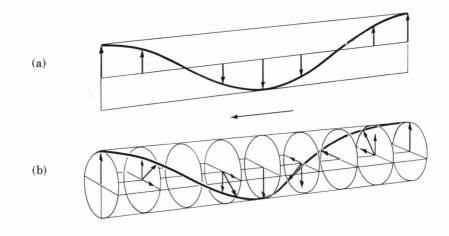

(a)

(b)

(c)

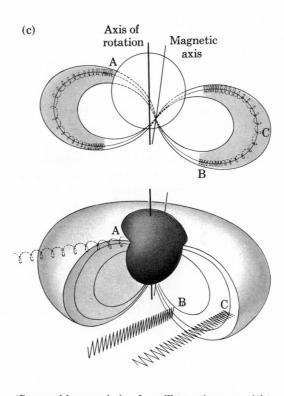

Axis of
rotation

Magnetic
axis

A

C

B

A

B

C

230   1240   1250   1300   1310

80°   190°   200°

may be obtained by a straightforward though somewhat more laborious analytical method, the major steps of which are shown below. Let E_y represent the resultant. Then

$$E_y = E_{y_1} + E_{y_2} = a_1 \cos \omega t + a_2 \cos (\omega t - \alpha) \qquad (16.3)$$

Upon expanding and making the substitutions indicated below,

$$(a_1 + a_2 \cos \alpha) \equiv R \cos \delta, \qquad a_2 \sin \alpha \equiv R \sin \delta \qquad (16.4)$$

we obtain:

$$E_y = R(\cos \delta \cos \omega t + \sin \delta \sin \omega t) = R \cos (\omega t - \delta) \qquad (16.5)$$

This calculation shows that the resultant is also a harmonic variation of the same frequency. The amplitude R is given by

$$R^2 = a_1^2 + a_2^2 + 2a_1 a_2 \cos \alpha \qquad (16.6)$$

while δ, the difference in phase between the resultant E_y and E_{y_1}, can be calculated from

$$\tan \delta = \frac{a_2 \sin \alpha}{a_1 + a_2 \cos \alpha} \qquad (16.7)$$

Frequently, it is necessary to obtain only the amplitude R of the resultant. Equation (16.6) shows that R can be evaluated directly in terms of the amplitudes of the individual field quantities and their phase difference. The equivalent graphical construction is shown in Fig. 16.1. The application of the law of cosines yields the value of R directly, and the phase difference δ between a_1 and the resultant may also be evaluated from the geometry.

The geometrical scheme for arriving at the magnitude of the

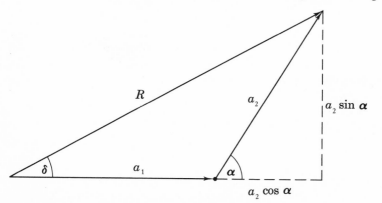

Figure 16.1   Resultant amplitude of two harmonic waves. The electric vector in each wave is parallel to a given direction.

resultant and the magnitude of the phase difference between it and a given component may be extended to three or more harmonically varying fields directed along the same straight line and of the same frequency. Thus, if the individual components are

$$E_{y_1} = a_1 \cos \omega t, \qquad\qquad E_{y_2} = a_2 \cos (\omega t - \alpha)$$
$$E_{y_3} = a_3 \cos (\omega t - \beta), \qquad E_{y_4} = a_4 \cos (\omega t - \gamma) \tag{16.8}$$

the resultant R may be found by combining the resultant of E_{y_1} and E_{y_2} with E_{y_3} and so on. The geometrical construction is

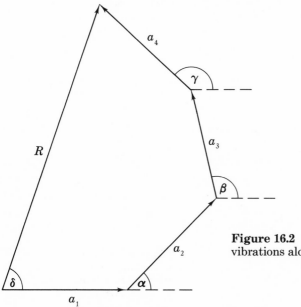

Figure 16.2   Resultant of four harmonic vibrations along the same straight line.

shown in Fig. 16.2, where α is the phase difference between the first and second, β is that between the first and third, and γ is that between the first and fourth.

16.3   Composition of Sinusoidal Electric Intensities at Right Angles

Consider two linearly polarized waves traveling in the $+x$ direction. Let the electric vector in one wave be parallel to the y direction, and let the electric vector in the second wave be parallel to the z direction. Let the individual time variations of the two electric intensities at a fixed point (say at $x = 0$) on the x-axis be represented by

$$E_y = a_y \sin \omega t \qquad (16.9)$$

$$E_z = a_z \sin (\omega t - \phi) \qquad (16.10)$$

These are two simple harmonic vibrations along mutually perpendicular directions. The vibrations have the same frequency but unequal amplitudes, and they differ in phase by ϕ. For arbitrary values of the phase difference ϕ, it may be shown that the terminus of the resultant electric vector traces out an ellipse. This is shown schematically in Fig. 16.3.

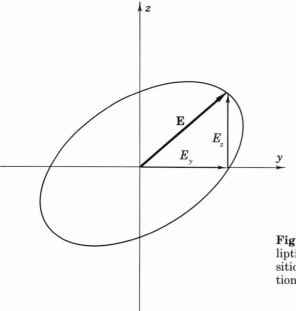

Figure 16.3 Production of elliptic polarization by the composition of two right-angle vibrations of arbitrary phase.

In the study of polarized light, it is necessary to consider certain special cases where the phase difference between the two mutually perpendicular harmonic motions assumes particular values, such as 0, $\pi/2$, π, and so on. In these instances the variation of the resultant vector may be determined readily from the procedure given above.

Case I, $\phi = 0$. Here,

$$E_y = a_y \sin \omega t, \qquad E_z = a_z \sin \omega t \qquad (16.11)$$

Hence, their ratio is

$$\frac{E_z}{E_y} = \frac{a_z}{a_y} = \tan \theta \qquad (16.12)$$

In this case, the resultant vector **E** always lies along a straight line in the first and third quadrants in the y,z plane. (See Fig. 16.4.) The slope of the line depends on the relative amplitudes

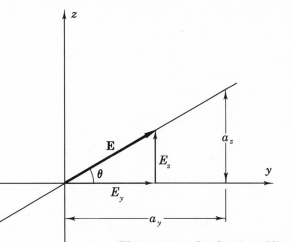

Figure 16.4   Production of linear polarization by the composition of two vibrations which are at right angles which are in phase.

of the two motions and is given by $\tan \theta$. Since the resultant electric vector at a fixed point in space always remains parallel to this line, the wave is said to be linearly polarized.

Case II, $\phi = \pi/2$. For this phase difference, the components may be written as

$$E_y = a_y \sin \omega t, \qquad E_z = a_z \cos \omega t \qquad (16.13)$$

That is,
$$\frac{E_y}{a_y} = \sin \omega t, \qquad \frac{E_z}{a_z} = \cos \omega t \qquad (16.14)$$

Upon squaring and adding, we obtain

$$\frac{E_y^2}{a_y^2} + \frac{E_z^2}{a_z^2} = 1 \qquad (16.15)$$

which is the equation of an ellipse whose axes coincide with the y- and z-axes. The resultant vector **E** therefore traces out an ellipse in the clockwise sense, since, in this example, the z component leads the y component by $\pi/2$. (See Fig. 16.5.) As in the more general case mentioned above, such a wave is said to *elliptically polarized.*

If, in addition, the amplitudes of the two motions are equal— i.e., $a_y = a_z$—then the resultant vector **E** sweeps out a circle

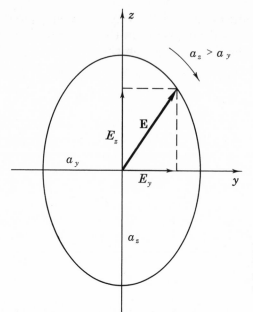

Figure 16.5 Elliptic polarization by composition of two mutually perpendicular oscillations; $\pi/2$ out of phase.

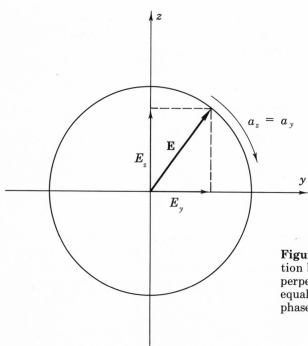

Figure 16.6 Circular polarization by the composition of two perpendicular vibrations having equal amplitudes but differing in phase by $\pi/2$.

and the wave is said to be circularly polarized. (See Fig. 16.6.)

Case III, $\phi = \pi$. The two components now reduce to

$$E_y = a_y \sin \omega t, \qquad E_z = -a_z \sin \omega t \qquad (16.16)$$

Hence, $$\frac{E_z}{E_y} = -\frac{a_z}{a_y} = -\tan \theta \qquad (16.17)$$

In this case the resultant lies along a straight line which is located in quadrants two and four (Fig. 16.7). This case also represents a linearly polarized wave, except that the vibration direction of the electric vector has been turned through 2θ compared to the situation in Case I.

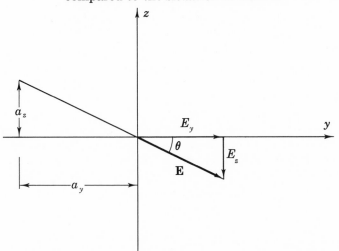

Figure 16.7 Linear polarization by the composition of two perpendicular vibrations differing in phase by π.

The preceding discussion shows that the resultant of two mutually perpendicular simple harmonic motions cannot be zero for all instants of time. The results of the special cases treated above are summarized in the following table:

Phase difference between components	Frequencies of components	Amplitudes of components	Path of resultant	State of polarization
0	Equal	Unequal	Straight line	Linear
$\pi/2$	Equal	Unequal	Ellipse	Elliptic
$\pi/2$	Equal	Equal	Circle	Circular
π	Equal	Unequal	Straight line	Linear

16.4   Huygens-Fresnel-Kirchhoff Principle

In general, the solution of problems dealing with (1) the propagation of an electromagnetic wave in a nonhomogeneous medium, (2) the modifications which arise at boundaries between media, and (3) the effects brought about by the insertion of obstacles or apertures in the path of a wave are accompanied by considerable mathematical and physical difficulties. However, it is possible to treat many cases of practical importance by a scheme first suggested by Huygens in the seventeenth century. For our purposes it is not feasible to present a rigorous proof in defense of the so-called Huygens' principle. We shall state the principle and apply it to a few elementary problems dealing with the modifications of a plane or spherical wave front incident upon plane or spherical boundaries separating nonabsorbing and homogeneous media.

In Fig. 16.8, let the closed spherical surface represent a wave front originating from a point source S located at the center of the sphere. Then regard each element of area, such as dA, as a source of secondary waves which are sent out in all directions.

The amplitude of the disturbance at a field point, such as P, is to be calculated by combining the effects at P due to second-

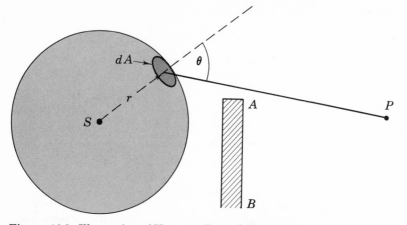

Figure 16.8 Illustration of Huygens-Fresnel-Kirchhoff principle. The wave from S will reach the imaginary surface drawn concentrically about S. Points of this wave surface are regarded as secondary sources. The behavior of the wave beyond the spherical surface is predicted by superposing the contribution from each secondary source.

ary waves originating from all elements of the wave front, with
due regard to their amplitudes and phases. In applying the principle of superposition to the waves which reach P, it is necessary to include the following features, dealing with the variation
in amplitude of the secondary waves originating from dA :

1. The amplitude of the secondary wave must be assumed to
vary with direction in accordance with the factor $(1 + \cos \theta)$,
where θ is the angle between the normal to the surface element
dA and the line joining dA to the point P. This is the so-called
obliquity factor, which was deduced by Kirchhoff from the wave
equation. This factor implies that each element radiates primarily in the forward direction, but not exclusively in that direction. There is no radiation in the backward direction ($\theta = \pi$).

2. The amplitude of the secondary wave is directly proportional to the area of the element dA and inversely proportional
to the distance of dA from the field point P.

This principle plays an important role in calculating the intensity at the point P when, for instance, an obstacle, such as
AB, is placed between the source S and the field point P.

Our immediate interest lies in the use of the principle in determining the progress in time of a given plane or spherical wave
front in a homogeneous medium. The method may be illustrated
by applying it to a plane wave front MN which is propagated in
the x direction. (See Fig. 16.9.) In the diagram, the trace MN
shows the location of the plane wave front at the time t_0. Tak-

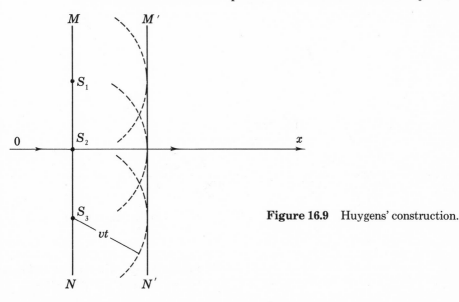

Figure 16.9   Huygens' construction.

ing S_1, S_2, and S_3 as hypothetical secondary sources on the plane wave front, we draw a series of spherical wavelets with a common radius vt, where v is the speed of propagation. The plane through $M'N'$ situated at a distance vt from MN and parallel to it is an envelope of the system of secondary wavelets and locates the position of the original wave front MN at the time $(t_0 + t)$. A similar construction enables us to predict the location of other types of wave fronts. The procedure gives correct results if the contribution of the secondary waves is confined to points which are tangent to the envelope in the forward direction of propagation.

16.5   Reflection and Refraction at a Plane Boundary

We shall now apply Huygens' principle and with the aid of a construction proceed to show how a reflected and a refracted wave front arise when a plane wave is incident obliquely on a plane surface SS'. In the construction given in Fig. 16.10, OP represents the incident wave front initially $(t = 0)$ as it intersects the surface SS' at the point O. At a later time $t = PQ/v_1$ (v_1 is the phase velocity in medium 1), had there been no change of media the wave front OP would have advanced to RQ. During the

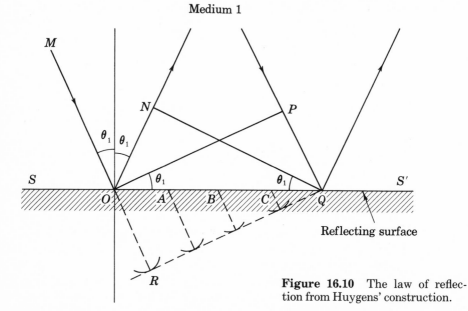

Figure 16.10 The law of reflection from Huygens' construction.

interval $t = 0$ to $t = PQ/v_1$, the surface points $O, A, B, C, \ldots$
were successively disturbed and became secondary sources. The
radii of the various wavelets shown in Fig. 16.10 are drawn at
the time the point P on the wave front has just reached the surface at Q. It is seen that the various secondary waves give rise
to a plane reflected wave front NQ which will move along ON.
Since the triangles POQ and ONQ are congruent, angle POQ
= angle NQO. But these are the angles that the incident ray
MO and the reflected ray ON make with the normal to SS'.
Hence we conclude that the angle of incidence equals the angle
of reflection.

To deduce the law of refraction (see Fig. 16.11) we note that
the radii of the individual wavelets AA', BB', CC' are to be
modified by the ratio v_2/v_1, since in the second medium the

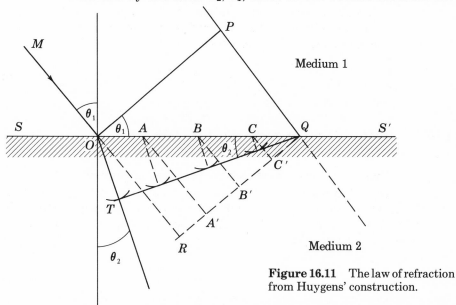

Figure 16.11 The law of refraction
from Huygens' construction.

phase velocity is v_2. (Again the diagram is drawn at the instant
the point P on the incident wave front strikes the surface at Q.
Also it is assumed that $v_2 < v_1$.) Thus the radius of the secondary wave from A is AA' (v_2/v_1), and similarly for the other
sources $B, C, \ldots$. In this case, TQ, the common envelope of the
secondary waves, represents the refracted ray which travels in
the second medium along the ray direction OT, which makes a
smaller angle θ_2 with the normal to the surface.

In the time it takes the point P to advance to the point Q in
medium 1, in medium 2 the point O, initially on the same wave

front, has moved to the point T. Hence $PQ/v_1 = OT/v_2$. But $PQ = OQ \sin \theta_1$ and $OT = OQ \sin \theta_2$; whence

$$\frac{\sin \theta_1}{\sin \theta_2} = \frac{v_1}{v_2} \qquad (16.18)$$

Dividing the numerator and denominator on the right by c, the velocity of light in a vacuum, upon rearrangement we obtain

$$n_1 \sin \theta_1 = n_2 \sin \theta_2 \qquad (16.19)$$

where n_1 and n_2, as defined by c/v_1 and c/v_2 respectively, are the refractive indices of medium 1 and of medium 2 for the particular frequency of the wave. The law of refraction given by (16.18) states that for a pair of homogeneous media the sine of the angle of incidence divided by the sine of the angle of refraction is a constant, independent of the angle of incidence. The constant is by definition the index of medium 2 relative to the index of medium 1. In symbols,

$$\frac{v_1}{v_2} = n_{2,1} = \frac{n_2}{n_1} \qquad (16.20)$$

16.6   Plane Waves at a Spherical Surface

Before proceeding with the problem of tracing reflected or refracted wave fronts having spherical shape, we digress to develop a relation for measuring $1/r$, the curvature of a sphere, in terms of the sagittal length x. (See Fig. 16.12.) From the diagram it follows that

$$r^2 = y^2 + (r - x)^2$$

or
$$x = \frac{y^2}{2r} + \frac{x^2}{2r}$$

If x is small relative to r, then within the allowed approximation

$$x \cong \frac{y^2}{2} \frac{1}{r} \qquad (16.21)$$

Hence, if the sagitta x is sufficiently small, it can be taken as a measure of the reciprocal of the radius.

The change suffered by an incident plane wave front upon reflection or refraction from a single spherical surface may be determined provided the incident, reflected, or refracted ray di-

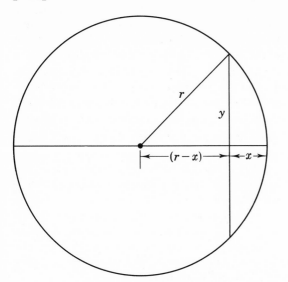

Figure 16.12   Diagram used to derive the sagittal theorem.

rections make small angles with the axis of the system. In Fig. 16.13, the incident plane wave front *MON* is shown at the instant it makes contact with *POQ*, the spherical boundary separating regions with refractive indices n_1 and n_2. Let $n_2 > n_1$; then the phase velocity v_2 in medium 2 is less than v_1, the veloc-

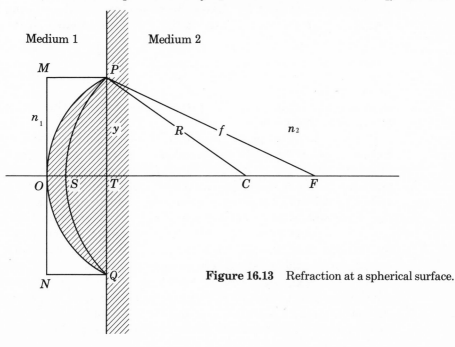

Figure 16.13   Refraction at a spherical surface.

ity in medium 1. In the time the point M on the incident wave front covers the distance MP in medium 1, the disturbance from O has reached the point S entirely in medium 2. (In the absence of the boundary, the wave front MON would have advanced to PTQ in the time interval in question.) The curved trace PSQ is taken as the refracted wave front. Its shape is assumed to be spherical. This is valid if the refracting spherical surface POQ is sufficiently small so that the sagitta relation given by (16.21) is a good approximation.

To determine the radius of the refracted front, we equate the time required for the incident front to advance from M to P while the refracted front goes from O to S—that is,

$$\frac{MP}{v_1} = \frac{OS}{v_2}$$

Multiplying each side by c, the speed of the waves in vacuum, and replacing OS by $(OT - ST)$, we have

$$n_1 MP = n_2(OT - ST)$$

or, since $MP = OT$,

$$(n_2 - n_1)\,OT = n_2 ST$$

The sagittas OT and ST have the same semichord y. Using (16.21), we can replace the sagittas by the corresponding curvatures and obtain

$$\frac{n_2}{f} = \frac{(n_2 - n_1)}{R} \tag{16.22}$$

where f is the radius of the refracted wave, and R is the radius of the refracting surface.

It is seen that the plane wave front incident upon the spherical boundary is converted into a spherical wave front as a result of refraction. If $n_2 > n_1$, the refracted wave fronts converge upon the center F and the refracted rays are brought to a focus at F. The system consisting of a series of incident and refracted rays and wave fronts is sketched in Fig. 16.14. The distance OF is the focal length f of the refracting surface and is defined as the distance from the pole O to the point where rays parallel to the axis of the spherical cap are brought to a focus.

For electromagnetic waves which have a wavelength corresponding to that emitted by a sodium light source ($\lambda = 5.89 \times 10^{-7}$ m), we may take $n_1 = 1.00$ and $n_2 = 1.50$ if the refracting surface is the boundary between air and glass. From these data,

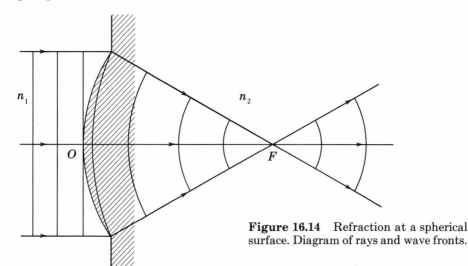

Figure 16.14   Refraction at a spherical surface. Diagram of rays and wave fronts.

the focal length f, as computed from (16.22), is found to be $3R$.

The case of reflection may be treated in a similar fashion by the use of the construction in Fig. 16.15, which shows a plane wave front MLN incident on a concave spherical reflector MON.

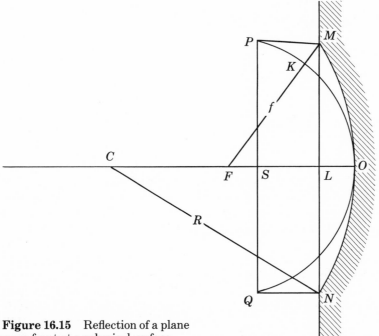

Figure 16.15   Reflection of a plane wave front at a spherical surface.

Here the incident wave front advances from L to O while the reflected front proceeds from M to K. As in the previous illustrations, the figure is grossly exaggerated. Within the accuracy of the sagittal formula, $KM \cong PM$. We carry out the rest of the calculation by noting that $OL = KM \cong PM = SL$, or $SL = (OS - OL)$. Hence, by the application of (16.21),

$$\frac{2}{R} = \frac{1}{f} \tag{16.23}$$

where R is the radius of the concave mirror and f is its focal length.

16.7   Spherical Wave Fronts at a Spherical Surface

Let a small source in Fig. 16.16 be located at A and let the spherical wave front diverging from A advance toward the spherical boundary KOJ. The incident front MON, whose radius

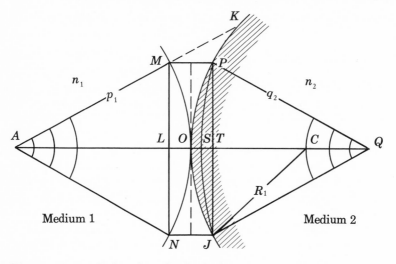

Figure 16.16   Refraction of spherical waves at a spherical surface.

is p_1, is shown touching the refracting surface on the axis. As before, $n_2 > n_1$, so that as the incident wave proceeds from M to K in medium 1, the refracted wave goes from O to S in medium 2. With small error MK is equal to MP, and a refracted front PSJ with radius q_2 is formed and appears to converge toward the point Q. Equating optical paths (geometrical length times index) as before, we have

$$n_1 MP = n_2 OS$$

Expressing the lengths in terms of the sagittal distances LO, OT, and ST, after rearrangement and simplification, we obtain

$$n_1 OL + n_2 ST = (n_2 - n_1)OT$$

or
$$\frac{n_1}{p_1} + \frac{n_2}{q_2} = \frac{(n_2 - n_1)}{R_1} \tag{16.24}$$

In (16.24), p_1 is the distance (in medium 1) of the source from the boundary, q_2 is the distance (in medium 2) of the image of the source also measured from the boundary, and R_1 is the radius of the surface which separates the source medium of index n_1 from the image medium of index n_2.

By adopting a sign convention it is possible to have a single formula apply to all cases of refraction from a single spherical surface. Locating an imaginary origin of coordinates at O (Fig. 16.16), we affix the positive sign to distances measured to the right of O along the axis AQ and the negative sign to distances to the left of O. When the sign convention is used, quantities in the general formula as well as numerical values substituted for them must be made subject to the convention. With this agreement regarding signs, (16.24) is written as

$$\frac{n_2}{q_2} - \frac{n_1}{p_1} = \frac{(n_2 - n_1)}{R_1} \tag{16.25}$$

When the wave front in the second medium emerges into a third medium—the boundary between them being spherical—(16.25) may be applied to the refraction at the second surface. The image distance q_2 now serves as the source distance p_2 for the second refraction. If q_3 is the image distance in medium 3 of index n_3, and if R_2 is the radius of curvature of the second boundary, the source distance p_1 and the final image distance q_3 are related by

$$\frac{n_3}{q_3} - \frac{n_1}{p_1} = \frac{(n_2 - n_1)}{R_1} - \frac{(n_2 - n_3)}{R_2} \tag{16.26}$$

The above relation may also be derived readily from fundamental considerations by referring to the diagram in Fig. 16.17 and by simplifying $n_1(AC) + n_3(CE) = n_2(BD)$, which is the condition on optical paths if BD is small.

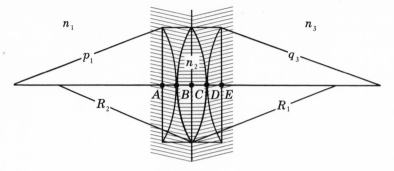

n_1 n_3

p_1 q_3

n_2

R_2 R_1

A B C D E

Figure 16.17   Two successive refractions of spherical waves.

In particular, if $n_1 = n_3 = 1.00$, then (16.26) reduces to

$$\frac{1}{q_3} - \frac{1}{p_1} = (n_2 - 1)\left[\frac{1}{R_1} - \frac{1}{R_2}\right] \qquad (16.27)$$

which is the standard formula applicable to thin glass lenses located in air, n_2 being the index of the glass for the particular wavelength in question.

16.8   Boundary Conditions for Reflection at Normal Incidence

In this section we shall derive expressions for the boundary conditions at reflection for the case of normal incidence by considering the case of propagation of plane waves in homogeneous and isotropic dielectrics. The case of oblique incidence for plane waves may also be treated by the application of boundary conditions to the electric and magnetic field vectors. Though laborious, the method is straightforward and leads to the laws of reflection and refraction of electromagnetic waves at the boundary separating two homogeneous and isotropic media.

When a linearly polarized wave traveling in one dielectric medium is incident normally on the boundary of a second dielectric medium, it gives rise to a reflected as well as to a transmitted wave. It follows from the two circuital relations (14.16) and (14.17) of the electromagnetic field that the tangential components of the vectors **H** and **E** must be continuous at the boundary. (See proofs of boundary conditions in Sections 4.8 and 9.9.) Let the y,z plane constitute the boundary separating the two media of index n_1 and n_2 where $n_2 > n_1$. Let the incident wave strike the boundary from the left with the electric and magnetic vectors parallel to the y- and z-axes respectively. Then the two vectors in the transmitted wave may have these same directions, but in the reflected wave the direction of either the magnetic or the electric vector must be reversed in phase. This reversal is necessary since the Poynting vector in the reflected beam is directed along the negative x-axis. The electric, magnetic, and Poynting vectors in the three waves are shown in Fig. 16.18, where the subscripts i, r, and t refer to the incident, reflected, and transmitted waves. The vectors in the reflected wave are

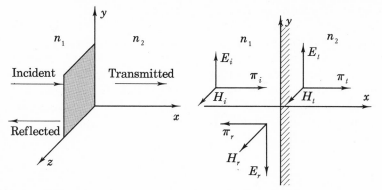

Figure 16.18   Boundary conditions. Reflection at normal incidence.

drawn for the case where $\mathbf{E}_r$ is assumed to be reversed in phase, while $\mathbf{H}_r$ has the same phase as $\mathbf{H}_i$. In the diagram of Fig. 16.18, the three sets of vectors are shown displaced, for clarity. They represent the fields at a particular point on the boundary, at a particular instant of time.

From the statement of the boundary conditions, we may write

$$E_i - E_r = E_t \tag{16.28}$$

$$H_i + H_r = H_t \tag{16.29}$$

Utilizing the relation between the amplitudes of the **H** and **E** vectors as given by (14.48), this equation assumes the form

$$n_1 E_i + n_1 E_r = n_2 E_t \tag{16.30}$$

Eliminating E_t between (16.28) and (16.30), we obtain

$$E_r = \frac{(n_2 - n_1)}{(n_2 + n_1)} E_i \tag{16.31}$$

which gives the relation between the magnitudes of the vectors in the incident and reflected waves. For the case where the wave passes from a region of index n_1 to a region of index n_2, where $n_2 > n_1$, (16.31) predicts that the reflected wave suffers a phase change of π radians, since the sign of E_r is as assumed in Fig. 16.18. The phase of H_r is not changed in this case. Thus, when light waves travel from air to glass ($n_2 > n_1$), the electric vector in the reflected wave will be 180° out of phase relative to the electric vector in the incident beam. In terms of speeds of propagation, a phase change occurs on reflection when the speed in the second medium is smaller than that in the first.

Relation (16.31) also shows that when $n_1 > n_2$, the sign of E_r is negative, so that in this case the direction of E_r would be opposite to that assumed in Fig. 16.18. Therefore, the electric vector in the reflected wave is in phase with that in the incident wave when the wave passes from an optically more dense to an optically less dense medium, e.g., from glass to water. In this case, it is the phase of H_r that is reversed.

Superposition, Reflection, and Refraction of Waves: **Problems**

16.1   Given three simple harmonic motions of equal amplitude A and the same frequency. The motions are parallel to the y-axis and are described by

$$y_1 = A \sin \omega t$$
$$y_2 = A \sin (\omega t + \phi)$$
$$y_3 = A \sin (\omega t + 2\phi)$$

Find the smallest value of ϕ for which the resultant amplitude of the three motions is: (a) $3A$, (b) A, (c) zero.

16.2   Two sets of plane waves traveling along the x-axis are described by

$$E_y = 3 \sin \frac{2\pi}{T}\left(t - \frac{x}{v}\right) \quad \text{and} \quad E_z = 4 \sin \frac{2\pi}{T}\left(t + \frac{x}{v} + \frac{T}{4}\right)$$

where E_y and E_z represent electric fields parallel to the y- and z-axis respectively. By an analytical or a graphical solution, describe the behavior in time of the resultant electric field at $x = 0$.

16.3   Three microwave sources, S_1, S_2, and S_3, are arranged along a straight line. The sources oscillate in phase and the wavelength of the radiation emitted by each source is 4.0 cm. The electric vector in each wave is perpendicular to the plane of the diagram. The sources are so adjusted that the amplitude of each wave train arriving at the field point P is 5 μv/m. The distances of the point P from each of the three sources are given by $S_1P = 24$ cm, $S_2P = 49$ cm, and $S_3P = 73$ cm.

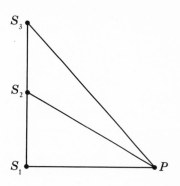

(a) At the point P, what is the phase difference between the wave trains emitted by S_1 and S_2?

(b) Calculate the resultant amplitude at the point P, considering the combined effect of the three sources.

16.4   Two microwave sources S_1 and S_2 emit continuous wave trains which have the same frequency and the same amplitude $E_0 = 4.0 \, \mu$v/m.

At the field point P, located on the perpendicular bisector of the line joining S_1 and S_2, the electric vector in each wave is perpendicular to the plane of the diagram.

(a) If the resultant amplitude at P is equal to the amplitude of either wave, what is the phase difference between S_1 and S_2?

(b) Assume that the phase difference between S_1 and S_2 is continuously variable from 0 to 2π. Write an expression for the square of the resultant amplitude at P for any phase difference ϕ ($0 \leq \phi \leq 2\pi$). Also draw a graph showing the intensity variation at P as a function of ϕ.

16.5   Consider two perpendicular vibrations:

$$x = A \sin \omega t$$
$$y = B \sin (\omega t + \phi)$$

Describe as completely as you can the resultant vibration if
   (a) $\phi = 0$ and $A = B$;
   (b) $\phi = \pi/2$ and $A = B$;
   (c) $\phi = \pi/2$ and $A \neq B$;
   (d) $\phi = \pi$ and $A \neq B$.

16.6   In each case below, consider the resultant of the given pair of wave trains. Specify the type of polarization and describe the orientation of the electric vector with respect to the coordinate axes as completely as possible.

(a) $E_y = E_0 \sin (\omega t - kx)$,
     $E_z = E_0 \cos (\omega t - kx)$.

(b) $E_y = E_0 \sin (\omega t - kx)$,
     $E_z = E_0 \sin [\omega t - kx + (\pi/6)]$.

(c) $E_y = E_0 \sin (\omega t - kx)$,
     $E_z = -E_0 \sin (\omega t - kx)$.

16.7   Two sets of electromagnetic waves traveling in a certain medium along the positive x direction are described by:

$$E_y = A \sin 2\pi \left(\frac{t}{T} - \frac{x}{\lambda_1} \right) \quad \text{and} \quad E_z = B \sin 2\pi \left(\frac{t}{T} - \frac{x}{\lambda_2} \right)$$

where E_y and E_z represent the magnitudes of the electric vector parallel to the y- and z-axes respectively, and where λ_1 and λ_2 are the wavelengths associated with the y and z wave trains.

(a) In a vacuum, the wavelength of either wave is equal to 4.0 cm. If the refractive indices of the medium for the wavelength λ_1 and λ_2 are 1.60 and 1.50 respectively, calculate the phase difference between the two waves at $x = 10$ cm.

(b) At $x = 30$ cm the phase difference between the two waves is $3\pi/2$. Describe the path followed by the tip of the resultant electric vector in a plane perpendicular to the x-axis at $x = 30$ cm.

16.8   Two microwave sources S_1 and S_2 which oscillate in phase emit continuous wave trains having the same frequency and the same amplitude. At the field point P, located on the perpendicular bisector of the line joining S_1 and S_2, the electric vector in each wave is perpendicular to the plane of the diagram and has peak amplitude $E_0 = 5.0$ $\mu v/m$.

(a) If the phase difference between S_1 and S_2 is continuously variable from 0 to 2π, calculate the phase difference necessary to produce a *resultant* peak amplitude at P of 5 $\mu v/m$.

(b) The antenna for source S_2 is rotated so that its electric field vector lies in the plane of the paper at P while S_1 continues to produce an electric vector perpendicular to the plane of the paper. With S_1 and S_2 in phase, what is the resultant peak amplitude at P? Is this resultant peak amplitude a function of phase difference between S_1 and S_2?

16.9 Two sources S_1 and S_2, located on the y-axis as shown, emit waves in the direction of a receiver R located on the x-axis. The wavelength of the waves is 0.10 m. The sources oscillate in phase and the electric vector at R due to each source is normal to the x,y plane.

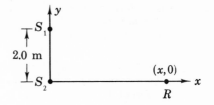

(a) What is the resultant amplitude at R when the path difference $S_1R - S_2R = 0.033$ m? Assume that the amplitude of the wave due to each source alone is 15 µv/m.

(b) As one moves along the x-axis from infinity toward S_2 one encounters a series of maxima. Obtain an expression for x_n, the x coordinate corresponding to the nth intensity maximum. Label the intensity maximum at infinity as the zeroeth fringe.

16.10 The axes of four dipole detectors D_1, D_2, D_3, and D_4 are placed at right angles to a straight line, the distance between adjacent dipoles being d. Each detector is tuned to the same wavelength λ and receives linearly polarized electromagnetic waves from a single distant source such as a radio star.

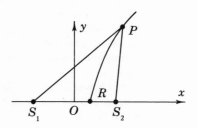

The electric vector in the waves and the dipole axes are perpendicular to the line joining the detectors. The outputs of the individual detectors are combined without the introduction of additional phase differences, the combined response being proportional to the resultant of the wave amplitudes at the individual dipoles.

(a) For any angle θ between 0° and 90° write an expression for the difference in phase between the wave trains arriving at a pair of adjacent detectors.

(b) Consider the special case where $\lambda = 3d/2$ and $\theta = 60°$. What is the magnitude of the resultant amplitude assuming that A represents the wave amplitude at each of the four detectors? Include a diagram showing how the resultant amplitude due to the four individual waves is obtained.

16.11 Two dipole sources S_1 and S_2 are 60 cm apart in air and are situated on the x-axis equidistant from the origin O. The sources oscillate in phase at the common frequency of 5.0×10^9 cycles/sec.

In the x,y plane, the curved path RP is chosen so that for any point on the curve such as P, the path difference $(PS_1 - PS_2)$ is a constant equal to C.

(a) Determine the value of C if the point R is located on the x-axis 9.75 cm from the origin.

(b) The speed of the emitted waves is 3.00×10^{10} cm/sec and the electric vectors in the waves are parallel to the z-axis but have different amplitudes of 4.0 and 3.0 μv/m at the point P. What is the magnitude of the resultant electric field at P? Include an appropriate diagram to show how the resultant is obtained.

16.12   Somewhat as in radio navigation, two antennas A_1 and A_2, 0.12 km apart, are driven by a master oscillator so that the waves emitted by them are 180° out of phase.

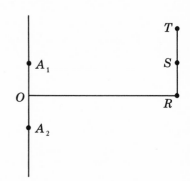

(a) Consider a receiver on a ship at sea located at R at a distance of 180 km from O, the midpoint of the line joining the two antennas. Assume that linearly polarized continuous wave trains of equal amplitude and frequency are emitted from A_1 and A_2 with the electric vector normal to the plane of the diagram. Is the receiver response (resultant electric field) at R a maximum or a minimum?

(b) The ship sails along RT, a line parallel to the line joining the antennas. S and T are the next two points where the receiver response is the same as that observed at R. If RT is 6 km, calculate the wavelength of the radio waves.

(In the actual case of radio navigation, pulses are emitted from pairs of antennas and the observer's position is determined by the difference in the time of arrival of signals.)

16.13 S is a source of microwaves (wavelength equal to 0.10 m) which is mounted on top of a tower TS (12 m high) located at the edge of a lake. The waves emitted from S are polarized with the electric vector parallel to the surface of the water. A boat B, whose receiving antenna R is also located 12 m above the surface of the water, is moving toward S. As the boat approaches S from a large distance, the signal received by R increases and reaches a maximum for the first time. Considering superposi-

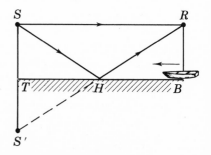

tion effects between the direct beam *SR* and the reflected beam *SHR*, calculate the magnitude of *TB*, the distance between the boat and the tower under this circumstance. For microwaves, the refractive index of the water is greater than that of air.

16.14 The reflecting power of a boundary surface is defined as the ratio of the reflected to the incident intensity. Express the intensities involved in terms of the corresponding Poynting vectors and obtain an expression for the reflecting power at normal incidence in terms of the indices of refraction of the media on either side of the boundary.

16.15 Extend the calculations given in Section 16.8 for the case of normal incidence and obtain the formula for the ratio

$$\frac{\text{Amplitude of the transmitted wave}}{\text{Amplitude of the incident wave}}$$

Does the result depend on the polarization of the incident wave? Also prove that in the absence of absorption the power incident on the boundary per unit area is equal to the power carried away by the reflected and transmitted waves.

16.16 A plane monochromatic wave front *AB* is located in air at time t_0. This wave front is incident upon the plane surface of a transparent solid, and at later time t the refracted wave front *A'B'* is as shown. Find the index of refraction of the medium if $AC = 1.5$ cm; $BD = 2.4$ cm; $CA' = 1.2$ cm; $DB' = 0.5$ cm.

16.17 In the diagram, *AB*, *DE*, and *GH* are plane wave fronts in the three media separated by plane parallel boundaries. The speed of the wave in free space is 3.00×10^{10} cm/sec and its frequency is 6.0×10^{14} per sec. The table on page 440 gives the times in seconds required to cover the indicated distances in cm.

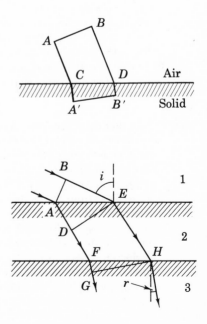

	Medium 1	Medium 2	Medium 3
Distance along ray in cm	$BE = 12.0$	$AD = 9.0$	$FG = 1.6$
Time in seconds to cover the distance	4.0×10^{-10}	4.0×10^{-10}	0.80×10^{-10}

(a) Supply the numerical value of the phase velocity in each of the three media.

(b) Supply the numerical value of the absolute refractive index in each medium.

(c) Apply the law of refraction to each boundary and evaluate the ratio $\sin i/\sin r$, where i is the angle of incidence in medium 1 and r is the angle of refraction in medium 3 (see diagram on page 439).

16.18   The conditions for reflection and refraction of plane waves at a plane boundary separating transparent media of index n_1 and n_2 are given by

$$\theta_1 = \theta_1' \quad \text{and} \quad n_1 \sin \theta_1 = n_2 \sin \theta_2$$

where θ_1, θ_1', and θ_2 are the angles of incidence, reflection, and refraction.

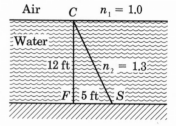

A cork C floats on the surface of a pond whose depth is 12 ft. Its shadow S on the bottom of the pond is 5 ft away from F, the foot of the normal passing through C.

(a) What is the angle between the sun's rays and the surface of the pond? Draw a ray diagram and label all angles.

(b) What is the maximum value of the distance FS as the inclination of the sun's rays changes? Carry out the numerical calculation involved.

16.19   The spherical wave front A_1AA_2 of radius p is incident upon the spherical boundary which separates two media whose indices are n_1 and n_2, with $n_2 > n_1$. The refracted wave front B_1BB_2 has zero curvature.

Using the symbols given in the diagram, write a relation between the distances AB and A_1B_1 and express p in terms of r, n_1, and n_2 utilizing the sagittal relation $1/R = 2x/y^2$.

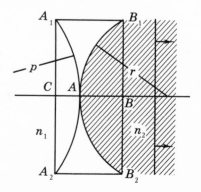

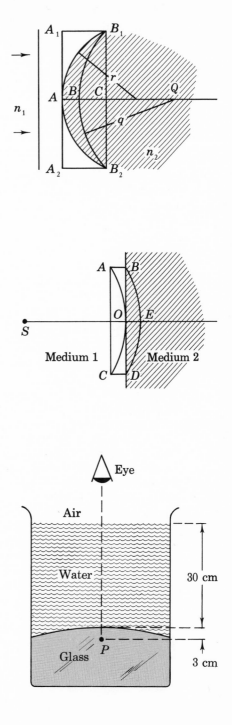

16.20   Plane waves moving in a medium of index n_1 are refracted at the convex surface B_1AB_2 of radius r and pass into a second medium whose index is n_2, $(n_2 > n_1)$. The refracted wave front is B_1BB_2, whose radius of curvature is q.

Using the symbols shown in the diagram, complete the equation

$$n_1\, A_1B_1 =$$

and express q in terms of r, n_1, and n_2, making use of the sagittal relation $1/R = 2x/y^2$.

16.21   Spherical wave fronts originating from a small source S are propagated in medium 1, whose refractive index is 1.2. The wave front AOC is refracted at the plane boundary BD and passes into medium 2, whose index is 1.5.

(a) If $AC = 9.6$ cm and $AB = 0.10$ cm, what is the distance of the source S from the boundary BD?

(b) Determine the distance OE.

(c) What is the radius of curvature of the refracted wave front BED?

16.22   A small object P is embedded in a piece of glass which has a polished convex surface whose radius of curvature is 20 cm. The object is located at a distance of 3 cm below the vertex of the spherical surface. The glass is placed in a jar which is filled with water to a depth of 30 cm above the vertex of the convex surface. What is the apparent distance of the object below the surface of the water? Assume the eye is located in air on the axis of the curved surface. (Index of glass 1.50, index of water 1.30.)

Appendix A.
Vector Algebra

A.1   Definitions

A working knowledge of vector analysis is essential to the study of electromagnetism. It is advantageous to utilize vector representations even in an introductory treatment. The following nonrigorous description of definitions and elementary operations includes the rudiments of vector algebra.

Certain physical quantities, after a suitable choice of units, are completely characterized by a numerical magnitude. Such quantities are called *scalars*. Thus density, temperature, and time are scalars. Other quantities, such as velocity, acceleration, and electric intensity, require the specification of magnitude and direction. These are referred to as *vectors* and are geometrically represented by a directed line segment whose length is proportional to the magnitude of the vector. Thus in Fig. A.1, the length OP de-

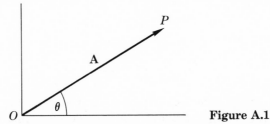

Figure A.1

notes the magnitude of the vector **A**. The end at O is called the origin, while the end at P is called the *terminus* of **A**. The direction of the vector is specified by the angle (here θ) that OP makes with a reference line, while the arrowhead at P designates the

443

sense of the vector. In printed matter, vectors are denoted by a letter in **boldface type** or by a bar or an arrow over the symbol. The magnitude of the vector is indicated by printing the same letter in italics or by placing the symbol within vertical bars or by omitting the bar or the arrow. In this text a vector is represented by a letter in **boldface type**, while its magnitude is indicated by a letter in *italics*.

The symbol $-\mathbf{A}$ represents the negative of the vector $\mathbf{A}$. It has the same length as $\mathbf{A}$ but is drawn in the opposite sense.

Two vectors $\mathbf{A}$ and $\mathbf{B}$ are equal if they possess the same magnitude, direction, and sense.

A.2   Addition and Subtraction of Vectors

Consider the two vectors $\mathbf{A}$ and $\mathbf{B}$, drawn so that the origin of $\mathbf{B}$ is coincident with the terminus of $\mathbf{A}$. (See Fig. A.2.) The third vector $\mathbf{C}$, drawn from the origin of $\mathbf{A}$ to the terminus of $\mathbf{B}$, represents the sum

$$\mathbf{C} = \mathbf{A} + \mathbf{B} \tag{A.1}$$

If the origin of $\mathbf{A}$ is made coincident with the terminus of $\mathbf{B}$, the sum $\mathbf{B} + \mathbf{A}$ will again equal $\mathbf{C}$, since the opposite sides of a parallelogram are equal and parallel.

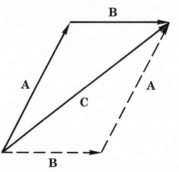

Figure A.2

The difference $\mathbf{D}$ between the vectors $\mathbf{A}$ and $\mathbf{B}$ is defined as the vector which extends from the terminus of $\mathbf{B}$ to the terminus of $\mathbf{A}$ when $\mathbf{A}$ and $\mathbf{B}$ are drawn from the same origin (Fig. A.3). This is equivalent to $\mathbf{A} + (-\mathbf{B})$ and yields the vector

$$\mathbf{D} = \mathbf{A} - \mathbf{B} \tag{A.2}$$

When the vector $\mathbf{A}$ is multiplied by a scalar S, the result $S\mathbf{A}$

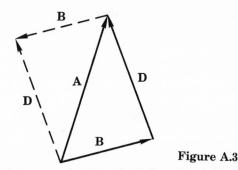

Figure A.3

is a vector S times as long as $\mathbf{A}$; it has the same sense as $\mathbf{A}$ if S is positive, and the opposite sense if S is negative.

A *unit vector* is a vector whose magnitude is unity. In the case of rectangular axes, the unit vectors respectively parallel to the positive x-, y-, and z-axes are denoted by $\mathbf{i}$, $\mathbf{j}$, and $\mathbf{k}$. (See Fig. A.4.) The axes are taken so as to form a right-handed set—that

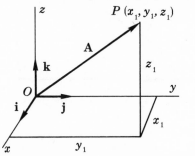

Figure A.4

is, the positive sense of the z-axis is determined by the sense of advance of a right-handed screw, which when rotated about the z-axis through $90°$ carries the x-axis into coincidence with the y-axis.

Let $P(x_1, y_1, z_1)$ represent the terminus of the vector $\mathbf{A}$. Then $\mathbf{A}$ is the sum of the three vectors $\mathbf{i}\,x_1$, $\mathbf{j}\,y_1$, and $\mathbf{k}\,z_1$. Symbolically,

$$\mathbf{A} = \mathbf{i}x_1 + \mathbf{j}y_1 + \mathbf{k}z_1 \qquad (A.3)$$

where x_1, y_1, and z_1 are the components of $\mathbf{A}$. The term component means the projection (with due regard to sign) of the vector along a coordinate axis. Another vector $\mathbf{B}$ (not shown in the diagram), with terminus at $P_2(x_2, y_2, z_2)$, can be represented by

$$\mathbf{B} = \mathbf{i}x_2 + \mathbf{j}y_2 + \mathbf{k}z_2 \qquad (A.4)$$

The sum of these vectors is

$$\mathbf{C} = \mathbf{A} + \mathbf{B} = \mathbf{i}(x_1 + x_2) + \mathbf{j}(y_1 + y_2) + \mathbf{k}(z_1 + z_2) \qquad (A.5)$$

It is seen that the components of $\mathbf{C}$ are obtained by scalar addition of the corresponding components of **A** and **B**. It also follows that if **A** and **B** are equal, their components are equal. Conversely, if the components of two vectors are equal—i.e., if $x_1 = x_2$, $y_1 = y_2$, and $z_1 = z_2$—then the two vectors are equal.

A.3   Scalar or Dot Product

The *scalar* or *dot* product of two vectors **A** and **B**, represented by $\mathbf{A} \cdot \mathbf{B}$, is a scalar defined by

$$\mathbf{A} \cdot \mathbf{B} = AB \cos \theta \qquad (A.6)$$

where θ is the angle between the vectors (Fig. A.5). The quantity $A \cos \theta$ is the component of **A** along **B**. The angle θ is some-

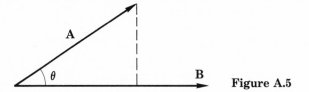

Figure A.5

times written as $(\mathbf{A}, \mathbf{B})$. From the definition in (A.6) it also follows that

$$\mathbf{A} \cdot \mathbf{B} = \mathbf{B} \cdot \mathbf{A} \qquad (A.7)$$

—that is, the scalar product obeys the commutative law. Without proof, it is stated that for the scalar multiplication of vectors, the distributive law

$$\mathbf{A} \cdot (\mathbf{B} + \mathbf{C}) = \mathbf{A} \cdot \mathbf{B} + \mathbf{A} \cdot \mathbf{C} \qquad (A.8)$$

also holds. Also by the commutative law

$$(\mathbf{B} + \mathbf{C}) \cdot \mathbf{A} = \mathbf{B} \cdot \mathbf{A} + \mathbf{C} \cdot \mathbf{A} \qquad (A.9)$$

In (A.6) when $\theta = 90°$, $\mathbf{A} \cdot \mathbf{B} = 0$. Conversely, if the dot product is zero, the two vectors are perpendicular, or else either **A** or **B** is zero. In the equality $\mathbf{A} \cdot \mathbf{B} = \mathbf{A} \cdot \mathbf{C}$, it is not permissible to divide through by **A** and obtain $\mathbf{B} = \mathbf{C}$, since $\mathbf{A} \cdot \mathbf{B}$ can be zero without **A** or **B** being equal to zero.

The scalar product of a vector **A** with itself is the square of the magnitude of **A**—that is, $\mathbf{A} \cdot \mathbf{A} = A^2$.

In consequence of the definition of the dot product, the unit vectors satisfy the following equalities:

$$\mathbf{i} \cdot \mathbf{i} = 1, \qquad \mathbf{j} \cdot \mathbf{j} = 1, \qquad \mathbf{k} \cdot \mathbf{k} = 1 \qquad \text{(A.10)}$$

and $\qquad \mathbf{i} \cdot \mathbf{j} = 0, \qquad \mathbf{j} \cdot \mathbf{k} = 0, \qquad \mathbf{k} \cdot \mathbf{i} = 0$

With the aid of the above relations, we can expand the dot product of the vectors $\mathbf{A}$ and $\mathbf{B}$ in terms of their components. Thus from (A.3) and (A.4)

$$\mathbf{A} \cdot \mathbf{B} = (\mathbf{i}x_1 + \mathbf{j}y_1 + \mathbf{k}z_1) \cdot (\mathbf{i}x_2 + \mathbf{j}y_2 + \mathbf{k}z_2)$$

$$= x_1x_2 + y_1y_2 + z_1z_2 \qquad \text{(A.11)}$$

An example of the use of the dot product is encountered in computing the work done by a force. If $\mathbf{F}$ represents the force acting on a body, and if $d\mathbf{l}$ is a vector displacement of the body, then the increment of work done is given by $dW = \mathbf{F} \cdot d\mathbf{l}$. Again, in computing the volume v of an oblique cylinder of slant height h and base area a, we may use the dot product $v = \mathbf{h} \cdot \mathbf{a}$, where the vector $\mathbf{a}$ has the magnitude of the area but is drawn normally to it. We note that the work done dW and the volume v are scalars.

A.4   Vector Product

The *cross* or *vector product* of the two vectors $\mathbf{A}$ and $\mathbf{B}$ is defined as a third vector $\mathbf{C}$ which is perpendicular to both $\mathbf{A}$ and $\mathbf{B}$ and has the magnitude $AB \sin \theta$. In symbols,

$$\mathbf{C} = \mathbf{A} \times \mathbf{B} \qquad \text{(A.12)}$$

$$C = AB \sin \theta = AB \sin (\mathbf{A}, \mathbf{B}) \qquad \text{(A.13)}$$

As before, $(\mathbf{A}, \mathbf{B})$ represents the angle $\theta (\theta < \pi)$ between $\mathbf{A}$ and $\mathbf{B}$. As shown in Fig. A.6, $\mathbf{A}$ and $\mathbf{B}$ determine a plane and their

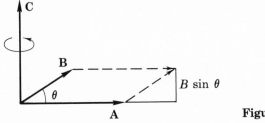

Figure A.6

vector product C is perpendicular to this plane. The sense is determined by the sense of advance of a right-handed screw which is rotated about C so as to bring A into coincidence with B. The angle through which A is rotated must be the smaller of the two angles ($\theta < \pi$) between A and B.

Geometrically, $AB \sin \theta$ represents the area of the parallelogram whose sides are A and B, and whose altitude is $B \sin \theta$.

The cross product does not obey the commutation law—that is, $A \times B \neq B \times A$—since the rotation which carries B into A reverses the sense of C although the magnitude of C remains unaltered. Therefore,

$$A \times B = -B \times A \tag{A.14}$$

If $\theta = 0$ or π, A is parallel to B and $\sin \theta = 0$, so that

$$A \times B = 0 \tag{A.15}$$

Conversely, if (A.15) is satisfied, either one of the vectors is zero or else the vectors have the same or opposite sense.

When the definition of the cross product is applied to the unit vectors in the rectangular system, the result is

$$i \times i = 0, \quad j \times j = 0, \quad k \times k = 0$$

$$i \times j = k, \quad j \times k = i, \quad k \times i = j \tag{A.16}$$

The above relations make it possible to expand the cross product of two vectors in terms of their rectangular components. Thus from (A.3) and (A.4), and by utilizing the identities in (A.16), we obtain

$$A \times B = i(y_1 z_2 - z_1 y_2)$$
$$+ j(z_1 x_2 - x_1 z_2) + k(x_1 y_2 - y_1 x_2) \tag{A.17}$$

The above expansion is readily obtained from the determinental form

$$A \times B = \begin{vmatrix} i & j & k \\ x_1 & y_1 & z_1 \\ x_2 & y_2 & z_2 \end{vmatrix} \tag{A.18}$$

As an example of the use of the vector cross product, consider the torque exerted by a force F applied at a point P in a rigid body. If O is a fixed point in the body, the point P is located by drawing the vector r from O to P. The force F gives rise to a torque T about an axis through O. The vector repre-

senting the torque is normal to the plane of **r** and **F**. The three
vectors are related by $\mathbf{T} = \mathbf{r} \times \mathbf{F}$.

As a second example, also from mechanics, we quote the for-
mula $\mathbf{v} = \omega \times \mathbf{r}$, where ω represents the angular velocity of a
rotating body, **r** is a vector which locates a point P in the body
relative to an origin, and **v** is the linear velocity of P.

As a third illustration, we cite the expression for the magnetic
force—namely, $\mathbf{f} = q\mathbf{v} \times \mathbf{B}$. Here **f** is the force exerted on a
point charge q which moves with a velocity **v** in a magnetic field
of induction **B**.

A.5   Line Integral

In Fig. A.7, let $\mathbf{F}_i$ be a vector which is defined at every point P_i
of the curve AB. Divide the curve AB into n segments each of
length Δl_i and form the sum

$$\sum_{i=1}^{i=n} \mathbf{F}_i \cdot \Delta \mathbf{l}_i$$

where $\Delta \mathbf{l}_i$ is a vector which joins the points P_{i+1} and P_i and

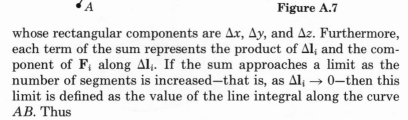

Figure A.7

whose rectangular components are Δx, Δy, and Δz. Furthermore,
each term of the sum represents the product of $\Delta \mathbf{l}_i$ and the component of $\mathbf{F}_i$ along $\Delta \mathbf{l}_i$. If the sum approaches a limit as the
number of segments is increased—that is, as $\Delta \mathbf{l}_i \to 0$—then this
limit is defined as the value of the line integral along the curve
AB. Thus

$$\lim_{\Delta l \to 0} \sum_{i=1}^{n} \mathbf{F}_i \cdot \Delta \mathbf{l}_i = \int_A^B \mathbf{F} \cdot d\mathbf{l} = \int_A^B F_l \, dl \qquad (A.19)$$

where F_l is the component of **F** in the direction of the infinitesimal vector $d\mathbf{l}$. In general, the value of the integral depends on the path as well as on the end points A and B.

Of the various types of line integrals which may be defined, the one in (A.19), involving the dot product of a vector $\mathbf{F}$ with a displacement $d\mathbf{l}$, finds many uses in physical problems. For instance, the work done when a force $\mathbf{F}$ acts along a specified path from the point A to the point B is represented by

$$\int_A^B \mathbf{F} \cdot d\mathbf{l}$$

Another example is found in electrostatics, where the vector is the electrostatic field intensity $\mathbf{E}$ and where the line integral

$$\int_A^B \mathbf{E} \cdot d\mathbf{l}$$

represents the potential difference between the two points. In the last example the value of the line integral is independent of the path, while in the case of mechanical work the line integral does not necessarily possess this property.

A.6   Surface Integral

Consider a surface S. Divide the surface into elements of area $\Delta A_1, \Delta A_2, \ldots, \Delta A_n$ by curves which are the intersections with S of the planes $x = $ Constant, $y = $ Constant. The areal elements are represented by vectors $\Delta \mathbf{A}_1, \Delta \mathbf{A}_2, \ldots, \Delta \mathbf{A}_3$ whose magnitude is equal to the area and whose direction is that of the normal to

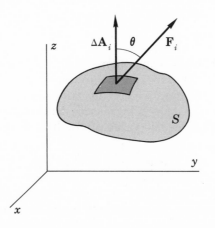

Figure A.8

the area. If the element is a part of a closed surface, the outward drawn normal is taken as positive. If the surface element belongs to an open surface, the positive sense of the normal is that of the advance of a right-handed screw which is rotated (about the normal as an axis) in the sense in which the periphery of the area is described. Thus, the positive sense of the normal is determined only if the positive sense of tracing the periphery is specified.

Let $\mathbf{F}$ denote a vector which is defined at each point of S. Let $\mathbf{F}_i$ denote the vector at some point in ΔA_i and form the sum of n scalar products

$$\sum_{i=1}^{n} \mathbf{F}_i \cdot \Delta \mathbf{A}_i$$

If this sum approaches a limit as the number of elements of area is increased—that is, as $\Delta A_i \to 0$—then the limit is defined as the value of the surface integral of $\mathbf{F}$ over the surface S. Thus

$$\lim_{\Delta A \to 0} \sum_{i=1}^{n} \mathbf{F} \cdot \Delta \mathbf{A}_i = \int_S \mathbf{F} \cdot d\mathbf{A} = \int_S F \cos \theta \, dA \qquad \text{(A.20)}$$

where $(F \cos \theta)$ is the component of $\mathbf{F}$ in the direction of the infinitesimal vector $d\mathbf{A}$.

The surface integral of a vector is called the *flux of* $\mathbf{F}$ through the surface. If the vector $\mathbf{F}$ is the product of the density of a fluid by its velocity, then $\mathbf{F} \cdot d\mathbf{A}$ is the mass of fluid crossing the element of surface dA per second, and the integral represents the mass of fluid passing through the whole surface S per second. Fluxes of electric intensity and magnetic induction are important quantities in the study of electromagnetic fields and are defined by surface integrals.

A.7 The Gradient

It is understood that functions which represent quantities of physical interest are single-valued and continuous, and possess continuous derivatives. The function f is said to be a *scalar point function* of position in space if every triad of positional coordinates x, y, z, defines a scalar number f. Physical quantities such as density, temperature, and potential are described by scalar functions. The region of space over which f is defined is called a *scalar field*. On the other hand, the function **f** is said to be a *vector function* of position if it associates a vector with each point x, y, z of space. A space of this sort is called a *vector field*. A common example is the gravitational force field. Regions surrounding charges and currents also represent force fields.

In this section we shall describe a differential operator which makes it possible to associate a vector field with a scalar field. If V is a scalar function at a point (x, y, z), then its value $(V + dV)$ at the point $(x + \Delta x, y + \Delta y, z + \Delta z)$ may be determined from the total differential

$$dV = \frac{\partial V}{\partial x}\,dx + \frac{\partial V}{\partial y}\,dy + \frac{\partial V}{\partial z}\,dz \qquad (A.21)$$

where the partial derivative $\partial V/\partial x$ indicates that the function V is to be differentiated with respect to x, with y and z considered to be constants. Similarly, in evaluating $\partial V/\partial y$ and $\partial V/\partial z$, the differentiation is carried out with respect to y or z, in each case with the other pair of coordinates treated as constants. The infinitesimal vector displacement between the two points may be written as

$$d\mathbf{l} = \mathbf{i}\,dx + \mathbf{j}\,dy + \mathbf{k}\,dz \qquad (A.22)$$

Next we define a quantity known as the gradient of V, which is denoted either as **grad** V or as $\boldsymbol{\nabla} V$. (The symbol $\boldsymbol{\nabla} V$ is read "del V.") The gradient is a differential operator (A.29) and

$$\boldsymbol{\nabla} V = \mathbf{i}\,\frac{\partial V}{\partial x} + \mathbf{j}\,\frac{\partial V}{\partial y} + \mathbf{k}\,\frac{\partial V}{\partial z} \qquad (A.23)$$

$\boldsymbol{\nabla} V$ is a vector whose components are the three partial derivatives shown in (A.21). The scalar product of the two vectors given by (A.22) and (A.23) is seen to be

$$\boldsymbol{\nabla} V \cdot d\mathbf{l} = \frac{\partial V}{\partial x}\,dx + \frac{\partial V}{\partial y}\,dy + \frac{\partial V}{\partial z}\,dz = dV \qquad (A.24)$$

where the second equality follows from (A.21).

For a given magnitude of $d\mathbf{l}$, dV, the change in V, is greatest when the cosine of the angle between $\boldsymbol{\nabla} V$ and $d\mathbf{l}$ is greatest— that is, when $d\mathbf{l}$ is in the same direction as $\boldsymbol{\nabla} V$. Therefore, $\boldsymbol{\nabla} V$ is a vector in the direction of the greatest space rate of change of V.

To obtain an intuitive feeling for the gradient, let $V(x, y, z)$ be the scalar function that is a measure of the potential energy of a small mass m at points in the field of a concentrated mass M

situated at the origin O. At the point P (see Fig. A.9), the potential energy of m is given by

$$V = \frac{CMm}{\sqrt{x^2 + y^2 + z^2}} \qquad (A.25)$$

where C is a constant and the distance $r = \sqrt{x^2 + y^2 + z^2}$ is

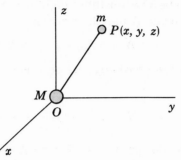

Figure A.9

measured from the origin O. Here V represents a scalar field. By the application of (A.23), we find

$$\nabla V = -\left(\mathbf{i}\frac{CMm}{r^2} \cdot \frac{x}{r} + \mathbf{j}\frac{CMm}{r^2} \cdot \frac{y}{r} + \mathbf{k}\frac{CMm}{r^2} \cdot \frac{z}{r} \right) \qquad (A.26)$$

The right-hand side is a vector $\mathbf{F}$ whose components are recognized as the cartesian components of the gravitational force of attraction between m and M. Hence, we may write

$$\mathbf{F} = -\nabla V = \mathbf{i}F_x + \mathbf{j}F_y + \mathbf{k}F_z \qquad (A.27)$$

This example shows that the gradient of the gravitational potential is the gravitational force. It also illustrates how a vector field may be associated with a scalar function. Note that the components F_x, F_y, and F_z are themselves functions of position in space, and that the symbol ∇ is not a vector itself but a symbol which indicates that certain partial differentiations are to be performed on a scalar function.

It is now possible to state under what conditions the line integral of a vector over a closed path vanishes. The requirement is that the vector be derivable from a scalar point function by taking the gradient of the scalar. Thus, in the gravitational field, $\oint \mathbf{F} \cdot d\mathbf{l} = 0$, since $\mathbf{F}$ is $-\mathbf{grad}\ V$.

A.8   The Divergence

Let $\mathbf{A}\,(x, y, z)$ be a vector function of position. In terms of its cartesian components $\mathbf{A}$ may be written as

$$\mathbf{A} = \mathbf{i}\,A_x + \mathbf{j}\,A_y + \mathbf{k}\,A_z \tag{A.28}$$

As we said in the preceding section, the differential operator $\boldsymbol{\nabla}$ is defined by

$$\boldsymbol{\nabla} \equiv \mathbf{i}\,\frac{\partial}{\partial x} + \mathbf{j}\,\frac{\partial}{\partial y} + \mathbf{k}\,\frac{\partial}{\partial z} \tag{A.29}$$

If we form the dot product of $\boldsymbol{\nabla}$ with $\mathbf{A}$ we obtain a scalar function known as the divergence of $\mathbf{A}$, which is usually written as div $\mathbf{A}$ or $\boldsymbol{\nabla} \cdot \mathbf{A}$. Thus

$$\boldsymbol{\nabla} \cdot \mathbf{A} = \frac{\partial A_x}{\partial x} + \frac{\partial A_y}{\partial y} + \frac{\partial A_z}{\partial z} \tag{A.30}$$

This quantity has important applications in hydrodynamics and in the theory of electricity. If we consider a closed surface in a region where there is mass flow of a fluid, the divergence represents the mass of fluid which flows out of this surface per unit time in excess of that which flows into the surface. Similarly, in electrostatics it represents the flux of the electric field leaving a closed surface in excess of that which enters it.

A.9   The Curl or Rotation

The curl of $\mathbf{A}$, denoted by curl $\mathbf{A}$ or $\boldsymbol{\nabla} \times \mathbf{A}$, is a vector function derived by forming the cross product of $\boldsymbol{\nabla}$ and $\mathbf{A}$. The result is

$$\boldsymbol{\nabla} \times \mathbf{A} = \mathbf{i}\left(\frac{\partial A_z}{\partial y} - \frac{\partial A_y}{\partial z}\right)$$

$$+ \mathbf{j}\left(\frac{\partial A_x}{\partial z} - \frac{\partial A_z}{\partial x}\right) + \mathbf{k}\left(\frac{\partial A_y}{\partial x} - \frac{\partial A_x}{\partial y}\right) \tag{A.31}$$

The expansion in (A.31) is conveniently remembered by the determinant

$$
\mathbf{\nabla} \times \mathbf{A} = \begin{vmatrix} \mathbf{i} & \mathbf{j} & \mathbf{k} \\ \dfrac{\partial}{\partial x} & \dfrac{\partial}{\partial y} & \dfrac{\partial}{\partial z} \\ A_x & A_y & A_z \end{vmatrix}
\tag{A.32}
$$

The curl of a vector field is a vector. The physical interpretation of the curl of a vector is more complex than that of the divergence. If $\mathbf{A}$ denotes the linear velocity at every point in an incompressible fluid in motion, then curl $\mathbf{A}$ gives a measure of the angular velocity at every point.

We summarize below the properties of the differential operators which we have mentioned.

Operation	Symbol	Is applied to a	Yields a
Gradient of V	$\mathbf{\nabla} V$	Scalar field	Vector field
Divergence of $\mathbf{A}$	$\mathbf{\nabla} \cdot \mathbf{A}$	Vector field	Scalar field
Curl of $\mathbf{A}$	$\mathbf{\nabla} \times \mathbf{A}$	Vector field	Vector field

Appendix B.
MKS Units

B.1 Definition

In the present text the "rationalized" mks (meter-kilogram-second) system of units has been used exclusively. The term "rationalized" means that a factor 4π has been introduced in Coulomb's and Ampère's laws of force in order to suppress the appearance of this factor in the field equations.

The mechanical unit of force in the mks system is called the newton. The newton is the force which will impart to a one kilogram mass an acceleration of one meter per second^2. In the cgs (centimeter-gram-second) system the unit of force is the dyne. The dyne is the force which will give a one gram mass an acceleration of one centimeter per second^2. Since 1 kg = 1000 g and 1 m = 100 cm, it follows that the newton equals 10^5 dynes.

The mks unit of work is the newton-meter or the joule. The joule is the amount of work done on a body by a constant force of 1 newton when the body is displaced by this force a distance of 1 meter in the direction of the force. In the cgs system the unit of work is the dyne-centimeter or the erg. It follows that the joule equals 10^7 ergs.

The definitions of electrical units in the mks system are based on the electrostatic and on the magnetic laws of force as the starting points. According to Coulomb's law the magnitude of the force of repulsion between two identical charges, each of magnitude q and separated by a distance r, is given by

$$F = \frac{1}{4\pi\varepsilon_0}\frac{q^2}{r^2} \tag{B.1}$$

In the above expression, the units of force and distance have already been established from mechanics. However the formula contains two other quantities ε_0 and q, and (B.1) can be used to define the unit of one of them provided the unit of the other is defined independently. It has become customary to define the unit of charge (the coulomb) in terms of the unit of current (the ampere) whose definition, as we shall see, is based on the law of magnetic force. Accordingly, in the mks system, (B.1) is chosen as the defining relation for ε_0, the permittivity of free space. The numerical value of ε_0 is determined experimentally by a somewhat indirect procedure, for instance, by measuring the capacitance in vacuum of a parallel-plate capacitor of known geometry.

In the absolute electrostatic system of units (cgs-esu), the unit of charge (the statcoulomb) is defined from Coulomb's law, which, for this purpose, is written in the form

$$F = \frac{q^2}{r^2} \tag{B.2}$$

Then the statcoulomb is defined as that charge which, when located at a distance of one centimeter from an identical charge in free space, experiences a repulsive force of one dyne. In terms of mechanical units, the esu of charge has the dimensions of (dyne)$^{1/2}$-centimeter.

The problem of determining the connection between the statcoulomb so defined and the mks unit of charge, the coulomb, must again be referred to laboratory measurement. The conversion factor between the two units of charge is: 1 coulomb equals 3.00×10^9 statcoulomb.

It is interesting to calculate the numerical value of ε_0 by utilizing relationships between the units of the quantities involved in Coulomb's law. In the terms of the electrostatic system of units we have two point charges, each one statcoulomb, placed one centimeter apart in vacuum, interacting with a force of one dyne. We convert the electrostatic quantities into their mks equivalents by utilizing the factors below:

1 dyne $= 10^{-5}$ newton; 1 centimeter $= 10^{-2}$ meter; and 1 coulomb $= 3.00 \times 10^9$ statcoulomb. Substitution in (B.1) gives

$$10^{-5} = \frac{1}{4\pi\varepsilon_0} \frac{\dfrac{1}{9 \times 10^{18}}}{10^{-4}}$$

whence $$\frac{1}{4\pi\varepsilon_0} = 9 \times 10^9 \text{ new-m}^2/\text{coul}^2$$

and $\qquad \varepsilon_0 = \dfrac{1}{36\pi \times 10^9} = 8.84 \times 10^{-12}$ coul^2/new-m^2

$\qquad\qquad\qquad\qquad\qquad\qquad\qquad\qquad\qquad$ (B.3)

The units of the result in (B.3) may also be expressed as farads per meter (see Section 11.1).

The definition of the mks unit of current is based on the magnetic interaction of two currents. Consider the special case of two parallel current elements in vacuum, each carrying the same current. According to (7.25) the interaction between the two current elements is of the form

$$F = C(i\, dl)^2/r^2 \qquad\qquad (B.4)$$

the constant C or its replacement $(\mu_0/4\pi)$ is set exactly equal to 10^{-7} mks units. Then, the unit of current (the ampere) is defined by stipulating that when the quantities i, dl, and r are each equal to unity, the interaction is exactly C newtons. Since current elements do not exist, a more realistic geometry is found in the case of two long straight filamentary currents situated in vacuum. From (7.27) the force per unit length on one of the conductors is

$$\left(\frac{F}{l}\right) = \frac{\mu_0 i^2}{2\pi r} \qquad\qquad (B.5)$$

provided that the current in each filamentary conductor is the same. The definition of the ampere follows: The current in each of two straight, very long filamentary conductors one meter apart and situated in free space is one ampere, if the magnetic force per meter of length is exactly 2×10^{-7} newton/meter. The unit of charge or the coulomb is now defined as the charge that crosses a section of a conductor in one second when there is a constant current of one ampere in the conductor.

In another system of units, known as the absolute electromagnetic (cgs-emu) system, the unit of current is the abampere which is defined by the use of $(i\, dl)^2/r^2$ in the following way: Consider two parallel current elements of equal length dl separated by a distance of one centimeter in vacuum. Let the elements carry equal current in the same direction. If the current elements attract each other with a force of one dyne per centimeter length of each element, the current in each is said to be one abampere. As in the mks system, the abcoulomb is defined as the charge transferred in one second by a current of one abampere. The dimensional constant C in (B.4) may be evaluated by expressing the various quantities found in (B.4) in terms of their mks equivalents. To accomplish this conversion from emu to mks units, we need to have the additional information that 1 abampere is equal to 10 ampere. Thus

$$10^{-5} = \left(\frac{\mu_0}{4\pi}\right) \times 10^2$$

whence
$$\frac{\mu_0}{4\pi} = 10^{-7} \text{ new/(amp)}^2 \qquad (B.6)$$

Other units of μ_0 are: weber/ampere-meter; henry/meter; in terms of mass, length, time, and charge the dimensions of μ_0 are kilogram-meter/coulomb^2.

In Section 14.5, it is pointed out that the speed of electromagnetic waves in vacuum is predicted to be

$$v = \frac{1}{\sqrt{\varepsilon_0 \mu_0}} \qquad (B.7)$$

so that the right side of (B.7) must have the dimensions meters per second. When the numerical value of v was calculated in Section 14.6 from the individual values of ε_0 and μ_0 adopted above, the result indicated that in free space electromagnetic waves were propagated with the speed of light c, which is a fundamental constant of nature.

There is an alternate way of arriving at the value of ε_0—that is, one can start with the experimentally determined value of c and compute ε_0. Then

$$\varepsilon_0 = \frac{1}{\mu_0 c^2} \qquad (B.8)$$

We recall that μ_0 is an exact number so that this procedure makes it possible to evaluate ε_0 with high precision, since the value of c is known experimentally with an uncertainty of about 1 part in 300,000.

It was stated that the main purpose of introducing the factor 4π in the force formulas was to simplify the form of the field equations which are used more often. As a further consequence, the factor 4π appears explicitly in problems involving spherical symmetry. The corresponding factor in the case of cylindrical or circular symmetry is 2π, while in rectangular geometry π does not appear. The student may verify this statement by comparing the results for the magnitude of the electric field originating from spherical, cylindrical, and plane charge distributions.

The mks system has an additional desirable feature because it includes the practical electrical units such as the volt, the ohm, the farad, and the henry. The relations which are used to define the units of these and other quantities are found in the text and will not be repeated here.

B.2   Other Systems of Units

Although in recent years the mks system of units has found wide acceptance, physicists and engineers sometimes use other systems of units such as atomic units, Heaviside-Lorentz units, gaussian units, etc.

We shall comment briefly on the gaussian system. This is a mixed system in which the unit of charge is the statcoulomb defined in (B.2), and the unit of current is the abampere as defined from a relation such as that given in (B.4) with the constant C placed equal to unity. Accordingly, the gaussian system is a combination of the electrostatic (esu) and electromagnetic (emu) systems of units already referred to. Based on these definitions, it is possible to obtain a consistent set of gaussian units, provided that the ratio between the statcoulomb and abcoulomb is determined experimentally. Measurements indicate the conversion factor between these units of charge is the speed of light c. The factor is applied so that a measurement expressed in statcoulombs when divided by c converts the units of the measurement into abcoulombs.

We present certain important formulas which are written in the gaussian system of units. In these units the force on a charged particle assumes the form

$$\mathbf{f} = q\left(\mathbf{E} + \frac{\mathbf{v}}{c} \times \mathbf{B}\right) \tag{B.9}$$

Moreover, when the differential forms of the field equations are expressed in the nonrationalized gaussian system, the factors 4π and c appear as indicated below:

$$\operatorname{div}\mathbf{D} = 4\pi\rho, \qquad \operatorname{div}\mathbf{B} = 0$$
$$\operatorname{curl}\mathbf{E} = -\frac{1}{c}\frac{\partial\mathbf{B}}{\partial t}, \qquad \operatorname{curl}\mathbf{H} = \frac{1}{c}\frac{\partial\mathbf{D}}{\partial t} + 4\pi\mathbf{j} \tag{B.10}$$

In the above formulations ρ, $\mathbf{E}$, and $\mathbf{D}$ are expressed in esu while $\mathbf{B}$, $\mathbf{H}$, and $\mathbf{j}$ are expressed in emu.

In the gaussian system the formula for the velocity of electro-magnetic waves becomes

$$v = \frac{c}{\sqrt{\varepsilon\mu}} \tag{B.11}$$

where now ε and μ are dimensionless. In free space $\varepsilon = \mu = 1$ so that $v = c$ as before.

In Table B.1 we present various electrical quantities along with the symbols by which each quantity is represented in the text. The names of the associated unit in the mks system are also given. Table B.2 is a brief collection of electrical quantities which shows numerical relations between the mks and the esu or emu system of units.

Table B-1. Electrical Quantities and Associated MKS Units

ELECTRIC FIELDS

Quantity	Symbol	Unit
Electric field	$\mathbf{E}$	v/m; new/coul
Displacement	$\mathbf{D}$	coul/m^2
Dipole moment	$\mathbf{p}$	coul-m
Polarization	$\mathbf{P}$	coul/m^2
Volume density of free charges	ρ	coul/m^3
Volume density of induced charges	ρ_i	coul/m^3
Surface density of free charges	σ	coul/m^2
Surface density of induced charges	σ_i	coul/m^2
Susceptibility	η	farad/m
Permittivity	ϵ	farad/m
Dielectric constant	k	ϵ/ϵ_0-dimensionless
Potential	V	v
Current	i	amp
Capacitance	C	farad
Resistance	R	ohm (Ω)

MAGNETIC FIELDS

Quantity	Symbol	Unit
Induction	$\mathbf{B}$	weber/m^2
Magnetic Intensity	$\mathbf{H}$	amp/m
Magnetic dipole moment $\mu_0 iA$	$\mathbf{m}$, $\mathfrak{m}$	weber-m
Magnetization	$\mathbf{M}$	weber/m^2
... Volume density of magnetic "poles"	ρ_M	weber/m^3
... Surface density of magnetic "poles"	σ_M	weber/m^2
Susceptibility	χ	henry/m; weber-amp/m
Permeability	μ	henry/m; weber-amp/m
Relative permeability	K_m	μ/μ_0, $\mu_0 = 4\pi/10^7$ henry/m
Magnetic potential (not used in text)	Ω	amp
Flux	ϕ	weber
Inductance	L, M	henry
Electromotive force	ε	v

MECHANICAL UNITS

Quantity	Unit	Quantity	Unit
Length	m	Force	new
Mass	kg	Energy	joule
Time	sec	Power	w

Table B-2.   A Brief Table of Conversion Factors

HOW TO USE THE TABLE: A physical measurement consists of a number and the unit in which the measurement is expressed. To convert from the mks system of units to the gaussian system, multiply the number of mks units by the conversion factor to obtain the number of gaussian units.

For convenience c is taken as 3.00×10^8 m/sec. A more precise value for the speed of electromagnetic radiation in free space is 2.99792×10^8 m/sec.

Quantity	Symbol	MKS Unit	Conversion Factor	Gaussian Unit (esu or emu as indicated)
Charge	q	coul	3×10^9	statcoulomb (esu)
Current	i	amp	10^{-1}	abampere (emu)
Electric field	**E**	v/m	$\frac{1}{3} \times 10^{-4}$	dyne/statcoulomb (esu)
Displacement	**D**	coul/m^2	$12\pi \times 10^5$	statcoulomb/cm^2 (esu)
Magnetic induction	**B**	weber/m^2	10^4	gauss (emu)
Magnetic intensity	**H**	amp/m	$4\pi \times 10^{-3}$	oersted (emu)
Magnetic flux	ϕ	weber	10^8	maxwell (emu)
Potential	V	v	$\frac{1}{300}$	statvolt (esu)
Resistance	R	ohm (Ω)	10^9	abohm (emu)
Capacitance	C	farad	9×10^{11}	cm (esu)
Inductance	L	henry	10^9	abhenry (emu)

Answers to Odd-Numbered Problems

Chapter 1

1.1 10^{-9} coul, negative

1.3 5.0×10^{-7} coul, negative

1.5 2π new/coul, along diameter to the left

1.7(a)

    (b) $A/8\varepsilon_0 R$, along $-x$-axis

1.9   21.6 new/coul, along BP, downward

1.11(a) $x = 0, y = (2 \times 10^4 t - 2.2 \times 10^{15} t^2)$ m;   (b) $x = 2 \times 10^4 t$ m, $y = -2.2 \times 10^{15} t^2$ m

1.13 $Q/4\pi\varepsilon_0 S^2$, where S is the distance from the center to the field point

Chapter 2

2.1 $\dfrac{\lambda}{4\pi\varepsilon_0} \ln \left(\dfrac{d + L}{d} \right)$ v

2.3 $V = (300h - 0.005h^2)$ v, where h is the height above the surface in meters

2.5 6×10^{-9} joule

2.7   100 v

2.9(a) $\dfrac{\sigma}{2\varepsilon_0} [(x^2 + R^2)^{\frac{1}{2}} - x]$ v;   (b) $\dfrac{\sigma}{2\varepsilon_0} \left[1 - \dfrac{x}{(x^2 + R^2)^{\frac{1}{2}}} \right]$ v/m, along $+x$ direction;
    (c) $\sigma/2\varepsilon_0$ v/m

2.11 4.05×10^{-2} v, circle at the higher potential

464

Chapter 3

3.1(a) $\sigma R^2/\varepsilon_0 r^2$ v/m;   (b) 0;   (c) $\sigma R/\varepsilon_0$ v, interior point at higher potential

3.3(a) 1 v;   (b) -5×10^{-12} coul

3.5(a) 2.54×10^{-5} coul;   (b) 1.13×10^4 v/m;   (c) 2.54×10^4 v, with the center at the higher potential

3.7(a) 0;   (b) σ/ε_0, normal to CD and directed away from CD

3.9 $\nabla^2 V = 0$

3.11(a) 0;   (b) $E_x = Cy, E_y = Cx$;   (c) $dy/dx = x/y$

3.15(a) 1.6×10^{-5} coul;   (b) 2.25×10^3 v/m

3.17(a) 9 v, point O at the higher potential;   (b) $\sigma = 2\varepsilon_0 x$ charge density positive and nonuniform

Chapter 4

4.1 $\varepsilon_0 E (k - 1)$

4.3 3.75×10^{28} atoms/m³, $p = 1.06 \times 10^{-34}$ coul-m, $l = 4.14 \times 10^{-17}$ m

4.9(a) 130 v;   (b) 5.4×10^{-7} coul/m²

4.11 $\dfrac{C_0}{1 - \dfrac{t}{d}\left(\dfrac{k-1}{k}\right)}$

Chapter 5

5.1 6.3×10^{-4} coul

5.3 5.0×10^{-8} amp; 3.0×10^{-8} amp

5.5 $2\pi\sigma V/\ln (b/a)$

5.7 $i_A = 50$ amp, $i_B = 25$ amp, $i_L = 75$ amp

5.9(a) 12 v;   (b) $V_A = 10$ v, $V_C = 26$ v;   (c) $i_{DC} = 4\frac{1}{3}$ amp

5.11 $R = 1 \ \Omega$

5.13 $12 \ \Omega$

5.15(a) $I_{AB} = 0$;   (b) $\mathcal{E}_1 = 14$ v, $\mathcal{E}_2 = 20$ v

5.17(a) 2 amp;   (b) 0;   (c) 6 amp

5.19 $5 \ \Omega$, 10 amp

5.21   0.50 amp, $V_1 = 25$ v, $V_2 = 80$ v

5.23(a) $R_1 = 6 \ \Omega, R_2 = 6 \ \Omega, R_3 = 7.2 \ \Omega$;   (b) 60 v;   (c) $5.4 \ \Omega$

Chapter 6

6.1(a) Path R;   (b) mv/eB

6.3(a) $dF = Ik \ dr/r$ new, $+z$ direction;   (b) $Ik \ln 2$ new

6.5(a) $ika \ dy/(y^2 + a^2)^{3/2}$, $-z$ direction;   (b) $ikL/a(a^2 + L^2)^{1/2}$

6.7(a) $dF = 6(1 + 3x^2) \ dx$;   (b) $+z$ direction, new;   (c) $6x(1 + 3x^2) \ dx$ new-m;   (d) 0;   (e) 3.75 new

6.9 3.2×10^{-18} new-m

6.11(a) 5×10^{-4} new-m;   (b) 4.16×10^{-2} m

6.13(a) Force on each side is 0.10 new, perpendicular to the side and away from the center of the triangle whose side is 0.05 m;   (b) $F_{AC} = 0$, $F_{CD} = 8.65 \times 10^{-2}$ new, perpendicular to and into plane of diagram; $F_{DA} = 8.65 \times 10^{-2}$ new, perpendicular and out of the plane of the diagram;   (c)   Net force is zero in both parts.

6.15(a) $iaB \cos \phi \, d\phi$ new, $+z$ direction;   (b) $ia^2B \cos^2 \phi \, d\phi$ new-m;   (c) $\pi ia^2B/2$ new-m

6.17(a) $\dfrac{kI \, dl}{a + l \sin \theta}$ new;   (b) $\dfrac{Ik}{\sin \theta} \ln \left(\dfrac{L \sin \theta + a}{a} \right)$ new

Chapter 7

7.1 $\mu_0 I/6R$ weber/m^2, perpendicular and into the plane of the diagram at P

7.3 4.62×10^{-6} weber/m^2

7.5(a) $\mu_0 Ni \, dx/2\pi W \sqrt{x^2 + a^2}$ weber/m^2;

(b) $\dfrac{\mu_0 Ni}{\pi W} \tan^{-1} \left(\dfrac{W}{2a} \right)$ weber/m^2

7.7(a) $C \equiv \mu_0 I/2\pi R^2$, $n = 1$;   (b) $C \equiv \mu_0 I/2\pi$, $n = -1$;   (c)   Normal to and outward from the plane of the diagram

7.9(a) 2×10^{-5} weber/m^2 at $x = 5$ cm
                                          0 at $x = 10$ cm
            6.67×10^{-6} weber/m^2 at $x = 15$ cm;
            (b)

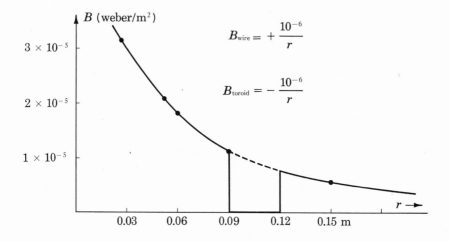

7.11 $\dfrac{\mu_0}{4\pi} \dfrac{ix \, dl}{(x^2 + y^2)^{3/2}}$ weber/m^2, $-z$ direction

Chapter 8

8.1(a) $-z$ direction; (b) $t_n = (2n - 1)$ sec, $n = 1, 2, 3, \ldots 3.0 \times 10^{-2}$ v;
(c) 1.91×10^{-2} v

8.3(a) vBL v; (b) $I = vBL/R$ amp; (c) IBL new; (d) $v = RW/B^2L^2$ m/sec

8.5(a) vBL v; (b) C at higher potential; (c) $(6 + vBL)$ v; (d) $Fv = (6vBL + v^2B^2L^2)/R$

8.7(a) 8×10^{-5} v; (b) 5.0×10^{-3} amp; (c) 0;
(d)

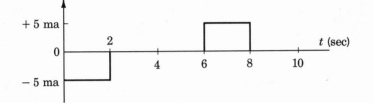

8.9(a) $\dfrac{\mu_0 il\, dr}{2\pi r}$; (b) $\dfrac{\mu_0 li}{2\pi} \ln\left(\dfrac{a + b}{a}\right)$ weber; (c) The time dependence of the current must be known

8.11(a) $10^{-10}I$ weber; (b) $i = 1.26 \times 10^{-6} \cos 377t$ amp

8.13(a) A to C; (b) $-4.5 \times 10^{-2}e^{-5t}$ v; (c) $t = 0, 4.5 \times 10^{-2}$ v

8.15 $t = 1/a$ sec. The motional emf and the emf arising from the Faraday effect have opposite signs. For $t > 1/a$ the motional emf remains smaller in magnitude.

Chapter 10

10.1 0.40 weber/m^2

10.3 $j_a^s = M/\mu_0$, out of the plane of the diagram

10.5(a) 1.13×10^{-4} weber/m^2; (b) Diamagnetic; (c) 1.26×10^{-4} weber/m^2

10.7 Portions in the second and fourth quadrants where H and B have opposite signs

10.9(a) $B = 0.07$ weber/m^2; (b) 6.92×10^{-3} weber/amp-m

10.11(a) $\mu_0 H + C$; (b) $\mu \to \mu_0$; (c) $\mu_0 ni$

10.13(a) 7.5×10^{-5} weber/m^2; (b) 0.67 weber/m^2

10.15(a) 500 amp-turn/m; (b) 0.40 amp

10.17(a) 3.99×10^{-2} weber/m^2; (b) Inner surface $j_a^s = 4.24 \times 10^4$ amp/m, directed up; outer surface $j_a^s = -2.54 \times 10^4$ amp/m, directed down; $i_a^s = 3990$ amp; j_a^s parallel to j in Cu; (c) Evaluate $\oint \mathbf{M} \cdot d\mathbf{l}$ over a path consisting of radial segments and arcs of circles with center on the axis; (d) No

10.19 2.88×10^{-5} weber/m^2

Chapter 11

11.1(a)   5.4 joule;   (b) $\sqrt{3} \times 10^9$ m/sec^2;   (c)   3.6 joule

11.3(a) $\frac{1}{2}\varepsilon_0(V/d)^2A$;   (b) $\frac{1}{2}\varepsilon_0 k(V/d)^2A$

11.9 $-3\mu_0\pi a^2 b^2 i_a i_b x/2(a^2 + x^2)^{5/2}$

11.11 4.02×10^5 new

11.15   Electrostatic energy of the electron $e^2/8\pi\varepsilon_0 a$; $a = 1.40 \times 10^{-15}$ m

11.17   0

11.19(a) $\mu_0 I^2/8\pi^2 r^2$, $a < r < b$;   (b) $\mu_0 I^2 \ln (b/a)/4\pi$;   (c) $\mu_0 I^2 \ln (b/a)/4\pi$

Chapter 12

12.1   Let $\mathcal{E}$ denote the emf and Q the final charge on the capacitor. Then $\frac{1}{2}\mathcal{E}Q$ is the energy stored in the capacitor. An equal amount is dissipated as heat during the charging process.

12.3

Time	Current in R	Charge on C	Energy in C
Just as S is closed	1.2×10^{-1} amp	4×10^{-4} coul	2×10^{-2} joule
When the steady state is reached	0	1.6×10^{-4} coul	3.2×10^{-3} joule

12.5(a) $-3.33 \times 10^{+2}$ amp/sec;   (b)   1 watt;   (c)   The integral represents the magnetic energy initially stored in the coil. The energy is dissipated as heat in the resistor.

12.7(a)   0.69 amp;   (b)   0.48 amp;   (c)   28.8 joule

12.9(a)   200 v;   (b)   100 Ω

12.11(a)   Straight line through origin;   (b) i/C, where i is the constant current; (c) $v_C = \mathcal{E}(1 - e^{-t/RC})$, where v_C is the potential across the capacitor and $\mathcal{E}$ the constant applied potential.

12.13(a)   5.0 amp, 200 v;   (b)   65 v;   (c) 8.12×10^{-2} joule

12.15 2.5×10^{-1} sec

12.17   60°

12.19(a) $\tan \phi = 1$;   (b)   Lags;   (c)   12 watt when $\omega = \omega_0$; 6 watt when $\omega = 2\omega_0$

12.21(a)   31.2 amp;   (b)   22 Ω;   (c)   The value of the capacitance or the inductance

12.23(a)   24 Ω;   (b)   24 Ω

12.25 $L\omega/(1 - LC\omega^2)$

Chapter 13

13.1   Set $y = f(\mu)$, where $\mu \equiv t - (x/v)$. Differentiation shows that $f(\mu)$ satisfies the wave equation, provided v is identified with the speed of the waves.

13.3(a) $\frac{1}{4} m\omega^2 A^2$;   (b) $\frac{1}{4} m\omega^2 A^2$;   (c)   Results in (a) and in (b) are equal

13.5(a) $-\frac{1}{4}$, phase change of π on reflection;   (b) $+\frac{1}{4}$, no phase change on reflection

13.7   From adiabatic gas law, $V = (C/P)^{1/\gamma}$. Then $\dfrac{1}{V}\dfrac{\partial V}{\partial P} = -\dfrac{1}{\gamma P}$. Then use defining relations $K = -\dfrac{1}{V}\dfrac{\partial V}{\partial P}$ and $B = \dfrac{1}{K}$

13.9   Minimum occurs when $\lambda = \sqrt{b/a} = 2\pi\sqrt{\sigma/\rho g}$, $v_{min} = (4ab)^{1/4} = (4g\sigma/\rho)^{1/4}$

13.11(a) $y\,|\,_{t=0} = -A\cos kx$, at $x = 0, y = -A$;   (b) $\omega = 151\ \text{rad/sec}, k = 126\ \text{m}^{-1}$

13.13 $\Delta\phi = 9°$, $T = 2\pi$ sec

13.15(a) $x_n = n\lambda/2, n = 1, 2, 3, \ldots$;   (b)   120 m/sec, 7.20×10^2 new

13.17(a) 0.04 m;   (b)   120 m

13.19(a) 0.331 m;   (b) 6.84×10^{-8} m/sec;   (c) 1.10×10^{-11} m;   (d) 3.02×10^{-15} joule/m³

Chapter 14

14.1(a) 1.54;   (b) 3.9×10^{-7} m

14.3(a) $E_y = \sqrt{\mu_0/\varepsilon_0}\ H_0 \sin(\omega t - kx)$;

(b)

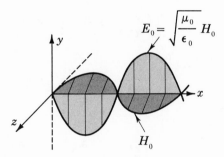

14.5(a) 3×10^8 m/sec;   (b)   30 microvolt;   (c)   Using $\partial E_y/\partial x = -(\partial B_z/\partial t)$, we find $B_z = B_0 \sin(\omega t - kx)$. Then the flux through loop

$$\phi = 1.2\, B_0 \int_{x_1}^{x_2} \sin(\omega t - kx)\, dx$$

$$\text{or}\ \ \phi = \frac{1.2\, B_0}{k}\left[\cos(\omega t - kx_2) - \cos(\omega t - kx_1)\right]$$

$$\varepsilon = -\frac{d\phi}{dt} = \frac{1.2\, B_0\omega}{k}\left[\sin(\omega t - kx_2) - \sin(\omega t - kx_1)\right]$$

where $x_2 = (x_1 + 0.5)$,

$$\varepsilon = 1.2\, E_0[E_y'' - E_y'] = 1.2[50 - 25] = 30\ \text{microvolt}.$$

14.7(a) II;   (b) $E_0/B_0 = C$

14.9(a)   In $\mathbf{\Pi} = \mathbf{E} \times \mathbf{H}$, substitute $\mathbf{H} = \mathbf{B}/\mu_0$, where $1/\mu_0 = \varepsilon_0 c^2$;   (b)   Using expressions for E_y and H_z evaluate $\frac{1}{2}\varepsilon_0 E_y^2$ and $\frac{1}{2}\mu_0 H_z^2$ and compare results; (c) $E_y/H_z = \mu_0\omega/k = \mu_0 c$, or $E_y/B_z = c$;   (d) $\mu_0 c = 4\pi \times 10^{-7} \times 3 \times 10^8 = 120\pi = 377\ \Omega$;

(e) $\Pi_x\Big|_{\text{avg}} = E_y H_z\Big|_{\text{avg}} = \dfrac{E_0^2}{\mu_0 c}\Big[\sin^2(\omega t - kx)\Big]_{\text{avg}} = \dfrac{1}{2}E_0^2\dfrac{1}{\mu_0 c}$

$\Pi_x\Big|_{\text{avg}} = 2.65 \times 10^{-3}\ E_{\text{rms}}^2\ \text{watt/m}^2$

(f)   From (b) $\frac{1}{2}\varepsilon_0 E_y^2 = \frac{1}{2}\mu_0 H_z^2$; total energy density $= \varepsilon_0 E_y^2$, $c \times \varepsilon_0 E_y^2 = E_y H_z = (1/\mu_0 c)E_y^2 = c\varepsilon_0 E_y^2$ since $c\varepsilon_0 = 1/\mu_0 c$

14.11(a) $\mathcal{E}_{\text{rms}} = 20\sqrt{2}\sin 12° = 5.87$ microvolt;   (b) $\Pi_x|_{\text{avg}} = 1.32 \times 10^{-13}\ \text{watt/m}^2$

14.13(a) $H_P = \dfrac{q_0\omega \cos \omega t}{2\pi R^2}r$, $E = \dfrac{q_0 \sin \omega t}{\pi R^2}$;

(b)   The Poynting vector is radial towards the axis, $\Pi_r = q_0^2\omega \sin 2\omega t/4\pi^2\varepsilon_0 R^3$;   (c)   Power input $\Pi_\gamma \times 2\pi R d = q_0^2\omega(\sin \omega t \cos \omega t)d/\pi R^2\varepsilon_0$; (d)   Rate of increase of electric energy

$$\frac{d}{dt}\left(\frac{q^2}{2C}\right) = \frac{q_0^2\omega(\sin \omega t \cos \omega t)d}{\pi R^2\varepsilon_0}$$

14.15 $E_{\text{rms}} = 1.25 \times 10^5\ \text{v/m}$

14.17 $E_{\text{max}} = 1.73 \times 10^{-2}\ \text{v/m}$

Chapter 15

15.1(a) $C' = \dfrac{2\pi\varepsilon_0}{\ln(b/a)}$, $L' = \dfrac{\mu_0}{2\pi}\ln\left(\dfrac{b}{a}\right)$;   (b) $\dfrac{\partial^2 q}{\partial t^2} = \dfrac{1}{L'C'}\dfrac{\partial^2 q}{\partial x^2}$,

where q is the linear density of charge

15.3   Applying the given restrictions placed on $\mathbf{E}$, from the relation $\nabla \cdot \mathbf{D}$ we find that $\partial D_x/\partial x = 0$, i.e., D_x is a function of t alone. Since we are interested in wave motion we set $D_x = \varepsilon_0 E_x = 0$. This leaves E_y and E_z each a function of $(x - vt)$.

Also from the x component of the $\nabla \times \mathbf{E}$, $\dot{B}_x = 0$, that is, B_x is not a function of t, hence B_x cannot represent a wave. As before we set $B_x = \mu_0 H_x = 0$. The given relations follow upon substituting $E_x = H_x = 0$ into (15.17) and (15.18).

15.5 $\dfrac{A^2\beta ab}{2\mu\omega}\sin^2(\omega t - \beta x)$

15.7 $v_{\text{gr}} = \dfrac{1}{d\beta/d\omega}$; but $\beta = \left(\dfrac{\omega^2}{v^2} - k^2\right)^{\frac{1}{2}}$, where $k^2 = -\left[\left(\dfrac{n\pi}{b}\right)^2 + \left(\dfrac{m\pi}{a}\right)^2\right]$.

Hence, $v_{\text{gr}} = \dfrac{v^2}{\omega}\left(\dfrac{\omega^2}{v^2} - k^2\right)^{\frac{1}{2}}$. Also $v_{\text{ph}} = \dfrac{\omega}{\beta} = \dfrac{\omega}{\left(\dfrac{\omega^2}{v^2} - k^2\right)^{\frac{1}{2}}}$

Therefore, $v_{ph}v_{gr} = v^2$.

15.9(a)   The magnitude of the Poynting vector in the radial direction is

$$\frac{A^2\omega^2}{\varepsilon_0 c^3} \cdot \frac{1}{r^2} \cdot \sin^2\theta \cos^2\omega\left(t - \frac{r}{c}\right)$$

Integrate this quantity over the surface of a sphere of radius r using $2\pi r^2 \sin\theta\, d\theta$ as the element of area.   (b)   Substitute $i_0^2 = q_0^2\omega^2$ into result of (a). Then the rate of emission is

$$\frac{q_0^2 l^2\omega^4}{6\pi\varepsilon_0 c^3} \cos^2\omega\left(t - \frac{r}{c}\right)$$

15..11(a) $i_{\text{refl}} = i_0\cos(\omega t + kx)$;   (b) $i_{\text{inc}} + i_{\text{refl}} = 2i_0\cos\omega t\cos kx$. This expression vanishes for all t, provided

$$kL = \frac{2\pi}{\lambda_m}L = \frac{\pi}{2}, \frac{3\pi}{2}, \frac{5\pi}{2}, \cdots (2m+1)\frac{\pi}{2}, m = 0, 1, 2, \cdots$$

or when the wavelength assumes the discrete values given by $\lambda_m = 4L/(2m+1)$ where L is the fixed length of the line. There is always a current loop at $x = 0$. When $m = 0$, there is a node at $x = L$ and the length of the line is equal to $\lambda_0/4$. When $m = 1$, there are nodes at $x = \lambda_1/4$ and at $x = L$ and the length of the line is equal to $3\lambda_1/4$. Similarly at shorter discrete values of the wavelength additional nodes appear along the fixed length L. In general there are $(m+1)$ nodes for a given value of m.

Chapter 16

16.1(a) $\phi = 0$;   (b) $\phi = \pi/2$;   (c) $\phi = 2\pi/3$

16.3(a) $\Delta\phi = 12\frac{1}{2}\pi$ radians;   (b) $R = 11.20$ microvolt/m

16.5(a)   Linear, slope $= A/B$;   (b) Circular;   (c) Elliptical;   (d) Linear, slope $= -A/B$

16.7(a) $\Delta\phi = \pi/2$ radians;   (b) Resultant moves in an ellipse with semi-axes A and B

16.9(a)   15 microvolt/m;   (b) $(400 - n^2)/20n = x_n$ m

16.11(a) $C = 19.50$ cm;   (b) 5 microvolt/m

16.13   Distance is 5760 m

16.15(a) $E_t/E_i = 2n_1/(n_1 + n_2)$, polarization does not matter;   (b) $|\Pi_{\text{refl}}| + |\Pi_{\text{trans}}| = |\Pi_{\text{inc}}|$

16.17(a) $3 \times 10^{10}, 2.25 \times 10^{10}, 2.0 \times 10^{10}$ cm/sec;   (b) $1.00, 1.33, 1.5$;   (c) $\sin i/\sin r = 1.5$

16.19 $n_1 A_1 B_1 = n_2 AB$, $n_1/p = (n_2 - n_1)/r$

16.21(a) $SO = R = 1.15$ m;   (b) $OE = 8 \times 10^{-4}$ m;   (c) $q = 1.44$ m

Index

A   5
B   6
C   7
D   8
E   9
F   0
G   1
H   2
I   3
J   4